W9-BSO-172

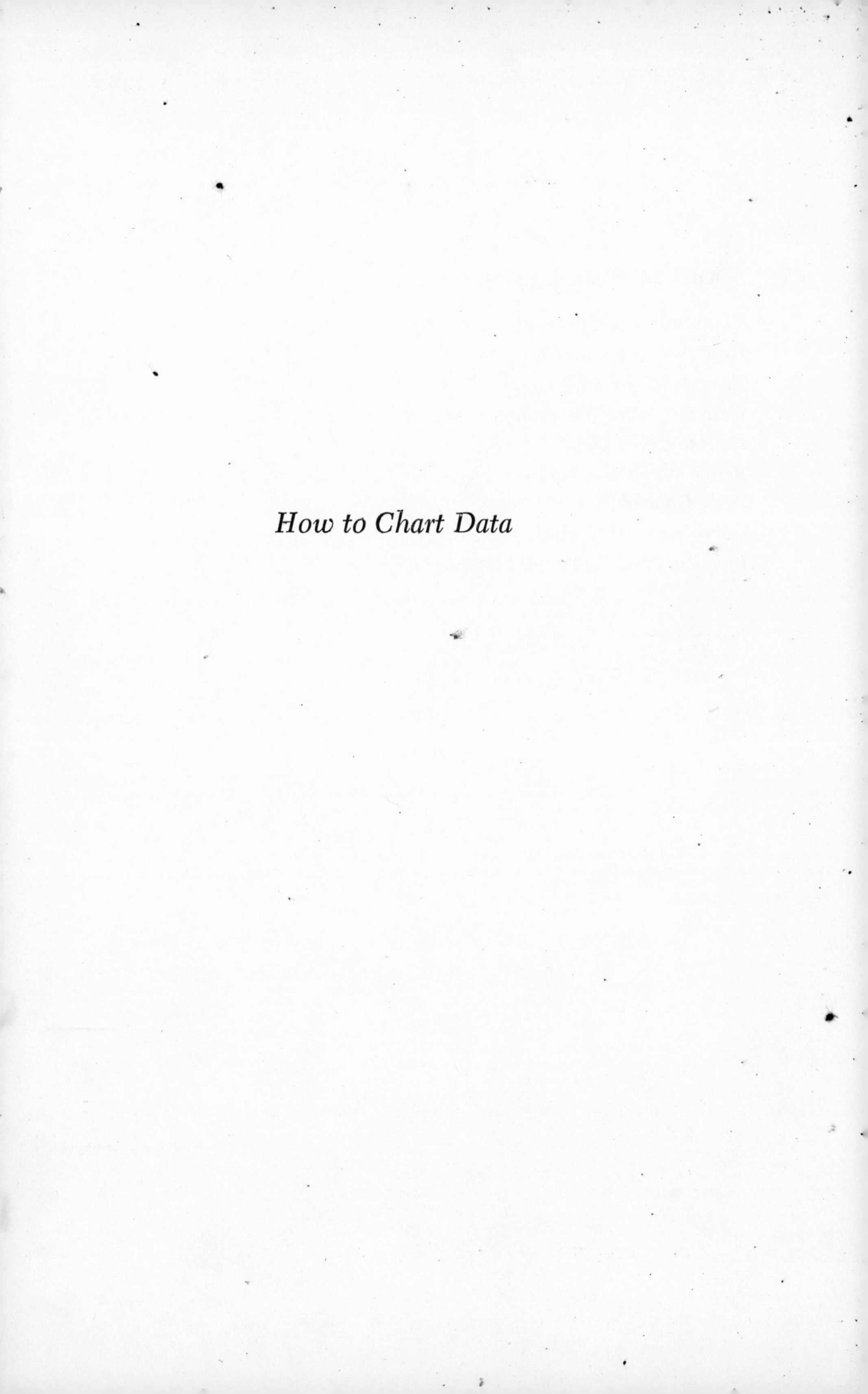

How to Chart Data

BOOKS BY PHIL CARROLL

Timestudy Fundamentals for Foremen
How Foremen Can Control Costs
Timestudy for Cost Control
How to Control Production Costs
How to Chart Data
Better Wage Incentives
Profit Control
Overhead Cost Control
Practical Production and Inventory Control

How to Chart Data

PHIL CARROLL

Professional Engineer

McGRAW-HILL BOOK COMPANY

New York San Francisco Toronto London

HOW TO CHART DATA

(Revision of the book originally published under the title "How to Chart Timestudy Data")

 Library of Congress Catalog Card Number: 60–6963

10129

6789–MP–987

Preface

Operations Research is a new name for the process of getting answers to multi-variable problems. It is an orderly way of taking into account all of the factors, usually in equation form.

Few of us, however, have sufficient skill in mathematics to work out these complex equations. Yet all of us can solve many such problems by taking one factor at a time. That is the method we have used in timestudy since Taylor devised "element" breakdown in 1881.

Later, some men used nomographs or alignment charts to obtain solutions by graphics. Most of those I have seen are line diagrams used to get answers to engineering formulas. From a speaking acquaintance with nomographs I worked out my first four variable chart in number form in 1924. As you look at it in Chap. 16, and at others in this book, you will see nothing unusual.

Anyone who can add two plus two and get the right answer can make charts to solve very complex problems. Thus, charting is a method any of us can use to get all the answers within the ranges of multi-variable factors. All you have to do is complete one step at a time.

Besides, charting affords a way for you to explain your answers to complex problems. You can show executives how the several factors affect end results without confusing them by shifting from one piece of paper to another.

Keep in mind both parts of problem solving. Getting answers is only one. Taking the actions indicated is the necessary second part if your solution is to have any practical value. So "selling" your ideas is essential. In this step, your success depends upon gaining confidence. Here is where the non-mysterious forms of charting can help you attain more ready acceptance of your solutions.

Now look ahead. You can see by some of the examples how charting can be used in wholly new fields. You can utilize charts to get answers to many complex problems of profit control through better forecasts, budgets, and product costs. Also, it provides the best method I know to overcome the "impractical" and "uneconomical" reasons given for not measuring overhead operations as reported in April 1959 issue of *Factory*.

Finding ways to economically set standards for non-repetitive types of work is the chief reason why these charts were developed in the first place. Many improvements have been suggested to me by associates and client personnel. These men deserve much of the credit for the better ideas explained here. Specific mentions are made in the text of those men I can identify with the ideas.

This book is my second attempt. For the original, my daughter Margaret worked on parts during a whole summer after she learned to type. My daughter Jeane drew some of the sketches while taking her courses in art. Charles A. Thomas, Jr., and my former secretary, Miss Atlee O'Brien, now Mrs. Phil Carroll Jr., worked out many of the step by step illustrations.

In this revision, I have utilized suggestions and materials given to me by Stanley Robinson, Alan Harper, Robert Seybert, Harry Trott, Kenneth Barth, and Auburn Shuff. Virginia Secor typed and retyped the manuscript as well as copying many of the new charts. I acknowledge my indebtedness to all those named and many others by whose help I have gained without remembering when or how.

Withal, the material in this book is little more than suggestive. Meager as it is, my hope is that the fundamentals explained will prove to be helpful to you. Remember, however, that a book is never finished. So your criticisms are welcomed. Your comments for improvement will be greatly appreciated.

PHIL CARROLL

Contents

CHAPTER 1

Variable Factor Problems

Men in business and industry are seeking answers to the complex problems of today. Managers, in particular, are trying to anticipate the results of their decisions. They want to know, "What will happen if we follow this, that, or some other course of action?"

The solutions to their problems are complex because several different factors control. These factors, in the main, are variables. They move in diverse directions. Some are dependent upon other variables in the problems themselves. For example, costs are related to volumes in the simple profitgraph (Fig. 1).

In contrast, some variables are independent of inherent factors. To illustrate, the income in our profitgraph is determined by our customers. They, in turn, are influenced by our own product prices, the general economic weather, and the competition of prices charged for all the other things our customers want to buy.

Operations Research

You can readily see that problems involving such factors will have many different answers. Each new assumption for each one of the variables can produce a new answer. To illustrate, refer again to our profitgraph (Fig. 1). If our business were built up around three products—Shirts, Shorts, and Sheets—we could expect profits to shift with changes in Volume, Product Mix, Prices, and Costs.

Experts could put all these factors together in equation form and feed our many different questions into a high-speed electronic computer. In no time, they could get a flock of answers. Using only Volume and Mix, a greatly simplified picture of these answers might look like Fig. 2.

Our new approach to multi-variable problem solving is called "Operations Research." It was first utilized by our military forces during World War II. Lately, it is defined as "a scientific method of

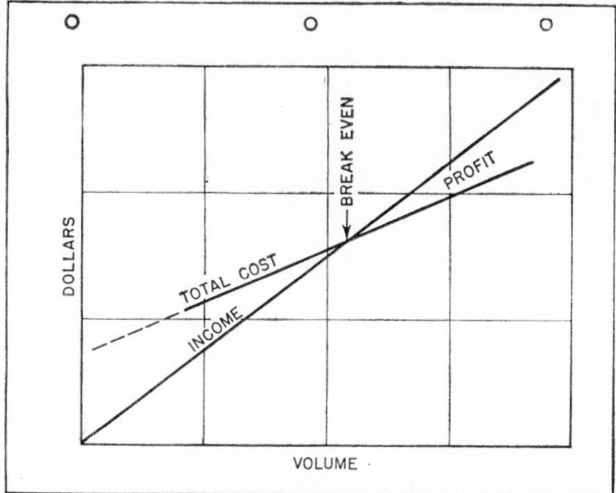

Fig. 1. Our company income is determined by customer's wants and competition whereas costs are related to our volume of output.

SHIRTS THOUSANDS DOLLARS																		
40	60	(80)	100	120														
	40				60	80	100	120										
60		SHORTS			40	60	80	100	120									
		40				40	60	80	100	120								
	60				0		40	60	80	100	120							
80			40			0		40	60	80	100	120						
		(60)					0		(40)	60	80	100	120					
	80			40				0		40	60	80	100	120				
100			60						0		40	60	80	100	120			
		80								0		40	60	80	100	120		
	100			60							0		40	60	80	100	120	
120			80									0		40	60	80	100	120
		100						SHEETS					0		40	60	80	100
	120			80										0		40	60	80
			100												0		40	60
		120														0		40
					0	2	4	6	8	10	12	14	16	18	20	22	24	26

PROFIT—THOUSANDS DOLLARS

Fig. 2. For the mix of sales of $80,000 Shirts, $60,000 Shorts and $40,000 Sheets the profit anticipated is $8,000.

providing executives with quantitive basis for decisions regarding operations under their control."[1]

Along with nearly every discussion of Operations Research is some

[1] Grabbe, Eugene M., "Automation in Business and Industry," p. 25, John Wiley & Sons, Inc., New York, 1957.

mention of high-speed electronic computers. Increasingly, these are being used to work out the complete ranges of answers to questions set up by operation researchers. These computers can turn out answers with amazing speed. But only after the research man or team has asked the questions. This preparation, often called "programming," may be simple or very complex.

The manager's problems that must take into account our customers and our competitors seem difficult to solve. Herein may be one reason why sales forecasts are only now beginning to make their appearances in a relatively few companies.

Intangible vs Tangible

My explanation is that customer attitudes, economic weather, competitive actions, and like external variables are intangible. You may prefer the term "unknown." In contrast, we think of internal factors like costs and volumes as being more tangible—knowns.

Thus, when we try to solve some types of problems, we must consider factors that are unknown. We must make assumptions. For example, to play a "decision-making" game related to business operation, we may assume that the market for a certain product is a constant. Then, the "decisions" made by the competing teams can only rearrange the total sales. Or again, we might assume that someone will put a colony of human beings into the stratosphere and that the market will change some stated amount.

Everyday Examples

By making assumptions, we have been solving some complex problems in industry for years. Here is one instance. To work out what shall be our product inventory, we can readily compute the tangible costs of capital tied up. We may have pretty good ideas of obsolescence costs. But we have had to decide how often we dared to disappoint our customers before we could solve the problem.

As a second example, we can schedule production by machine loading. We may have both work standards and wage incentives to aid our predictions. But we have assumed that Joe Workman's wife kissed him happily this morning and that he will want to work at his usual pace. Otherwise our production does not conform with our schedules.

As a third case, we can plan to make improvements in methods. We can predict the probable changes in cost. But we must assume some quantity of production before we can figure the estimated savings to be made.

Easier to Solve

You may say, "These latter types of problems are easier to solve." They are. But let me ask you, "Are they easier because we use rules to go by?" For instance, to figure estimated savings in methods improvement, we may use last year's production. This rule of using prior output makes the decisions for us and conceals the assumption I mentioned.

Again, those who schedule production may say, "This department averages 128.7 per cent performance," and proceed to load their work stations accordingly.

We may look upon these garden-variety problems as being easier to solve for another reason. We may think of the factors involved as being tangible—internal—under our control.

Here is one such problem of the kind I know something about. We set work standards in advance from standard time data. To do so, we may assume, for instance, that the casting to be machined will have a certain amount of stock on it. Also, we assume that the job will be run on a given type of machine.

Multi-variable Problems

If the stock or the machine type changes, a new or plus standard is required. To make the revision, we use standard time data that covers the changed conditions. Or as in too many plants, we let the job run on "day work" and, maybe, pay average earnings to boot.

More to the point, we need data for all the conditions, regular and irregular, that arise in a type of work before we can set standards to get total coverage. To cite examples, in Drill Press operations we have ranges in time for

Piece Handling   Jig Loading   Machining

Then, too, we have many combinations of drill, ream, and tap together with diameters, depths, and metals.

Some types of work are more complex, some are less complex to measure. Nearly all involve ranges of several variables. Problems of this type are solved to the extent that we get data to cover the ranges.

As a parallel, more and more companies are trying to take out some of their unknowns by getting data. Some are doing market research, studying business trend indices, supporting trade associations, making surveys, and attending professional-society meetings, to cite a few examples.

More facts, more answers to the unknowns cut down on the ranges of possible results. Still, our complex problems must be solved if we are to prepare ahead of time for probable changes.

Our multi-variable problems can be solved in many ways. Until Operations Research and electronic computers were developed, we used methods we already had. Some of those less modern ways are still thoroughly practical to use in many instances.

Besides, we should keep in mind that about 90 per cent of our business enterprises have less than 500 employees. Small-plant managers may never get to the computer stage of answering questions. And, of course, there are the computing costs to consider.

Some may take special problems to service groups that will do the computing for fees. That way of solving problems introduces the need for planning ahead and for some delay times. Also, going outside for help seems contrary to our tendencies to want to be self-sufficient. Remember, too, that you must get facts or make assumptions before you can use Operations Research, electronic computers, or the charts I want to explain in this book. Keep in mind one more point as we move along. Charting can be used to solve complex problems that are and will be worked out by more costly methods. Big and little plants, with and without electronic computers, all can use charting to advantage in "providing executives with quantitive basis for decisions regarding operations under their control."

Variable Charting

To work out many multi-variable problems, we can use charting methods. These are ready and inexpensive. They can be made up by men who may not understand differential equations.

Probably, charts will always be used to record results, however calculated. It is our usual way of setting up number data that we want to compare or portray. A common case is the tabulation side by side of company-operating results for the past month with those for the same month a year ago and for the year to date. But here, I am talking about charting as a way to compute multiple answers.

For this purpose, charting has a primary advantage. I call it the "wholesale" method for computing answers. To point up this use, let's take another look at Fig. 2. There, we show ranges from $40,000 to $120,000 of sales for our three products—Shirts, Shorts, and Sheets. At the end is the expected profit for any combination of sales, within the ranges.

All these answers were built up in making the chart. In contrast, we usually solve such problems singly. Our usual method might be to work out in the following manner the combination of sales indicated by the dotted line on the chart.

	Income	*Var. Cost*	*Profit*
Shirts	$ 80,000	$ 64,000	
Shorts	60,000	42,000	
Sheets	40,000	36,000	
Constant Cost		30,000	
	$180,000	$172,000	$8,000

Even computers, although very, very speedily, calculate only one answer at a time.

Now note another advantage of charting. You can assume a different sales volume for one, two, or three of our products and read off another expected profit from the same chart (Fig. 2). This advantage has seemed important to me in explaining the results of change. With it, you can show non-engineers a series of changes without losing them in a maze of papers. I learned about this advantage the hard way. I used to confuse managers by trying to shift their attention from one set of figures on one sheet to comparable sets on other pieces of paper.

For reasons given, we can list certain advantages of charting as

1. Economical ways to work out the answers to multi-variable problems
2. Practical computing devices for getting whole ranges of multiple answers that can be worked out by men who understand simple arithmetic
3. Easy methods for wholesale computing of answers to multiple alternative decision-making conditions
4. Understandable forms for the composite portraying of probable results to be attained among a variety of alternatives

Utilize Charts

To gain the chief advantages from charting, the first thing you should know is that there are several forms you can use. Some are easier to make than others. Looked at from the other side, some forms are more suitable than others for solving certain types of problems. Thus, you should know how to construct different types of charts. Then you can choose the one you believe to be best-adapted to solving the problem at hand.

Second, you can profit from using charts to solve multi-variable problems. For instance, George Smith told me in April, 1958, "I got my money back from your workshop in Worcester. That one thing you said about turning charts inside out helped me to solve a problem that stumped me for years."

Every day we do many kinds of computing that could be charted. As I put it, "After you multiply 2 by 2 and get 4 often enough, why not write it down?"

Better Methods

The "how-to-make" I shall describe in later chapters is the outgrowth of experiences. As we say, "Necessity is the mother of invention." My own necessity was to find cheaper ways to set work standards for job shop and non-repetitive operations.

Most of my experience has been in plants where vice presidents have said, "You can't set standards for our operations. No two orders are alike. To measure our work, we would need a timestudy man for every employee."

Such deductions are not true. That many think so is evident by our extensive failures to measure overhead and indirect labor operations. One reason is given us by Josh Billings in the latter half of his quip, "'Tain't the things we don't know what makes us so ignorant, it's the things we know that ain't so."

"Can't be done" is to me more often an excuse than a reason. That we have profitably set standards for one-piece order, setup, maintenance, tool room, and office work is proof enough. Two factors have contributed to many such installations. One is the use of standard time data developed from timestudies. This use of timestudy results again and again is the "ain't so" part of the frequent supposition that every job must be studied.

The other factor is the charting of standard data. To digress for a moment, let me emphasize how charting can cut the cost of setting work standards. It is brought out in an example given by Marty Doring. He reports how he was called into a plant to check on the use of standard time data for wooden box making. After some study, he set up a multi-variable chart. "When this was completed, it was possible to set a standard in 30 seconds with fewer errors than they had been making. When we compare this with the average time of 90 minutes under the old method, we have a saving of 89½ minutes per standard."[1]

[1] Doring, Martin R., "Why Timestudy Standards Cost Too Much," *Journal of Industrial Engineering*, p. 12, September, 1954.

Better Analysis

One explanation of this type of saving is stated by Robert M. Wellington. He says, "Engineering is the art of doing for one dollar what a bungler can do for two dollars."

To me, engineering in our sense means analysis. That is the first step in getting away from repeated calculations. We must ask, "Why do it this way day after day?" Only when we realize "there must be a better way" can we improve methods.

Then, the next step is to study the ranges of the variables. In timestudy, we do this by plotting curves. In solving many multi-variable problems, I suggest curve drawing may be the most convenient approach. For this reason, and because this book was originally directed toward solutions of timestudy problems, I will go through curve making as the initial stage.

Before we go into the mechanics, however, you might like to get a quick picture of charting in its several forms. With that as a plan, our next chapter will be sort of a survey of end products. These will be examples of several ways to solve the profitgraph problem briefly described in this chapter.

CHAPTER 2

Forms of Charting

Charts may take many forms. Some are better than others. Like production tools, their costs are affected by degree of perfection. The proper choice from a variety is essential to secure the maximum economies for a given set of conditions. But some of the forms I have seen were the result of incomplete analysis as contrasted with informed selection. Perhaps an analogy will help to develop our theme.

Your choice of chart form is somewhat like the question that comes up every day in some shops about lathe operations. Many parts to be machined can be made on an engine lathe, turret lathe, semi- or full-automatic. Thus, there are important costs to be compared in planning where to run the current order. In the average shop, the machine to use is often determined by comparing the Setup with the Piece Time. When the Quantity multiplied by the operation Standard plus the Setup is the least total amount, it is assumed to indicate the proper equipment to use.

In general, we expect the operation Standard to vary inversely with the extent of Setup. To reduce the Piece Time, usually we spend more time on the Setup. You should use this same type of thinking when choosing the form for your charting. The factors are the same. First, there is a cost of Setup—the preparation of your chart. Second, the operation Standard is likened to the computing time. The Quantity is the probable number of calculations to be made before you are required to revise your chart.

Straight-line Curves

Perhaps the simplest ways to get wholesale answers are to plot curves. One common example is the curve made to compare wage rates with point evaluations. Another is the series of curves made in budget building where expense trends are related to volumes of production or sales. A third example is the many curves plotted in time-study analysis to find how element standard times change with work content. You can think of others used in engineering, market analysis, aptitude testing, and quality control, to name a few.

The curve is our basic tool for analyzing variables. We turn to it almost automatically when we want to find or to portray the relation of one variable to another. In our profitgraph, Fig. 3*a*, we have done this with several sets of curves. Figure 3*b* represents the constant cost of what I call the "nucleus of an organization." Some describe it as the "cost to open the doors." The other sets of curves on Fig. 3 show variable cost trends and incomes for our four company products.

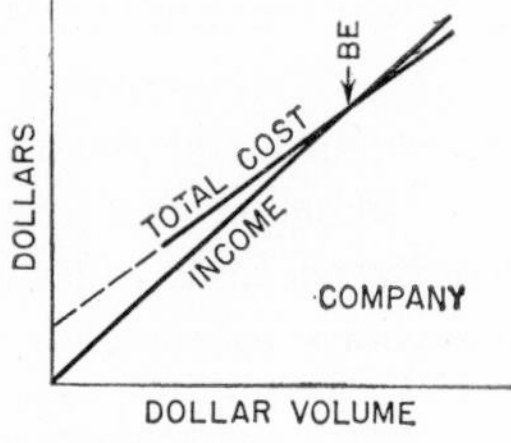

a. Profitgraph of a company showing total income and total cost trend lines.

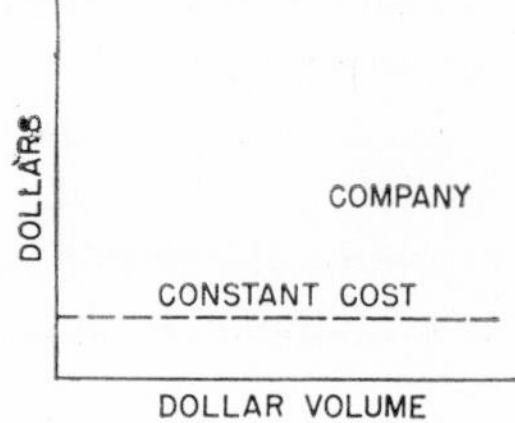

b. Constant cost separated from variable costs.

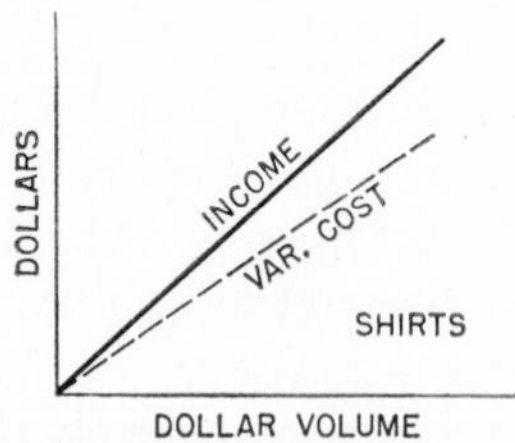

c. Shirts are one product with income and variable cost trends.

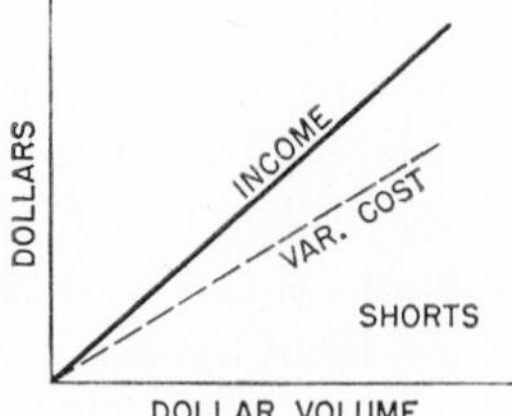

d. Shorts have another set of income and variable cost trend lines.

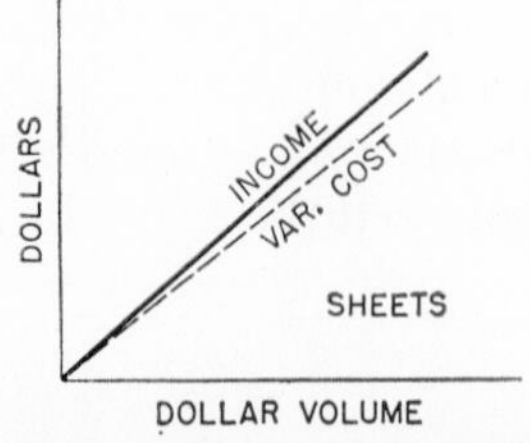

e. Sheets income and variable cost trends show small profit potential.

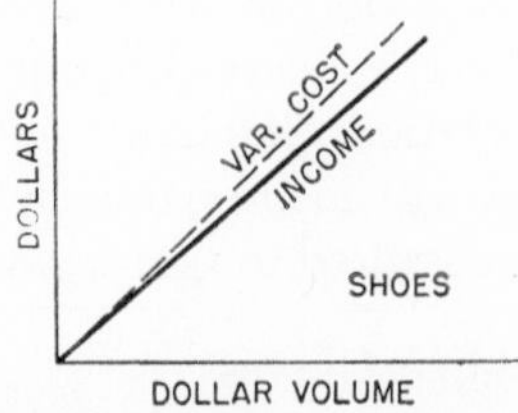

f. Shoes variable cost trend is higher than the income line.

Fig. 3. Curves or trend lines may be used to portray and analyze the profit potentials of a company.

Each of these four products was assumed to be 25 per cent of our total volume of income to make our company's profitgraph. This assumption makes the break-even point come at $240,000 in sales volume. The break-even volume would change, as you can see from Fig. 3*c*, *d*, *e*, *f*, were we to change these proportions.

Curves like these are easy to construct. With them, we can work out the likely profits or losses for various combinations of our four products. Too, we can determine where the break-even point will be for any combination of our four products.

But curves have disadvantages as working tools. They may be read in error, at least three different ways. Besides, curves seem mysterious to many folks. This is particularly true with timestudy data curves. For that and other reasons, I always translate standard time data curves into numbers.

Lists of Data

To change curves to numbers, most folks would set up tables in uniform steps. In these instances, we might choose steps of $10,000 in volume of income. We would write these down in columns as in Fig. 4. Then we would read the costs that correspond and write them alongside the incomes.

Income	Variable Costs			
	Shirts	Shorts	Sheets	Shoes
$ 40,000	$32,000	$28,000	$36,000	$ 44,000
50,000	40,000	35,000	45,000	55,000
60,000	48,000	42,000	54,000	66,000
70,000	56,000	49,000	63,000	77,000
80,000	64,000	56,000	72,000	88,000
90,000	72,000	63,000	81,000	99,000
100,000	80,000	70,000	90,000	110,000
	Plus $30,000 Constant cost			

FIG. 4. For easier understanding, curve readings may be tabulated in numbers at suitable intervals.

From such tables, we can figure what profit or loss we might expect. We can pick various combinations of our four products. For each forecast, we would take the income and variable cost for each product, write them down in order, and add the company constant cost to the sum of the variable costs. Then the difference between this total cost and total income would be our probable profit or loss. Here is an example taken from Fig. 4.

	Income	*Var. Cost*	*Profit*
Shirts	$ 60,000	$ 48,000	
Shorts	100,000	70,000	
Sheets	80,000	72,000	
Shoes	40,000	44,000	
Constant		30,000	
	280,000	264,000	$16,000

Tables like those on Fig. 4 are somewhat faster to use than curves. Certainly, they are more readily understood by most people. But the adding of nine numbers in two totals as we have done here opens up chances for error also.

Straight-line Equations

Rather than go to tables, some folks would work out the equations for their curves. This is fairly easy to do when the curves are straight lines. The "how to" will be explained in Chap 7.

Here we can say that our income lines all have $1 of income for $1 of volume. Our variable cost lines, however, have differing rates. These are

c. Shirts	.80	*e*. Sheets	.90
d. Shorts	.70	*f*. Shoes	1.10

From these, we can set up an equation.

(*A*) Profit or Loss = Income − ($ Shirts × .80 + $ Shorts × .70 + $Sheets × .90 + $Shoes × 1.10 + $30,000)

In this formula, the income is the sum of all the sales of our four products. Names with the $ represent the sales for each separate product. The $30,000 is our constant cost.

We can make our equation look somewhat simpler by using letters instead of products names and dropping the brackets. Also, we can assume that a minus profit is a loss. Then we get

$$(B)\ \text{Profit} = \text{Income} - .8\,Ic - .7\,Id - .9\,Ie - 1.1\,If - \$30{,}000$$

Using our equation to compute the likely profit from the product mix forecast in the previous example, we have

$$\text{Profit} = \$280{,}000 - .8 \times \$60{,}000 - .7 \times \$100{,}000 - .9 \times \$80{,}000 - 1.1 \times \$40{,}000 - \$30{,}000$$

$$\text{Profit} = \$280{,}000 - \$48{,}000 - \$70{,}000 - \$72{,}000 - \$44{,}000 - \$30{,}000$$

$$\text{Profit} = \$16{,}000$$

Equations afford us a good way to analyze and to express a problem. But often, they are complex to work out and are not readily understood by many people.

Two-way Charts

Perhaps the obvious way to combine variables and constants is by means of our common two-variable chart. This is the kind we see in most handbooks. Such charts may be made directly from curves, from their equations, or from tabulated data. By any process, more time is consumed in combining variables. Therefore, charts are somewhat more expensive to prepare. However, they are not subject to the same errors of interpretation as your curves. They are not nearly as puzzling as equations are to those who are not familiar with algebraic signs. You will agree, too, I'm sure, that charts like those shown in Fig. 5 are more readily understood by those you may want

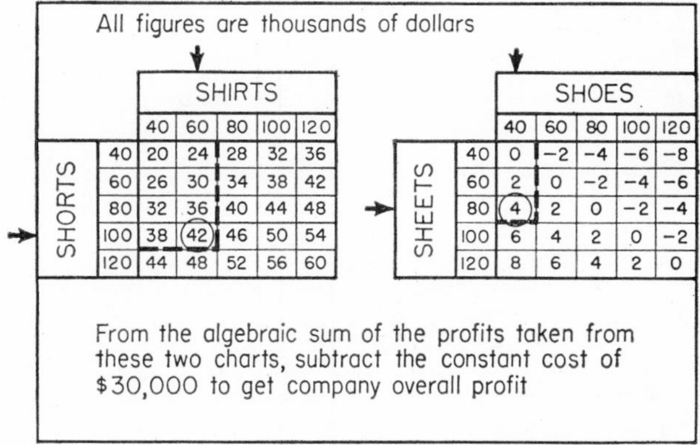

FIG. 5. Our four products may be set up in two charts to show profit potentials. Example is $42,000 from $60,000 Shirts and $100,000 Shorts plus $4,000 from $40,000 Shoes and $80,000 Sheets minus $30,000 constant cost equals $16,000 overall profit.

to explain them to. Here we have set up the profit potentials of our four products in two charts.

Such charts have many applications in recording timestudy working data. This is one of the best forms for setting down work element standards that are used in quantity—multiplied or divided. Instances are 1 to 10 vents in Squeezer Molding and Gauge 1 in 1 to 50 after some machining operation.

Nomographs—Alignment Charts

Another form for combining variables is called a "nomograph" or an "alignment chart." This form of chart is more like a group of curves than a table. It is a line diagram arranged to do arithmetic by placing a straight edge across it. In general, the scales on the nomograph are laid out graphically. Thus, certain small errors may be introduced. Even so, the nomograph offers another means for combining results given in several curves or charts, together with constant times and factors. Naturally, the nomograph is somewhat more mysterious than one or more curves. Part of this difficulty arises from the fact that not many people know how to make or use one. Often, the average manager, accountant, and shop man is not acquainted with nomographs.

Yet a nomograph is one of the quickest ways to get the many answers required for ranges of variables. Perhaps that is why we have as many as 10 books about making alignment charts for every book on any other form of charting. Your examination of these books will quickly reveal that, in the main, they are directed at solving engineering formulas.

That's no reason why we should pass up the utility this type of

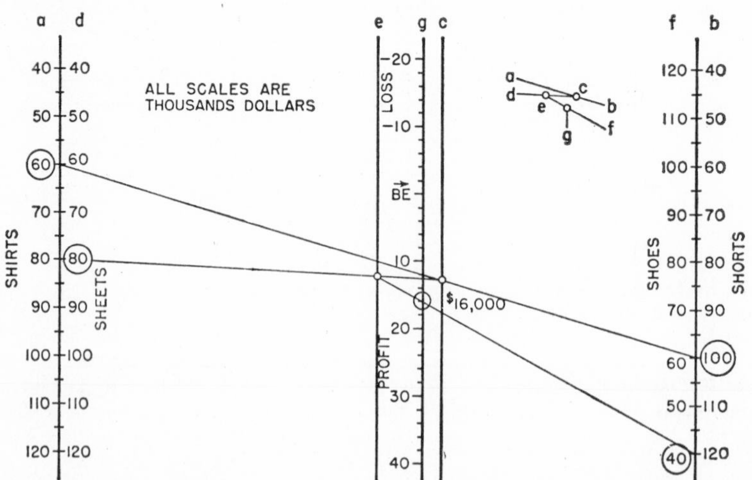

FIG. 6. Schematic diagram shows (1) $60,000 Shirts connected with $100,000 Shorts, (2) hold intersection on line c and turn straight edge to connect with $80,000 Sheets, (3) hold intersection on line e and turn to $40,000 Shoes, (4) result $16,000 profit is intersected on scale g.

chart has for us in many cases. For instance, I have used it in Fig. 6 to show how we can combine the potential profits of our four products.

Family of Curves

Like the nomograph, families of curves can be used to combine several variables, constants, and factors. As a rule, they are less expensive to construct than nomographs designed to accomplish the same result. While they are easier to explain and to understand than nomographs, they do appear to be more complex.

Here again is a fairly easy solution to construct that few seem to have discovered. As evidence, I have only one book that is made up of such charts. There may be others. Even so, you need only to locate two points for most curves and draw them. Let me underline the word "locate," however. Not all families are made up of parallel lines, as you may infer from Fig. 7. Some may fan out, as you will see in Chaps. 10 and 11.

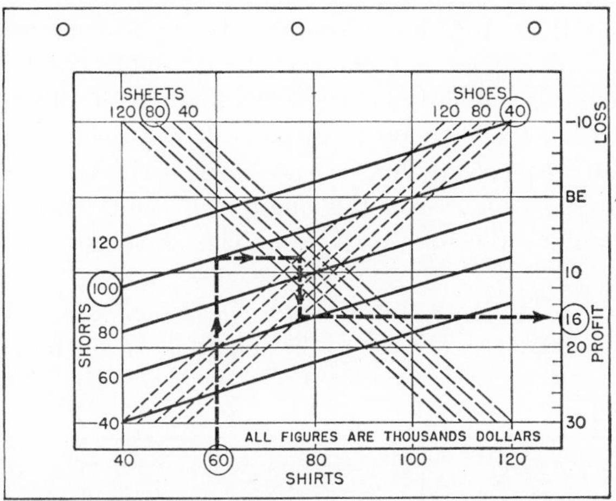

FIG. 7. Start on bottom scale with $60,000 Shirts, go up to $100,000 Shorts, sideways to $80,000 Sheets, down to $40,000 Shoes and out to right hand vertical scale. Read off $16,000 company profit.

Keep in mind this type of solution. It is another cheap way to combine multi-variables. How it works can be seen if you will follow through the mix in sales of our four products.

Multi-variable Charts

When you have to combine many factors, a chart will do the job. "Multi-variable" is the term I use to indicate a chart that combines more than two variables. Generally speaking, it is the most expensive of all forms to prepare. However, because it is a combination of tabulated numbers, it is easy to understand and to explain.

Charts are not as accurate as curves because the number of answers you can determine from a curve is greatly reduced when set up in tabular form. Many possible answers are eliminated because you read your curves at intervals. This is not a drawback. Absolute accuracy is not attainable nor is it necessary in many types of multivariable solutions.

Primarily, I am prejudiced in favor of numbers because curves seem mysterious to the uninitiated. Workmen in the shops and even some vice presidents are reluctant to believe the answers taken from curves. Thus, when mechanisms used to get your answers must be brought into their explanations, you run risks of failure in selling.

That, and the necessity to reduce standard setting costs, pushed me in 1924 to find ways to combine variables in number form. My first problem had four variables. It took me quite a while to figure out how to put these together. You see, I was like most men—I had never seen other than our common two-variable chart. I can still hear my boss, Loyal Benedict, bawling me out for sitting three days looking off into space trying to invent. It was in these mental gymnastics that I conceived the idea of "turning charts inside out," as I call the process. Once over this hump, it became simply more of the same to combine the four variables. This "first" for me is shown in Chap. 16.

That shown in Fig. 8 looks much the same. Here, I have used this form of chart to work out profit potentials of our four products.

ALL FIGURES THOUSANDS OF DOLLARS										40	60	(80)	100	120	(40)	SHOES
						SHEETS			40	60	80	100	120		60	
SHIRTS								40	60	80	100	120			80	
							40	60	80	100	120				100	
40	(60)	80	100	120		40	60	80	100	120					120	
	40					−14	−12	−10	−8	−6	−4	−2		2		
60	SHORTS					−12	−10	−8	−6	−4	−2		2	4		
		40			LOSS	−10	−8	−6	−4	−2		2	4	6		
	60					−8	−6	−4	−2		2	4	6	8		
80			40			−6	−4	−2		2	4	6	8	10		
		60				−4	−2		2	4	6	8	10	12		
	80			40		−2		2	4	6	8	10	12	14		
100			60				2	4	6	8	10	12	14	16		
		80				2	4	6	8	10	12	14	16	18		
	(100)			60		4	6	8	10	12	14	(16)	18	20		
120			80		PROFIT	6	8	10	12	14	16	18	20	22		
		100				8	10	12	14	16	18	20	22	24		
	120			80		10	12	14	16	18	20	22	24	26		
			100			12	14	16	18	20	22	24	26	28		
		120				14	16	18	20	22	24	26	28	30		

FIG. 8. Start with $60,000 Shirts, move down to $100,000 Shorts. Turn 90 and trace across. Hold that line, our answer lies along it somewhere. Now begin with $40,000 Shoes, move left to $80,000 Sheets. Turn 90 and move down until you intersect your horizontal line. There you read $16,000 profit for that product mix.

Better Tools

The foregoing are but thumbnail sketches of the five commonly used forms for combining variables. Each will be developed further. One or more chapters will be given to the construction and use of each form. Each has its useful applications. We can make the forms a kit of practical and handy computing tools.

As in the shop, we often make remarkable increases in production by introducing jigs and fixtures in processes that are already considered to be very efficient. So it is with devices that we can use to solve multi-variable problems. Some are more efficient than others.

You can profit from learning how to use all five of these charting tools. They are different ways to put numbers together. That is all the work part of problem solving consists of. One caution: Try to overcome the mental screening we all use in sorting out ideas we say do not apply to our work.

Try to look at the methods of construction and the examples shown in this book for purely selfish reasons. Try to overlook the fact that many of the charts shown and described are in timestudy terms. That happens only because the original of this book was written in an effort to help timestudy men cut the costs of setting work standards for non-repetitive operations.

Take another look at the examples in this chapter. All are charts of numbers. These happen to be sales and profit dollars. They could have been pounds, square feet, gallons, specific gravities, or standard times. So as we move on through later chapters, different kinds of numbers will be used in an effort to show the universal application of charting. My hope is to add some useful ideas to your kit of mental tools for *combining variable sets of numbers.*

CHAPTER 3

Standards for Curve Drawing

Curves are very important tools in the analysis of variables. They are used to determine how one factor in your problem changes with respect to another. They represent gradual progressions in the relation of one or more variables to another.

Curves are used in nearly every phase of business and industrial analysis. You see them in every commercial magazine and newspaper. The more common ones in the public eye show Car Loadings, Steel Production, Cost of Living, Bank Deposits, and Stock Prices. These have the factors named on vertical scales and time-date across the bottom. In your company, you may have similar curves for Sales, Production, Hourly Earnings, and Costs of many types.

Curve Layout

The curves we want to make are different. They do not have peaks and valleys. They have regular trends. They may be straight or curved lines. You may develop them singly. For example, the relation of one budget expense to volume of output. Or you may plot several as a family of curves. In timestudy, one case may be for the element Pick Up Piece where you use Weight as the main dimension and Distance moved as a second variable. This would bring out the fact that in moving a 30-pound piece, different distances would take differing times.

To plot the curves we need to analyze our problems, we use cross-section paper. The usual type has 20 squares to the inch. The preferred paper size is 8½ by 11 inches, and it is punched for standard three-ring binding.

But you would be surprised to see the number of different ways men can lay out the same kind of paper. Some place the dimension factor on the vertical scale. Some use only part of the scales available. Some start the scales so that 0 is way off the page. Conse-

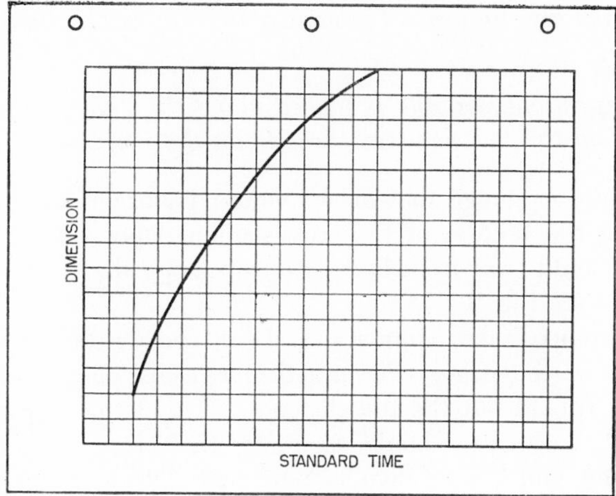

a Not correct

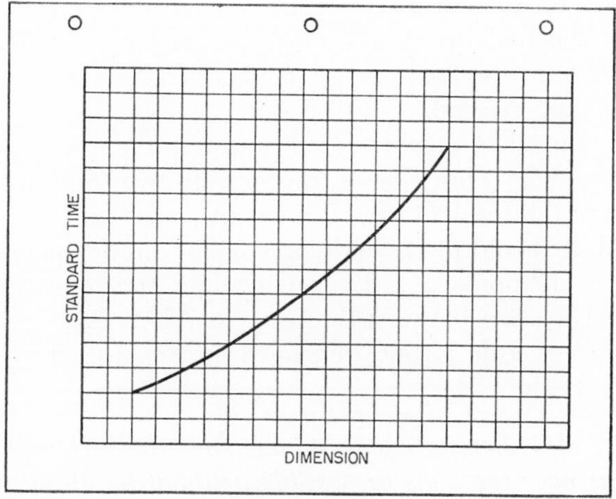

b Correct

FIG. 9. Curves for element timestudy analysis should be laid out with the Dimension Factor along the horizontal scale and Standard Time on the vertical scale.

quently, it seems a good idea to give some simple rules for curve drawing. A good reference pamphlet on the subject is "Engineering and Scientific Graphs for Publications."[1]

In this authoritative pamphlet, it says that the independent variable should increase from left to right. The dependent variable should

[1] ASA Z15.3, American Society of Mechanical Engineers, New York, 1943.

read from bottom to top. To summarize, we might insert an important rule:

1. *The dependent variable is placed along the vertical scale of a curve and the independent variable on the horizontal scale.*

In timestudy language that means your Dimension scale should be placed along the bottom of the cross-section paper. Your Standard Time scale would read from bottom to top along the vertical edge of the paper. (See Fig. 9.)

For appearance' sake, your scales should be written in along the full distance of the page. For practical reasons, choose your scales so that they spread out the full distance. This latter rule should be interpreted to mean you should use scales that are easily understood. Usually, some multiple of five is best with 20-square paper. The major divisions of your scale should correspond with the heavy lines on the cross-section paper.

Scales made up of odd divisions are inefficient to use. You have to count out the odd divisions each time you want to plot a point correctly or to read the final curve. Such scales are often read incorrectly. Errors are created.

The scales you select should extend from 0 to the maximums of the ranges anticipated. This should accomplish two things. First, it should magnify the results to the full extent permitted by your paper size. Second, it should place your curve about on the diagonal of the page. That will approach a 45-degree angle and approximate the best analytical relation between the two variables. Examples of correct and incorrect scale layout are shown on Fig. 10. Thus, we can set up a second rule.

2. *Choose scales that start with* 0 *and place the extremes of the ranges as near the ends as possible, without requiring the use of odd divisions of the cross-section paper.*

One other fundamental detail should be emphasized. All scales should start at 0. You may not agree that this is important. It is, however. Curves drawn with scales that begin with 0–0 more correctly portray the constants included. The starting amount at zero Dimension is apparent in curves drawn for job evaluation, expense budget, and timestudy variable analysis, to cite examples.

The point involved has more to do in aiding your correct analysis than anything else. Curves show their right proportions when plotted from 0–0. The inherent constant is correctly portrayed in relation to

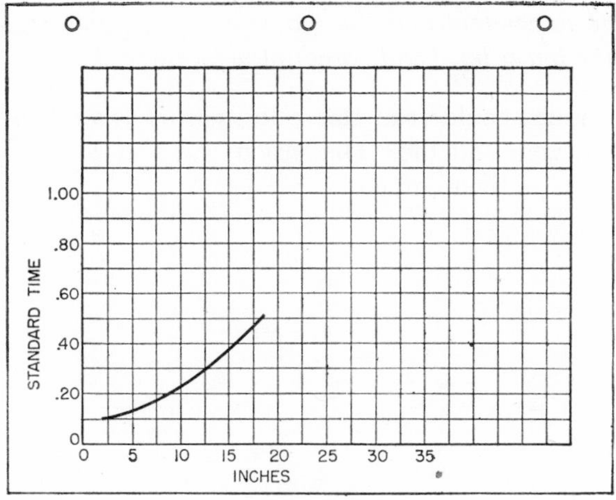

a Not correct

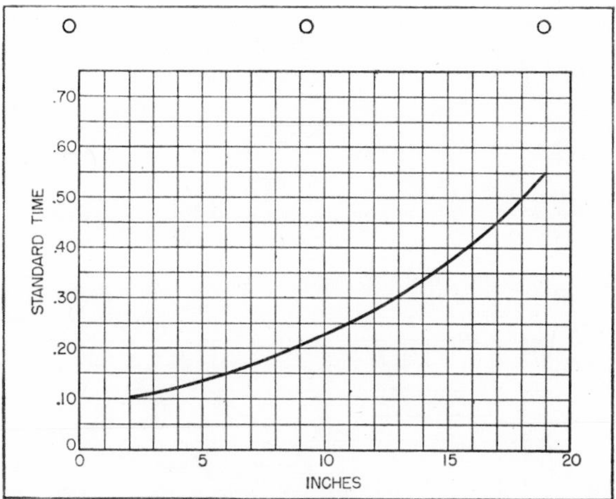

b Correct

FIG. 10. Two typical mistakes are illustrated in Curve *a*. The important one is that the scales chosen have too great a range. This is emphasized by the second mistake—the scales extend only part way along the edges of the page.

the slope. Note the effects of distortion caused by incorrect plotting in Fig. 11*a* and 11*b* as contrasted with Fig. 11*c*.

In Fig. 11*c* the scales are laid out correctly. Both start with 0. Figure 11*a* has omitted from it the time from 0 to .05. As a result, the inherent constant seems to be small. This constant appears larger than it should be in Fig. 11*b*. With these examples to emphasize this defect in curve plotting, we can set down a third rule.

3. *Start the dependent and the independent variable scales with 0–0 in the lower left-hand corner of your curve sheet.*

Timestudy men should read this rule so as to start their Standard Time scales at zero and their Dimension scales at zero in the lower left-hand corners of their curves.

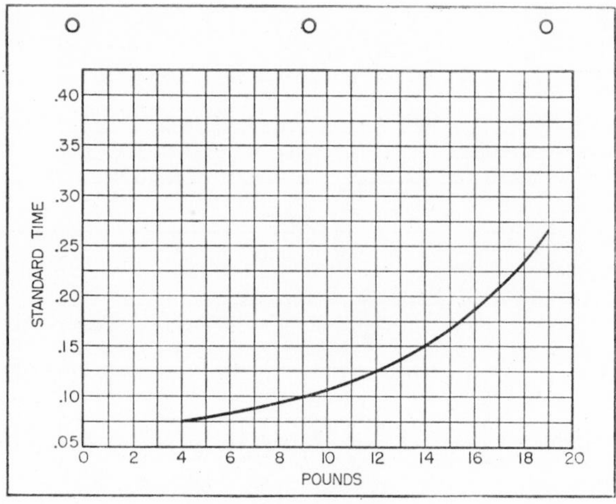

a Not correct

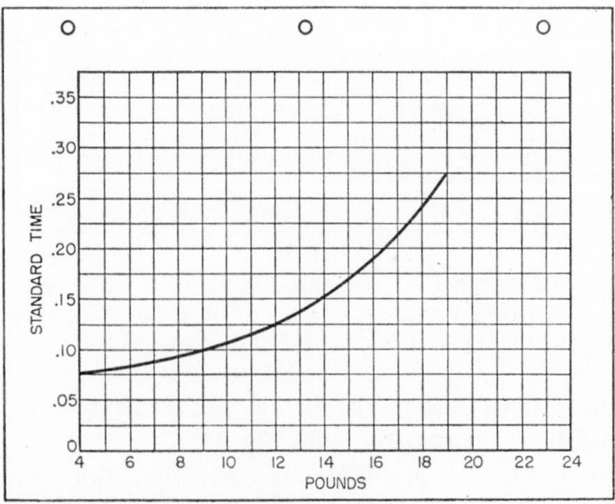

b Not correct

Fig. 11. Two curves drawn to illustrate the disproportionate size of the inherent constant that results when scales do not start at 0-0. Example *a* makes the constant standard time appear smaller than it is. Example *b* indicates a relatively larger constant. Example *c*, on the next page, shows a correctly drawn curve.

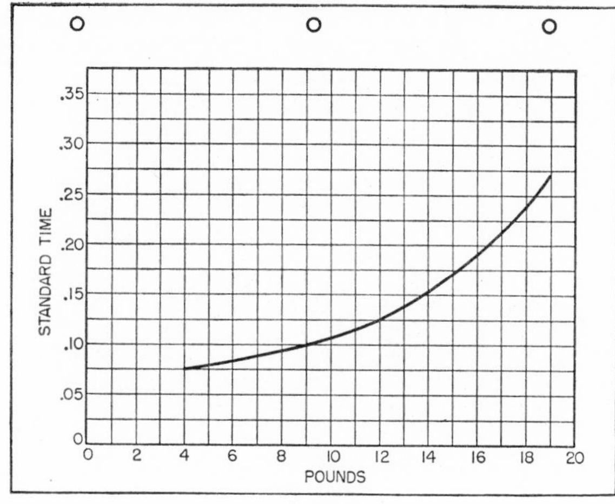

c Correct

Fig. 11 (*Continued*).

Descriptive Details

Scales should be placed outside the cross-section part of the sheet in the blank margins. The descriptions or names of the variable factors should be printed outside also, between the scales and the margins of the paper (Fig. 12). Lettering of any vertical-scale description should read from bottom to top as shown on all "correct" curves in this chapter. Here we can record another rule.

4. *Letter the scales outside the cross-section part of the curve paper.*

Curve Labels

Frequently, you may have several curves on one sheet. This happens because many of the variables you want to analyze are actually families of curves. Consequently, you will save yourself a lot of rework if you will distinguish one curve from another.

In plotting, designate each curve of a family by one specific symbol or color. Use symbols if the curves are to be reproduced. Obviously, colors will not show up in blueprinting. Color designations are usually satisfactory, however, because curves are not often reproduced. The reasons why will be gone into later on when we discuss charting. Each curve should be labeled. The titles should be placed close to the curves so there can be no mistake in correct identification. Arrows can be drawn from labels to curves, if necessary, to avoid confusion.

Draughting rules call for horizontal lettering of labels. But you cannot always follow the rules. Many times, your curves come too

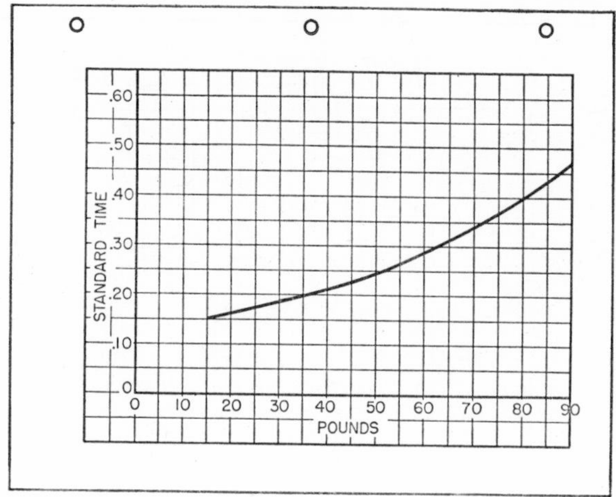

a Not correct

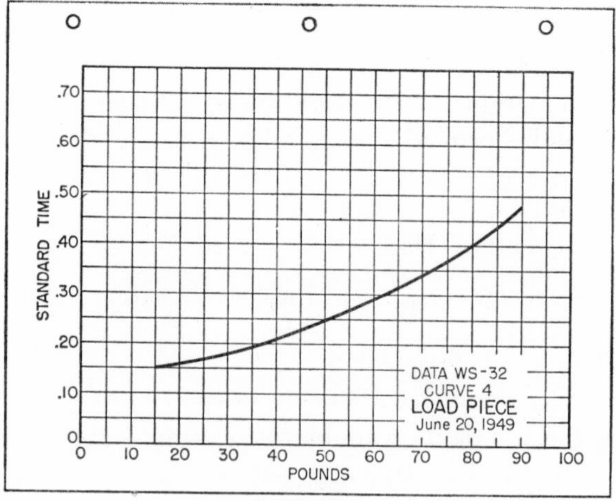

b Correct

FIG. 12. Scale figures and descriptions should be placed in the margins outside the cross-section paper. Curves should be fully identified with Date and Description. Curve Number is desirable when there are several.

close together. Often, the only labels necessary are figures used to show dimensional factors. These may be printed one space away from the curves and just above or at the ends. (See Fig. 13.) When they are printed at the ends, as I recommend, there is less confusion. However, when curves are used for standard setting, I prefer central labeling. Labels directly in front of the user will prevent some mis-

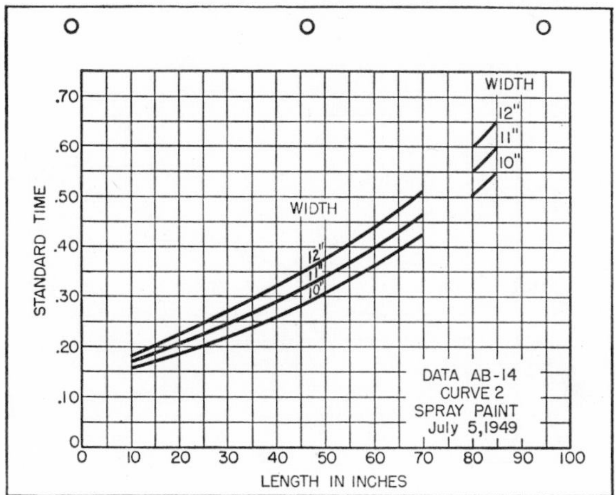

FIG. 13. Curve labels may be printed at the ends of the curve, or near the center.

takes. Labels at the ends require too much eye travel. Mistakes are easily made, especially when curves are close together.

5. *Use specific symbols to distinguish individual curves and clearly label each to identify it.*

Placing Your Curves

It may seem out of order to label your curves before they are drawn in. But the symbols and labels go together, so I discussed them under the same heading.

In between the assigning of symbols for plotting and the labeling of completed curves comes the drawing-in. These curves you finally draw may be straight lines or curves. Straight lines are easy to draw. Maybe that is why we draw so many straight when they should be curved. In all fairness, however, we should agree that there are many instances where the straight line is quite correct. Many cases occur where the range of the variable is so short that there is no significant difference between a curve and a straight line.

To locate a straight line, you may use either of two methods. The Method of Least Squares is advocated by some. It is a mathematically accurate way to locate a straight line through a series of points. This is the method suggested by many job-evaluation writers. It is described in Chap. 7 where we discuss equations.

My personal preference is to locate straight lines by using a stretched rubber band as a guide (Fig. 14). This method is not scientific. But I think it is more correct, especially in timestudy analysis, than

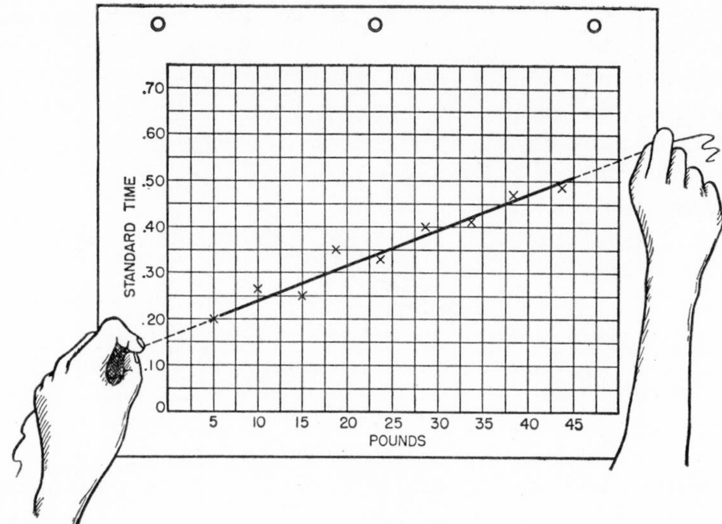

FIG. 14. You may stretch a rubber band or string through a series of points to locate a straight line. This method is preferred for its ease of analytical review.

the mathematically accurate method, for several reasons. In this field, our purpose is to determine fair standard times. What we want, therefore, is a line that represents each variable. This may require giving more weight to some points plotted than to others. For illustration, standards (points) set by skilled timestudy men should have more influence on where your line is drawn than those set by other observers whose skill and training are not up to specifications.

Straight-line curves are truly representative of many mathematical variables and most factors. Machine time is the most common example.

Such lines can often be located with only two points. If I were you, however, I would spot at least one other point near the center, just to be sure. It might be a curve. Also, if the three points fail to line up, you may have made a mistake in calculating any one of the three. So if you are not positive of your mathematics, locate several points. Then, when you are all set, you can draw the lines with a straight edge.

Curved lines are more difficult. And most timestudy curves are curved. They curve upward at an increasing rate. At the extreme outer range of the variable, your curve begins to point skyward. Sometimes you can "fit" curves with an irregular curve-drawing device. These can be shaped to fit the conditions. Years ago, we used to shape ribbon solder for a ruling guide. You may use ship's curves if you have them. If you resort to French curves, look out. Fitting these is difficult. You will have better than average luck if you stop drawing any one portion of your curve before it runs out. Then find another fit and blend the two sections.[1] In doing this, I have sometimes gradually and progressively tipped my ruling pen from vertical to a lesser angle as I drew in the curve.

Figure 15 shows a practical way to draw curved curves. This

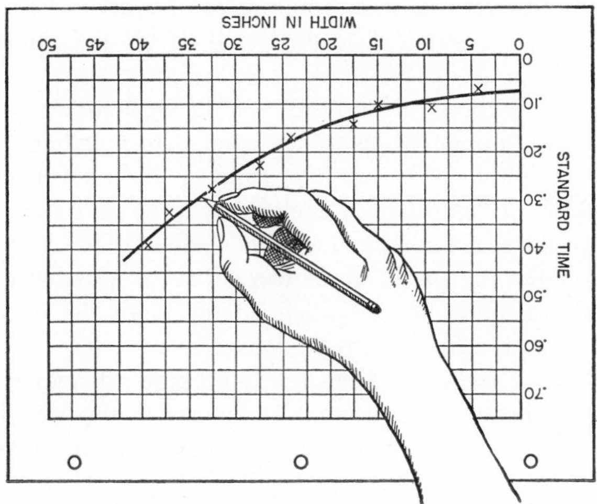

FIG. 15. A good way to sketch in a curved line is to turn the page upside down and utilize the circular motion of the arm.

sketch was made for us by my daughter Jeane. When you turn the sheet upside down, the natural circular motion of your arm helps to form the curve.

6. *Draw curves to represent the correct relations between dependent variables and their controlling dimensions.*

Curves for Everyday Use

Should you plan to use your curves as drawn, they should be specially set up. Perhaps "copied" or "traced" is more descriptive. At any rate, you should not use the originals containing all the plotted points. Primarily, the basic plotted curve should be carefully preserved for use when revisions become necessary.

[1] Riggleman, John R., "Graphic Methods for Presenting Business Statistics," 2d ed., p. 221, McGraw-Hill Book Company, Inc., New York, 1936.

Second, curves of timestudy element data used by standard setters should be sharply drawn lines, completely free from plotted points. Even so, they have some disadvantages. But there is one decided advantage. Variable element data is available for use immediately after the curve is drawn. And it should be used under certain conditions. The chief instance is when you have but a few standards to set.

Generally, you will want to reproduce curve solutions if you will be working with them in line form. In such cases, you should use distinctive rulings. You may draw dotted lines for certain factors. One example is the family-of-curves combination I worked out for Fig. 7, Chap. 2. There I used solid, dashed, and dotted lines to distinguish the three families.

If there are only three or four curves, a different ruling may be used to distinguish each one. If there are more than four lines, some pattern can be adopted. For example, suppose curves were used for a range in width or length of 6 inches, with ½-inch sizes included. Then, you could make all the inch lines solid. The ½-inch curves could be dotted. Again, if there were four to a pattern, the inch curves could be solid. The ½-inch curves might be dashed. The ¼-inch and ¾-inch curves could be dotted.

All these little details of design are important. They can save you both time and mistakes. You would take care of them in short order if you tried to use the curves every day to set operation time standards.

7. *Curves of families that are to be used repeatedly should be drawn in dotted, dashed, and solid lines to denote dimension types, and plotted points should not be shown.*

Curve and Chart Lettering

Our finished work should be good-looking. This requires a word about lettering or printing, as you may call it. Either way, we have to print letters and numbers on curves and charts. And we don't want our captions to bring out a comment like the one my drawing teacher made. He said, "Phil, you turn out a pretty fair drawing and then spoil it with punk lettering."

That hurt. So I began to letter instead of write. All my longhand reports were lettered. On the back of all my timestudies, everything was lettered. After a while, I could letter reasonably well, and almost as fast as I could write.

Part of my improvement came through the adoption of an easy-to-form style of lettering. It was between an engineering and an architectural type. The difference lay in using curved lines instead of straight ones in forming certain of the letters. In essence, you can tell when a line is not straight.

That reminds me of a story. Back when I was just out of high school, I worked on the Missouri Pacific Railroad. One summer, my boss was "lining track." He would sit on one rail and, with a spyglass, line the track for a mile or more ahead. He had the reputation for doing the best job of lining on the whole system. After watching this exacting process many times, one day I asked, "Mr. McCullough, if it takes all that effort to get the track straight, how in the world can you line a curve?" He said, "That's easy. You can tell when track ain't straight."

So if you will try using some curves instead of straight lines, you can make certain letters much easier. For instance, A, D, K, L, and R have curves as shown in the top line of the lettering example. See Fig. 16.[1]

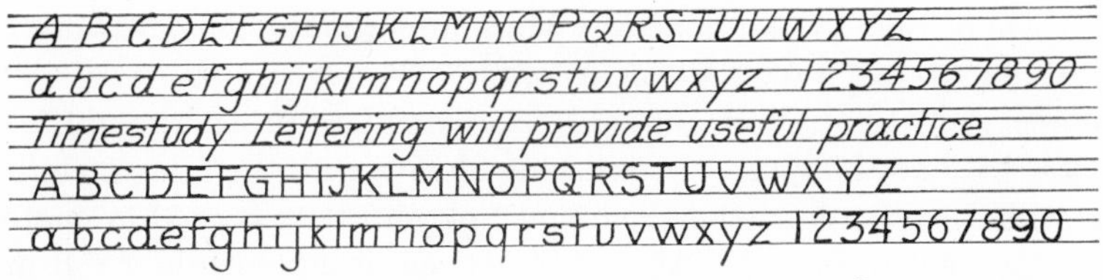

A B C D E F G H I J K L M N O P Q R S T U V W X Y Z
a b c d e f g h i j k l m n o p q r s t u v w x y z 1 2 3 4 5 6 7 8 9 0
Timestudy Lettering will provide useful practice
A B C D E F G H I J K L M N O P Q R S T U V W X Y Z
a b c d e f g h i j k l m n o p q r s t u v w x y z 1 2 3 4 5 6 7 8 9 0

FIG. 16. Adopt a style of lettering you can practice using until you can turn out a goodlooking product.

Notice another detail. B, E, F, and similar letters are divided above the center line. Again, you can tell when the cross-line is out if it is not in the center when it is supposed to be there. But if it is well above or below center, as in A or B, your small variations are not noticed.

If your lettering is not good, you should correct the difficulty. Often, all that is necessary is more practice. But you should not practice on a job that the boss is waiting to have turned in. You may spoil it. Do your practicing on something where quivering lines won't matter. If the style you are using is difficult to master, adopt an easier one. But practice until you can turn out a good-looking curve or chart, neatly lettered.

8. *Adopt an easy-to-form style of printing and practice it until your lettering is entirely acceptable.*

[1] For other pointers on drawing, see the excellent appendix in Riggleman, J. R., "Graphic Methods for Presenting Business Statistics," 2d ed., McGraw-Hill Book Company, Inc., New York, 1936.

Timestudy Data Plotting

Now I want to add a couple more rules primarily for timestudy men. The first has to do with plotting timestudy standards for variable elements. Most timestudy curves are drawn to measure the effect on standard time caused by some dimensional factor. In these cases, your dependent—effect—is Standard Time. Your independent variable—cause—is Dimension.

In the general case, each plotted point is a time standard. Ordinarily, it results from a timestudy that has been converted to normal pace with relax added. It is the standard time for an element that would have been allowed if an operation "rate" had been set from the individual timestudy.

I recommend that you plot only standard times. You can omit relax factors, although my personal preference is to include them. Actual times cannot logically be compared. Consequently, I consider it a waste of time to plot actuals. More importantly, they are very apt to lead you to reach wrong conclusions.

When you include both conversions as standard procedure, mistakes are less likely to happen. By working always with the relax included, you cannot overlook it when some part of your data is used in another operation or department. Also, it is less confusing to explain. It may appear like sleight of hand to foremen or mechanics if you add on or take off percentages of relax during an explanation of changes in standards. So we might set up an important rule for timestudy data plotting by saying that

9. *Points plotted on curves should be standard times, all converted to the same normal rating with proper relax factors included.*

Curve Heading

The second rule of concern to timestudy men relates to positive identification. Each standard data curve should have on it several notes to clearly identify it. You can best arrange for such descriptive notes by specially designed headings at the top of your curve sheet (Fig. 17). You can do this quite inexpensively when you use several hundred sheets of cross-section paper.

One way to make up standardized cross-section paper is by the photo-offset process. To prepare, make a dummy by pasting together the design features suitable for your Standards Department. The cross-section paper chosen would ordinarily be 20 squares per inch. However, one of the most skilled men I know prefers millimeter ruling.

Paste the selected type of cross-section ruling on a larger piece of white cardboard. Locate it to allow for proper margins. Then neatly letter your heading captions. Add other identifying notes like your Company name. These may be printed on strips of paper if your plant has equipment available. Mount the lettering on your cardboard dummy in proper alignment with the cross-section paper.

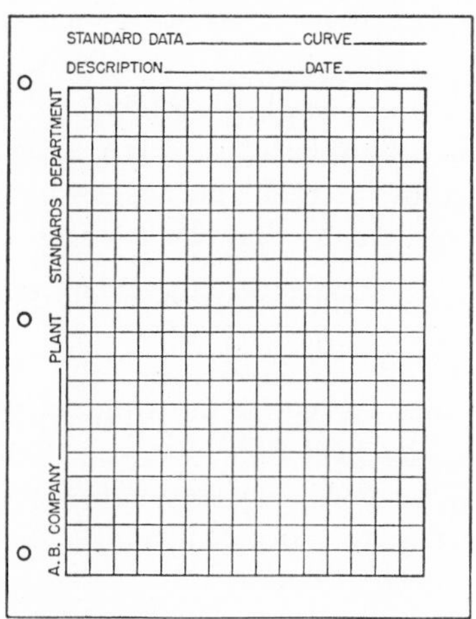

FIG. 17. Standardized curve headings may be printed on the cross-section paper when quantity to be used warrants it.

Next come the border lines. Remember the pasted dummy is oversize. It is to be reduced photographically to 8½ by 11 inches. So you should spot the approximate locations of your top and bottom margin lines. Suppose the space allotted measures 14½ inches. For this length, the width must be 14.5/11 times 8.5 or 11.2 inches. Allowing 1 inch for the margin where Dimension scale and lettering will go, provides about ¾ inch when reduced. Measuring from this line across a width of 11.2 inches locates the paper edge on the binding margin. This should be ample. An inch and a half after reduction is about right as a margin. If the over-all width thus determined does not give you the margins you want, then start the border lining from the width of your pasted dummy to determine your length margins.

When you have finally located your margin lines, there is another detail to include. I suggest a border line all around the completed cross-section paper. The purpose is to get back copies from Blueprinting that somewhat resemble an 8½- by 11-inch page. So if you are accustomed to blueprints trimmed on the bias, put an ink border line all around the dummy. Then draw pencil lines outside that border about ¼ inch away from it for the photo-offset printer to work to for paper size when photographing the dummy.

Black printing is cheaper, of course, but I do not recommend it. Plottings stand out much better on colored rulings. Orange or green printing provides better working conditions when you are doing an extensive job of curve plotting.

The headings you want to print on your curve paper will vary with plant requirements. But several are very necessary when you use these sheets for element timestudy data analysis. They are, first and most important, the *Date*, second, the *Element* description, and third, the *Data* designation. This latter is often a code number. Curve *Number* is very useful for reference purposes when your standard data includes more than one curve. But don't forget the *Date*.

10. *Put the Date on each curve, together with Element description and other positive identification.*

With these basic rules for curve drawing set down, we can move on to curve analysis. This next step, although going on simultaneously with curve drawing, is purposely separated for easier discussion. Thus, our next chapter treats more of where than of how to draw your curves.

CHAPTER 4

Analyze Variables

Curve plotting is one of our best ways to analyze variables. I think it is also the easiest way. Perhaps it is this easy phase that leads some of us to make mistakes in using this analytical tool. We tend to over-simplify—to average unlike conditions.

Averaging is a poor way to avoid the mental work of analysis. Therefore, to gain better analyses, we must be more exacting in our curve plottings. This is not difficult. Nor does it take a lot more time. But you have to do more thinking before you make marks on paper.

Do Not Over-simplify

At the outset we must keep in mind that we are working with effect. We are trying to find the cause or causes of variation. Usually, these are multiple. Yet most of us try to find simple solutions to complex problems. We can't be bothered with refinement. We plot all our points in the same symbol. That is, the first time. But the points do not line up. See Fig. 18*a, c, e.*

At this stage, some may fudge a solution. A few will rub out the unruly points. The professional-minded man will make a fresh start. But time has been wasted. What is worse, one line may be drawn that includes a broad average of variable conditions.

You should avoid this type of mistake by assuming there are multiple causes. You should prove that a simple solution is correct before you apply it. The easiest way is to plot with symbols or colored pencils. You should use a different symbol to designate each suspected difference. Then, if different symbols fall on the same line, to that degree your suspicions were unfounded.

Notice in Figs. 18*b, d, f* how two or more curves are indicated by the different symbols. Figure 18*b* compares a community survey of wage rates with those of your company, shall we say. Normally, you

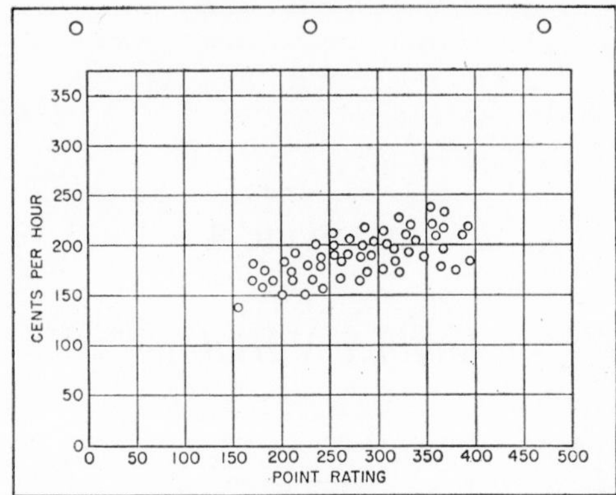

a. Not correct. One curve would average a spread of about 35 per cent.

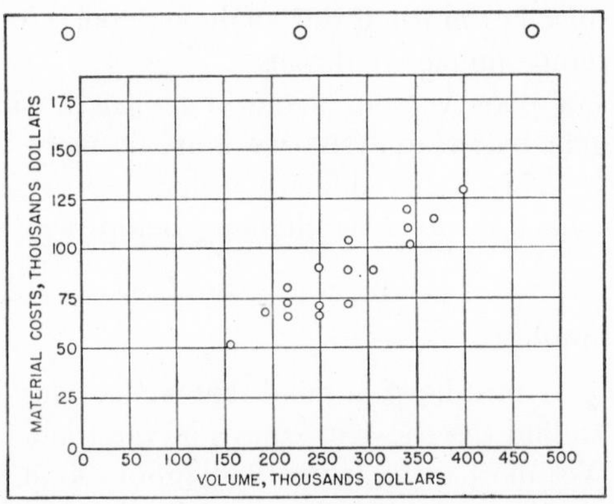

c. Not correct. Maximum spread shown is around 45 per cent.

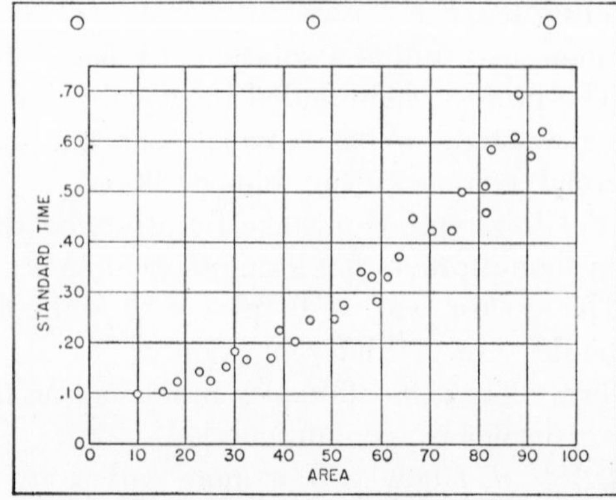

e. Not correct. Spread ranges from 20 to 30 per cent.

FIG. 18. Multiple causes should be

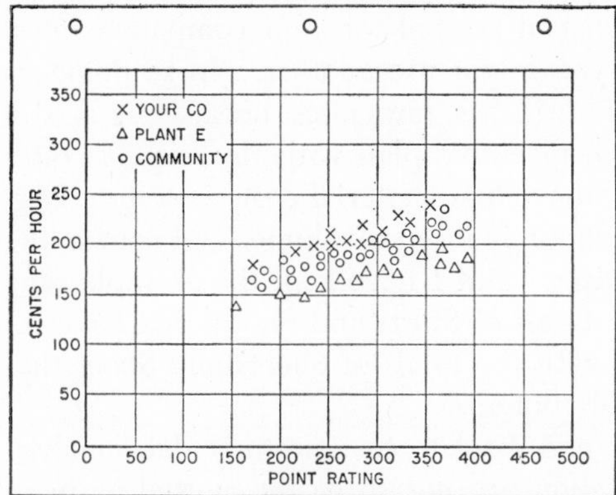

b. Correct. Three symbols separate your co. and Plant E from community.

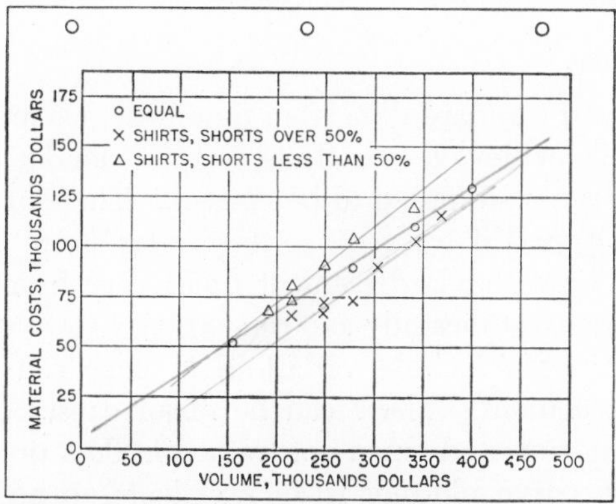

d. Correct. Three groupings show need for distinguishing product mix.

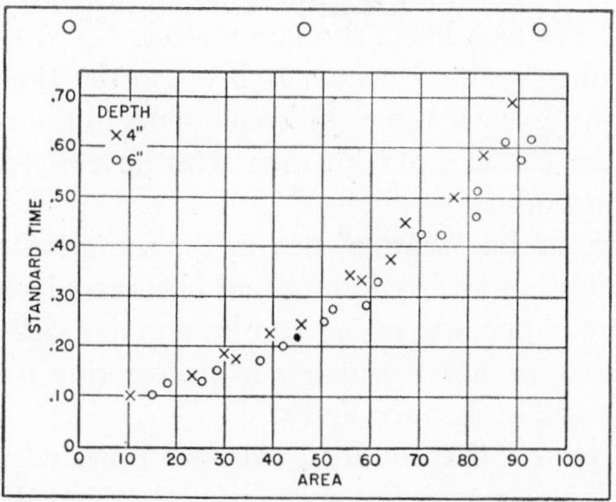

f. Correct. Recognizing depth as factor reduces the error of averaging. distinguished by different symbols.

would use a special symbol for your company's rates. For the community rates, you might use another. In so doing, you could fail to show that Plant *E* has low rates because it is still using an old-fashioned wage incentive plan with "loose piece rates."

Figure 18*d* shows how material costs vary to a large extent according to the product mix in sales volume. Of course, there are hundreds of probable mixes. But I have kept the example simple by grouping. I compare the totals of Shirts and Shorts that have comparatively low material costs with the totals of Sheets and Shoes that have relatively higher material contents.

Figures 18*e* and *f* relate to timestudy data analysis. In this field, causes of variation are not so easily spotted as in our two previous examples. So before describing these curves, I want to discuss some timestudy factors that may cause "scatter."

Effect and Cause

To build sound standard data from timestudy, we must find out why time varies. To achieve this analysis, we plot standard element times. These standards are supposed to be correct. These are the times that we would have used if we were setting "rates" from individual timestudies. But these standard element times vary from each other for two sets of reasons—timestudy and dimensions.

Timestudy reasons include variations in pace rating, watch reading, and work content. These can be major causes of element time variation among timestudy men not trained in data preparation. Said the other way, curve plotting is an excellent "go–no-go" gauge that clearly shows whether or not the observers are qualified timestudy men. My belief is that they are not qualified when the plotted results of their timestudies look like a shotgun scatter.

One reason the "scatter" occurs is because the timestudy men did not read their watches at the right breakpoints in the operation cycles. This effect often shows up with men who have been "setting rates" from single timestudies.

A second reason for "scatter" lies in the variations in rating pace. These can be substantial because not all observers have had the training they require. Because rating can be a major variable, my recommendation is that extensive training in pace rating be given to bring the variations within tolerance limits.

If, then, we assume that the foregoing two timestudy variations have been corrected, the remaining spread in plottings should be caused mainly by dimensional factors. Such variations should be separated on the timestudies by finer breakdown. Where this is not possible because of the way the work is done, then the element descriptions on the timestudies must be altered to clearly indicate differences in work content. Certainly, plottings will spread all over the map if they include mixtures of "horses and apples."

The variations related to dimensions should be the only important ones causing a spread in plotted points. The spread should depict the variables you are obligated to measure. Figure 18*f* is one example of how variations in work content should be sought out and defined.

Remember also, data is never finished. Changes will come later. Engineers in a going concern are sure to change designs to maintain progress. Competitors and your customers are going to rearrange any average you may have set up. When these changes occur, they will affect your data. New studies will have to be taken. New points will be plotted. These new points will extend or expand your data. At this and successive stages, it will be most convenient to have your curves show the original analyses in designating symbols. So let's make it a rule to

1. *Plot every suspected difference in an identifying symbol or color.*

Sales Dollars

If we have plugged all the leaks mentioned thus far, the plotted points may still be all over the lot. That may result from an error in selecting your dimensional measure. For example, you may be plotting Labor Costs in order to set up some form of cost control. You may have selected Sales Dollars as a measure of Volume of business. Many do. That's why I worked out Figs. 19*a*, *b*. Let me say, "If there is one wrong measure worse than most, it is sales dollars." To emphasize, let me point out that the sales dollars in this case have four different values in terms of cost. These are

Shirts \$1.25 Shorts \$1.43 Sheets \$1.11 Shoes \$.91

Besides these variations, there are those caused by differences in material content. These amounts in our four sales dollars are

Shirts \$.24 Shorts \$.14 Sheets \$.45 Shoes \$.44

Also if, as should be the case, most companies had different overheads for their several products, we would have a third variable concealed in sales dollars.[1]

As you can see, these three—profit, material, and overhead—might

[1] Carroll, Phil, "How to Control Production Costs," McGraw-Hill Book Company, Inc., New York, 1953.

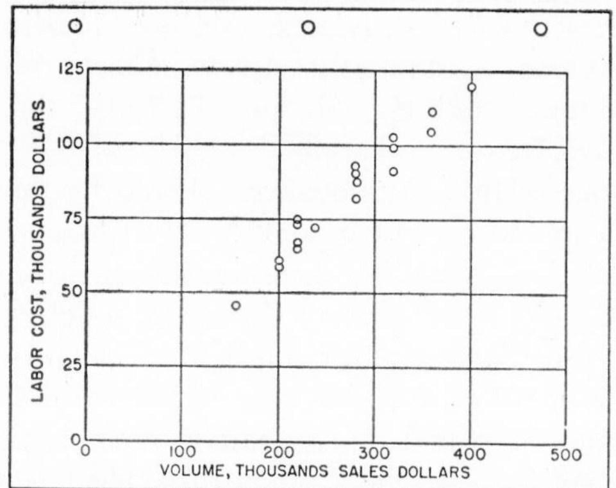

a. Not correct. Sales dollars in themselves contain several variables.

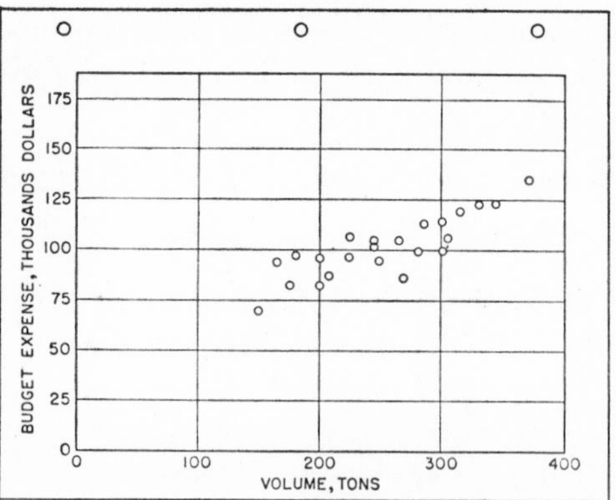

c. Not correct. Tons do not correctly measure mixed production.

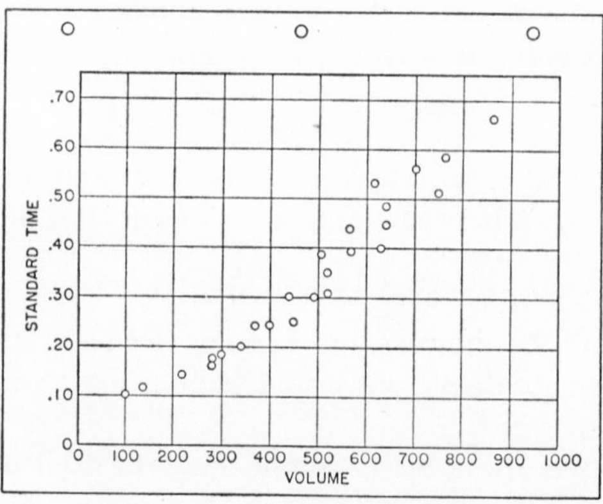

e. Not correct. Points seem to line up when plotted against Volume.

FIG. 19. Be careful of the Dimensions

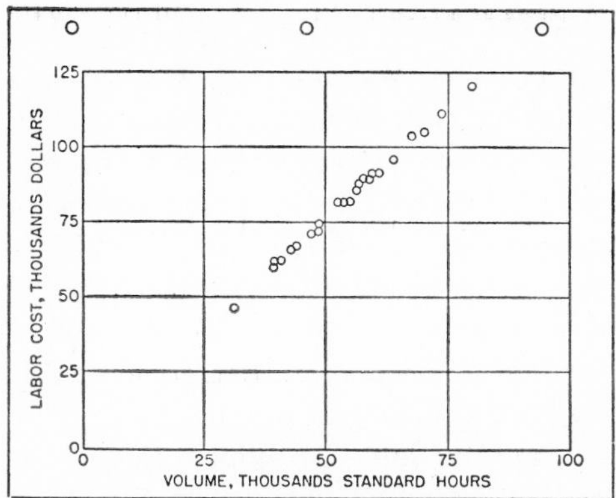

b. Correct. Standard hours is a much better measure of output.

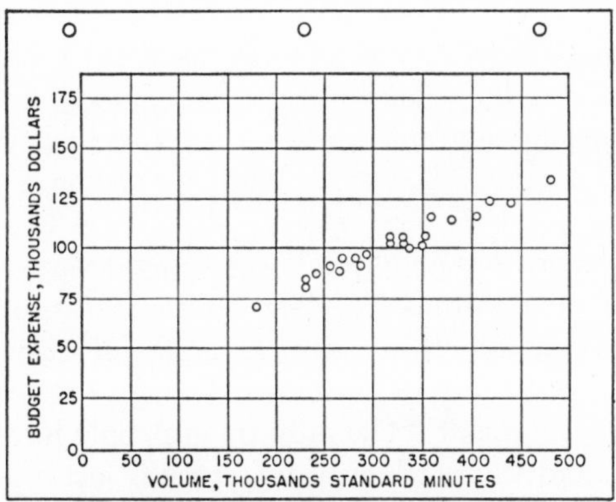

d. Correct. Standard Minutes is the best measure of conversion.

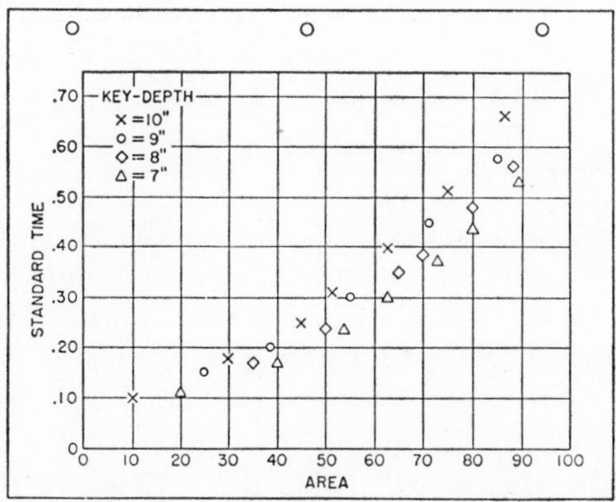

f. Correct. Four distinct curves show up when Area and Depth are used. you choose for curve plotting.

combine to show weird results in the many uses made of the erroneous sales-dollar measure. That reminds me of a manager who tried to prove we were making cost savings with per cents of sales dollars. True, the per cent of labor cost had declined over the periods reported. Actually however, we had sold an increased proportion of production that contained more costly materials.

The three variables concealed in sales dollars combine here to show a scatter spread in Fig. 19*a* of about 17 per cent. What we have actually is a large family of curves. Each one would have to carry a symbol that designated the current product mix. The better measure of Standard Hours used in Fig. 19*b* reduces this to around 5 per cent. This smaller variation is caused by the changing mix of wage rates.

Tons of Material

Another wrong dimension commonly used in Tons. Most of the foundry managers I have known were raised to think that Tons did measure their production and sales. My farfetched way of trying to disprove this is to say. "The more work we do on a ton, the less it weighs."

Figure 19*c* shows how widely a budget might vary if it were based on total tons of mixed products. The alternative is to use symbols in an effort to unscramble this complex family of curves. Looked at differently, most plants are in business to convert—to apply their skills. As Boss Kettering states it, "The only thing people have to sell is their time and effort and the product of a factory is just a packing crate in which the people working there ship out their labor and get money in return for it."[1]

Material is the vehicle of transfer. So "value added" is what we are trying to measure. For this purpose, Standard Minutes of production or sales is a much better dimension (Fig. 19*d*).

Volume versus Area

Similar mistakes can be made in selecting the dimension for measuring variable elements in timestudy. For example, you may plot standard element times against Volume when you should have used Area. For instance, take a look at Fig. 19*e*. The points seem to line up reasonably well. Actually there is about 35 per cent spread between low and high trend lines of the scatter. A line drawn through the center of the spread will halve this. Even so, the tightness or

[1] Boyd, T. A., "Professional Amateur," p. 201, E. P. Dutton & Co., Inc., New York, 1957.

looseness would be roughly 17.5 per cent. That's too much. Such work standards would be unfair.

In contrast, by separately distinguishing Area and Depth, the points line up on distinct curves (Fig. 19*f*) with about 10 per cent spread. Averaging has been avoided. The analysis is clear for the problem as it exists. In addition, the groundwork is already laid for expansion when new Depths are introduced.

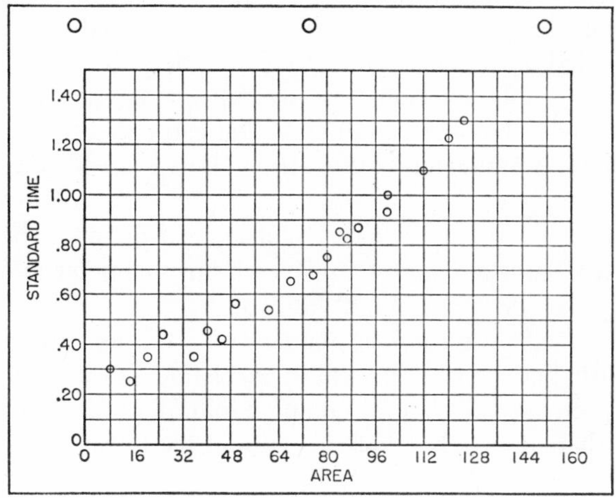

a Not correct

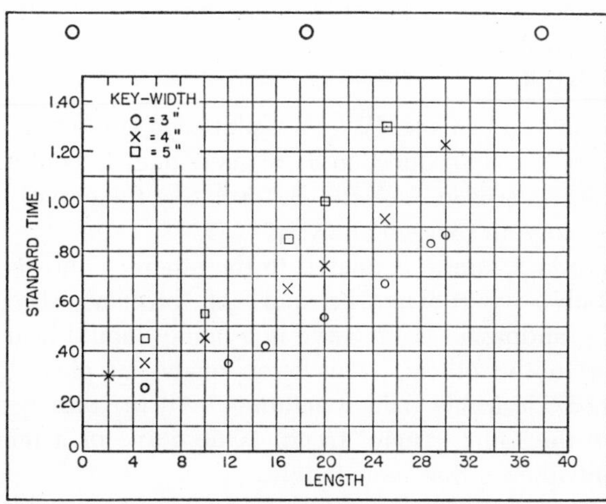

b Correct

Fig. 20. Plot suspected differences in distinguishing symbols instead of seeking an over-simplified solution.

The same type of mistake is often made by using Area when Length and Width would be more correct. This is true particularly when there is a directional influence. Painting is an example. With working limited to a vertical stroke, area no longer can be a correct denominator for work measurement. True, there may be no apparent errors in large dimensions. But compare the Area with $L \times W$ analysis in the smaller ranges. Notice how the dispersion of plottings increases for the low areas in Fig. 20*a*, marked "Not Correct."

What I have tried to explain here must be interpreted properly. I am talking about correct analysis. My point is that the problems are complicated, as a rule. Since they are complex, you should avoid the errors of simple solutions, of coverup averages. But analysis is different from mechanical execution. You can correctly analyze without going into complicated arithmetic. Here is an illustration of the distinction. Suppose you have a variable element depending upon circumference. You can correctly plot against diameter because it is related by the constant factor 3.1416. Using diameter is a saving in mechanics yet no error is brought into your analysis.

Easier and faster ways are recommended. But be careful. Be sure to distinguish between short cuts in mechanics and short circuits in analytics. You should plan for complex solutions. If they turn out to be simple, that's fine. But look ahead and try to save the backtracking—rework. So another rule might be

2. *Expect a family of curves instead of a single curve that might average a compound variable.*

Per Cent Relations

At this point you can say, "Why not plot each curve of a family on a separate sheet?" Your question is a good one, if confusion results from too many curves in one set. But isolating the curves has a major disadvantage in your over-all analysis.

Each curve in a family is related to the others. This fact was best stated by Bob Seybert when he spoke of "brothers, sisters, cousins, uncles, and grandpas." Each curve in a family should bear a percentage relation to the others. This is an analytical phase that makes grouping more desirable than separating. All the curves of a family should have the same general trend. One curve of a family should not cross any other in that same family.

The number of curves in a family is infinite, we might say. Certainly this is true of most of the curves previously shown. One exception is those for the wage survey. There, we could have only as many as the number of companies represented. (Note, this wage rate series is not a family of curves in the meaning I am applying in this book because they are not interrelated.)

The number you draw is determined by the degree of accuracy you want to hold. In standard data building for job shop operations and indirect work measurement, my recommendation is to draw a curve for each 10 per cent of the vertical spread. More about this under the caption "How Many Curves?" later in this chapter.

Method Variable

To be more specific about families of timestudy data curves, one cause of different curves is variation in work method. Any change introduces a different work content into the element standard. To connect the curve of one method with that of another requires a step. This method of drawing is not logical. Actually each method should have its distinct curve. The error is obvious if you extend the curves to overlap. The dotted lines in Fig. 21 show what would be revealed

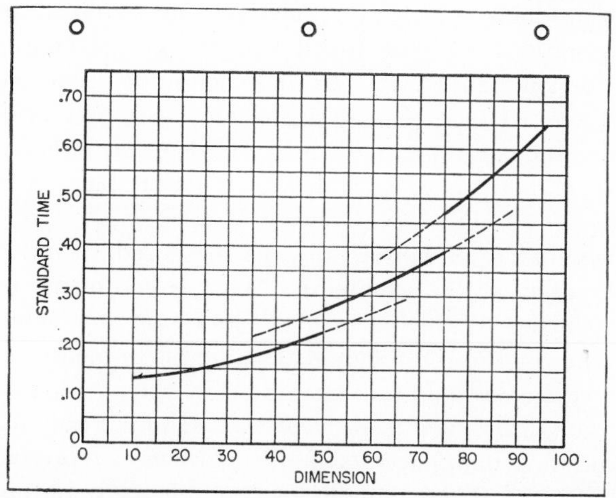

FIG. 21. The curves in this illustration have a spread of 20 per cent between them. That is the relation of one to the other but each is a portion of an individual curve. Each is not a part of one curve.

by timestudy if the three methods shown in this example were being used beyond the ranges assumed.

Another variation may occur that will cause curves to show a tendency to cross. For example, suppose your studies were taken in a small department. Suppose also that one man did all the jobs at one end of the range in size. His way of performing the element being analyzed could be different enough to throw off the curve. Plottings that include these slight variations may suggest that your curve should take a bend to the east that doesn't look right. It isn't.

"What to do?" you ask. The answer is to draw the curve where it should be. That is the purpose of this discussion about percentage relationship applied to timestudy data analysis. The point is this. People differ. They have different skills. They were trained or they learned by trial and error how to do their work. Even if all men working on a specific type of operation had been trained to use identical methods, still there would be noticeable differences after a few months of producing on their own. All of this refers to small differences that cannot be separated with the watch.

"What about micro-analysis?" is your obvious thought. "Maybe we should use motion pictures" is another. But remember, here we are using timestudy. Timestudy will be the method discussed for two reasons. In this book, I want to point out among other uses how charting can be used to get economical measurement and incentives on work now largely overlooked. I refer specifically to jobbing, tailor-made products, maintenance, clerical, and the like. Such small-quantity operations are not tuned up, are not standardized, and, usually, are not measured. When these conditions continue in plants practicing the exact type of analysis, we must assume that exactness is too expensive for non-repetitive work. That means either we have to use economical methods of work measurement or abandon the attempt to measure.

Now if we insist upon getting all work measured, then we must look to the methods of setting standards. That is one of my purposes in writing this book. With that in mind, let's look at exactness in data analysis. The question is, "Should we attempt to measure exactly all the tiny variations brought into operations by the people doing them?" We know they differ even if all were trained to use only one method.

Thus, timestudy data curves should be drawn to represent only one set of conditions. Those conditions, not of work but of method, should represent those skills and abilities defined as normal in your job descriptions. In so doing, you express in numbers what is described in words and thereby set fair work standards for normal qualified people.

Going from the specific of one curve to the general family, we apply the same reasoning. All your curves should represent the same normal skill. Therefore, they should bear percentage relationships to each other. The differences between them should be assignable to only the dimensional causes you are measuring.

3. *Curves of a family should bear percentage relationships to each other.*

How Many Curves?

You can use Rule 3 to help you answer the question, "How many curves are there in a family?" To begin the answer, take another look as the two curves on Figs. 19*e*, *f*. In connection with these, you read the statement about a spread of 35 per cent. Obviously, the per cent at the top of the range is different from that at the low end. That is a detail. You can take care of it after you grasp the idea explained here.

In Fig. 19*f* marked "Correct," the difference between curves is 10 per cent. That broad an average may be too much for your purposes. So much depends upon the applications you expect to make of your solutions. If you are working with any kind of assumptions like sales forecasts or budgets, chances are that 10 per cent spread will be inside the variations of actuals from assumptions.

In work measurement, I consider 10 per cent spread too much for repetitive operations. In contrast, long experience proves it to be *practically* accurate for jobbing work. The point is that accuracy costs money. This fact applies in all types of computation. Therefore, as I become more specific in discussing this cost in timestudy data applications, I hope you will easily translate my comments into the other fields you may be more immediately interested in.

Cost of standard setting like all types of overhead expense should be thought of just the same as milling, drilling, or most other shop operations. You want to find economical ways to measure work that many people say will "cost too much." What is "too much" may be understood better if explained in terms of tolerances as we use them in the shop. Repetitive and interchangeable parts are made to close tolerances. Tailor-made products usually have bigger tolerances. Part of the difference results directly from the degree of tooling. We do not make tools for small-quantity orders. We can't afford them. Consequently, we cannot get the accuracy. That is different, I know. We can get more accuracy in timestudy if we do spend the money. My question is, "How can we measure economically the many operations that have not yet been put on incentive?"

One detail of standard-setting cost lies in the answer to this question, "How many curves in a family?" It must give weight to the factors of both fairness and cost. Inaccuracies in work standards are unfair, either to the employee or to the company, as we erroneously express it. We should say, "unfair to the consumer."

Naturally, any number of curves selected is deliberately creating some inaccuracies. Thus, we must know what we are doing. To get down to cases, let's solve a specific problem. Take Fig. 22 as an example. In it, you have a common, everyday, complex variable.

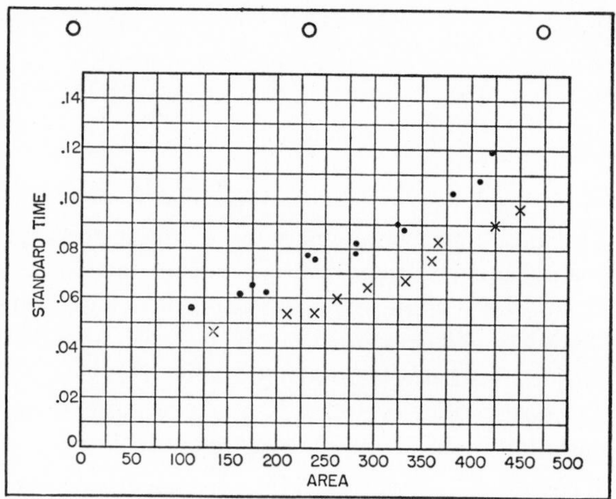

FIG. 22. The spread in these curves is about 30 per cent. Only the top and bottom points of the spread are shown to make this an example requiring further analysis.

The Area ranges from 100 to 450 square inches and the plottings show a spread of about 30 per cent.

What Curve Spacing?

"How many curves should we draw?" Your answer would be, "More than one, anyway," if you agree with me that 15 per cent plus and minus is too big an error. Then you might start in as most men do by adopting steps in Depth, say 1-inch increments. That approach would give you four or five curves since the Depth varies from 2½ to 6 inches. You could say you had the right number if you made the decision to use 1-inch steps. One of your timestudy analysts might have chosen ½-inch steps. He would have come up with eight curves. This dimension-step method of approach produces inconsistencies, as you can see. The reason is that these adopted solutions do not have reasons behind them. They may even be expensive to select because you may argue for 1-inch spacing and your timestudy man wants to use ½-inch intervals.

Both are wrong for one reason. The dimensional approach usually results in non-uniform per cent time increments. To have consistency in per cent, you must start with uniform per cent intervals in standard times.

To make an example using "about 30 per cent" as one spread in Fig. 22, here's the way I go about curve spacing. I say, "30 per cent divided by 10 per cent is 3 spaces or 4 curves." Getting down to the actual arithmetic is a little more complicated. We have to work with compounding percentages. So we resort to the compound interest formula where i is the interest rate and n is the number of periods interest is to be accumulated.

$$\text{Amount} = \text{Principle } (1 + i)^n$$

Utilizing this formula to set up curve spacing, we can think of it first in general terms. These could be

$$\text{Top curve} = \text{Bottom curve } (1 + \text{per cent space})^{\text{number spaces}}$$

In our problem, suppose we take a top-curve reading as .10 and one on the bottom as .08 minutes. These coupled with the 3 spaces just mentioned give us the equation

$$.10 \text{ min} = .08 \text{ min } (1 + \text{per cent space})^3$$

Now .10 divided by .08 equals 1.25. Then on my big, water-cooled, "guessing-stick," I find the cube root of 1.25 to be 1.0773. Using this as our per cent spacing where the total spread is actually only 25 per cent, our curve points are .0800, .0862, .0929 and .1000 minute.

You should go through this step of proper curve spacing for another reason. To apply Rule 1, in many cases, you have to pick arbitrary sub-divisions of your vertical spread in order to assign symbols for plotting suspected differences. As a result, you would expect the per cent spreads between your indicated curves to vary. Thus, two further steps become necessary.

1. Determine the number of curves you need to correctly portray the family and use the compounded per cent method to establish where these should be drawn.
2. Redefine the arbitrary grouping you used for analytical plotting so as to correctly specify the ranges in dimensions represented by your new curves.

The percentage spread you will use to determine "how many curves" in a family is something you will have to decide. When you do decide, you will have established a consistency. To give you something to chew on, let me put down the tolerance ranges I recommend:

1. For repetitive operation, 5 per cent
2. For non-repetitive work, 10 per cent
3. For some types of miscellaneous maintenance and indirect jobs, 15 and even 20 per cent

Those are generalities. But they grow out of many experiences in measuring the "impossible" types of operations. More will be written on this per cent method when we get into the construction of multi-variable charts. Hence we will conclude with Rule 4:

4. *Use a uniform per cent spacing in setting up the number of curves in a family.*

Four more rules for curve analysis and drawing will be discussed in the next chapter. They are separated from the foregoing general rules because they relate more specifically to timestudy data curves. You will find it worth-while to study them, however, even if you think you are not interested because, in certain respects, their principles apply to curves of analysis in most fields.

CHAPTER 5

Timestudy Data Curves

You have a picture from Chap. 4 of how curves should be arranged up and down. Now we should look at them the other way. This question is, "How far across the page should they extend?" My answer, "Studies must be taken over the entire range of the variables." Our purpose is to find out how standard times should change to compensate for differences in dimensional conditions. Of course, the extent of any range will differ from one plant to another. It may vary within the plant. It is in this connection that we want to outline the next rule of analysis.

Plants are expanded departments. Back in their beginning, a few men made the product in a little shed somewhere. As each business grew beyond the abilities of one man to supervise, separate departments were set up. Often, the subdividing cut up the ranges of our variable elements into several sections. To take our simplest timestudy example, maybe the Piece Handling now occurs as follows:

Department	*A*	*B*	*C*
Piece weight, pounds	5 to 35	20 to 50	40 to 80

Naturally, you would take timestudies over this entire range if all sizes were in one department. You would plot all handling element standards on one curve sheet. Probably, you would draw one continuous curve to represent the standards for *Pick Up Piece.*

But usually, when timestudies are started in any plant, we overlook this important detail. We take our studies and work up data for Department *A*. Later, maybe some other men are assigned to timestudy the work in Department *B*. To make the point, let's assume the worst condition, namely, that still another group does the study of Department *C*.

Study the Range

Already, you are way ahead of me. The three final Pick Up Piece curves would probably not form one continuous curve when brought together. They might look like Fig. 23. But we know that the breaks in the summary curve Fig. 23, exaggerated to illustrate, should not exist. The curve should be smooth. That means all the element standards for Pick Up Piece should be plotted on one curve.

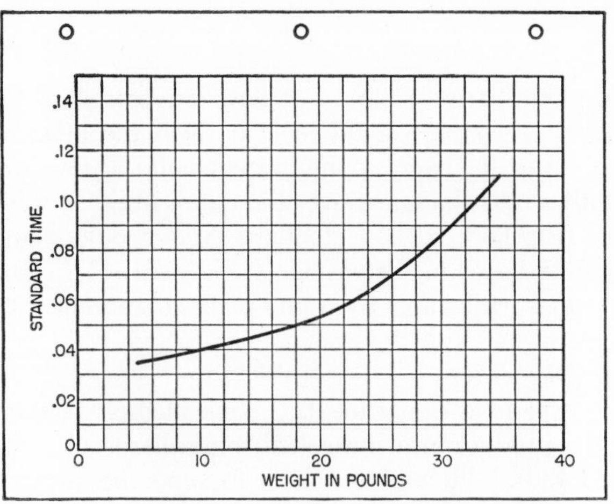

a Department *A*. Piece handling curve.

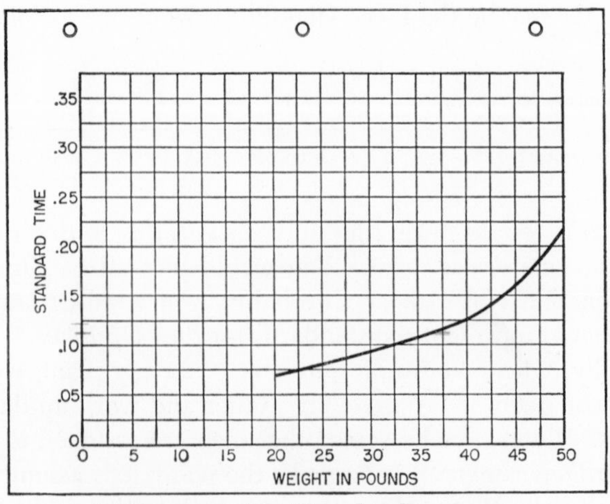

b Department *B*. Piece handling curve.

FIG. 23.

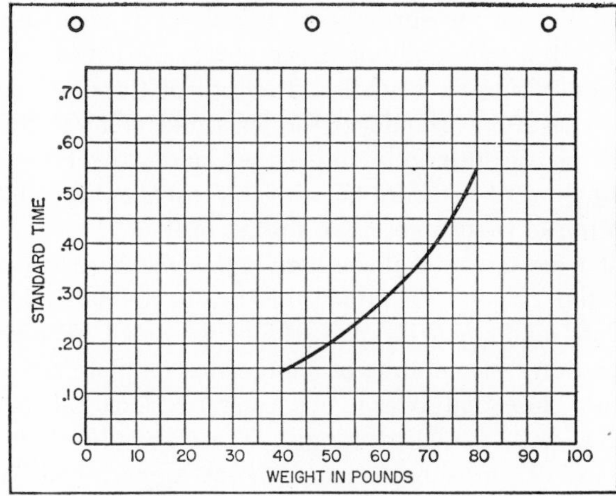

c Department *C*. Piece handling curve.

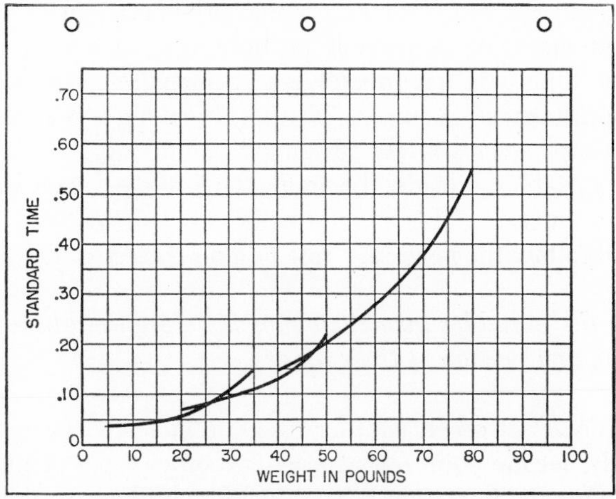

d Summary curve.

Fig. 23. (*Continued*). Overlaps in curves result when the three separately drawn curves in this example are brought together. Each curve looks all right by itself. But the exaggeration shown here can happen when parts of a range are studied separately.

You counter with, "But we set up the standards in Department *A* way back in June last year. Joe's group started in Department *B* seven months later. Shucks, Bill didn't start his studies in Department *C* until April." This can and does happen. It is more apt to be the rule than the exception. But study again the Summary curve. You know it is wrong. Yet yours may come out that way, too, if you have the responsibility for measuring work in several departments or plants. The reason is that the ends of every curve are extremes. The end sizes occur only once in a while. Because of this fact, you can get fewer studies than you should of the least and greatest sizes. While we have lots of pressure on us to get the standards set, we don't exert that same amount of pressure to bring the extreme sizes into production more often so we can get more studies of them.

The point I am trying to make here is that we must get consistency throughout the range. To attain this result, we must look beyond the immediate assignment for the studies we need. We will have to study all the range at one time or another to complete the job of work measurement. For that reason, we can't overlook the necessity for taking studies over the entire range. These may be limited to sampling because of pressure to cover some department "yesterday." And I can go along with this, because I do not believe in waiting until standards can be set for everything. That holds up coverage.

Your objective is to get standards that are consistent over the entire range. You may not succeed if portions are set up independently. At the same time, you have to solve each installation problem according to circumstances. Usually, "it's the squeaking wheel that gets the grease." That leaves you the alternative of taking studies to at least check the variables outside the immediate range. You must "hurry to get on incentive." This suggestion is one practical way to do your job and still follow the necessary rule to gain consistency.

5. *Study the variables over their ranges before establishing standards on any portion of their ranges.*

Now before I set down another rule you can read as applying only to timestudy, let me point out at least two other types of ranges that it includes. One is in expense analysis for budget setting. In this field, you should get the widest range in volume with corresponding expenses you can obtain. To exaggerate the error of depending upon a narrow range, think of how many different curves you could draw through one point.

The other type of range I want to mention is in wage-salary evaluation. If you recall the history, first we developed job evaluation. A straight line curve was drawn. Later, salary or position evaluation was worked out. When the two curves were brought together, in some plants at least, they crossed like those in Fig. 23*d*. Therefore, keep in mind that independent studies of parts of any range may reveal inconsistencies when brought together.

Do Not Extend the Range

Along with the study of range goes another important factor in curve making. It is a detail. Yet failure to observe it can lead to errors. It is brought up here because the error is made in analysis. You might contradict by saying that it is a detail of curve drawing.

The fact is this. Assume that you have a group of plotted points. You are all set to draw the curves. You may not do what some have done, but just the same, it is a mistake to extend your curves beyond the limits studied. It is so easy to extend the lines a little bit. Perhaps this is done without a second thought. But here's what happens. In the first place, most timestudy curves are concave upward. Consequently, an extension on either end is likely to produce tight standards. Second, it is a mistake to go beyond the data. You have no right to do that. That is guessing. And if you can guess an extra 10 per cent beyond your studies, your successor may go you one better. Before many years have passed, you wouldn't recognize your original curve.

Back in 1919 at Westinghouse, my boss insisted that we draw big roadblocks in India ink at both ends of a curve. He figured that it would be obvious if any extending were done. That is one approach. I do not recommend that one. It savors a little of the childish. But the idea behind the roadblock is thoroughly sound.

6. *Do not extend curves beyond the limits of your timestudy data.*

You can see from this discussion how you could make mistakes by extending curves in other fields. For example, what happens to certain operating expenses as you approach capacity—of one shift, two shifts? How do freight and selling expenses move when you expand territories? Until you know what new trend your curves will take, you will be wiser to follow this rule.

Analyze the Family

With Rule 6 before us, I want to couple it with Rule 3 that states, "Curves of a family should bear percentage relationships to each other." Together, these give us another analytical tool for working with curve families. It must be used with caution. Like anything else, it can be overdone. Remember, I said analytical tool. So use your head.

In curve families, frequently each curve has a different range. Some of the differences result from actual limitations in sizes. Also—and this is the principle—we need not study all the sizes. We can follow the rule used when there is only one curve. We say that we need a representative number of studies all along the range. Then why not understand that often a family of curves is only a vertical expansion of one curve introduced by a modifying variable?

It follows that you can tackle many problems in curve families more effectively by using some planning:

1. Concentrate your studies on the sizes that make up the major part of the range on one curve factor.
2. Study the curve to get it most accurately placed.
3. Spot the other curves with studies representative of their weighted activity.
4. Take enough studies, regardless of activity, to obtain a representative trend line.
5. Draw in the remaining curves in percentage relationship when this rule applies.

The procedure outlined *logically* permits you to extend all curves to the limits studied on any one. Remember however, this seeming contradiction of Rule 6 must be used with lots of good common sense.

What Shape of Curve?

None of the factors of curve analysis discussed thus far helps you to shape your curves. I did mention, however, that most curves are concave upward in my caution about extending them. "How do you know?" is the question we want to answer now. Perhaps the easiest way to explain is by example. Take Piece Handling, to illustrate. The curve heads skyward for the heavy weights. The reason becomes clear when you think about it. Suppose the heaviest weight you could lift was 150 pounds. If that is all you can possibly lift, then you could not lift 151 pounds even if you were allowed all day to do it.

As you approach the maximum, each added pound takes more effort than the pound just before it. That extra amount is what causes the bend upward. It means that we must allow more time or relax for the eighty-first pound than we do for the thirty-first pound. The same general effect is produced by added lengths, areas, and volumes. The larger ones tax the reach, strength, and other capacities of people. Because of this approach to capacity as dimensions increase, we get the concave upward curve in standard time data.

You may object by saying, "But I have seen a lot of straight-line curves in timestudy." That is true. Some could have been straight and correctly so. There are plenty of straight-line curves that are mathematically straight lines. Machine-time curves are common examples.

Contrariwise, we see many curve lines that are drawn straight because it is the easy thing to do. But wait. Some of these straight lines are correct within limits. Take a simple example. You have seen or heard about the Western prairies. They look as flat as a tabletop. But we know they curve somewhat in relation to the earth's surface. Obviously, then, we must think in terms of degree. In reality, we are back again to the per cent accuracy discussed previously.

Control the Error

Look at the curves in Fig. 24. Curve *a* represents a possible range of a variable. In this instance, a single straight line would be greatly in error if drawn in place of the curve. The maximum spread between the curve and the straight line is about 24 per cent. However, we can break up the curve into a series of straight lines. Curve *b* shows the approximations. Curve *b* is only an example set up to indicate how the full range may be sectionalized under actual shop conditions. When this happens, straight lines can be used while holding the error within prescribed tolerances. See Fig. 25 for the method to use.

Let's move on to the next step. In Curve *c* of Fig. 24, we show how the curve would look if our range were only from 10 to 45 pounds. This curve has been drawn in accordance with Rule 2 in Chap. 3. There we specified that the dimension and time scales chosen should be the largest we could use practically. As a result, the section that is noticeably curved in Curve *b* seems almost straight in Curve *c*. It would be even straighter if the section of the range were shorter so that the dimension scale could be stretched out farther. So we come down to the question, "How straight is a curve?" And our answer must depend upon per cent of accuracy. We can use a straight line when the error is within limits.

Two important cautions must be stated before we go on. First, remember our Rule 6 that prohibits the extension of your curves beyond the range of your timestudy observations. Applied here, the result could be that, at some future time, you would have to change a straight-line substitute back to a curve. This would become necessary more in error than prescribed by the limits you have set as standard when the extended part of your data showed the straight line to be tolerance.

The Curve Constant

The second caution is also another part of our analytical efforts. The caution is to watch out for the constant element that usually exists with every curve. The constant is the amount of standard time allowed at 0 Dimension. This constant may show up only when the curve is projected to the time axis. But there is some constant in almost every timestudy curve.

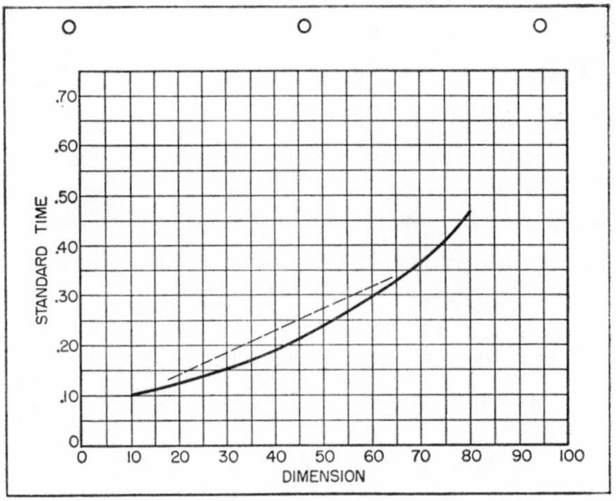

a Not correct—Maximum error about 24 per cent.

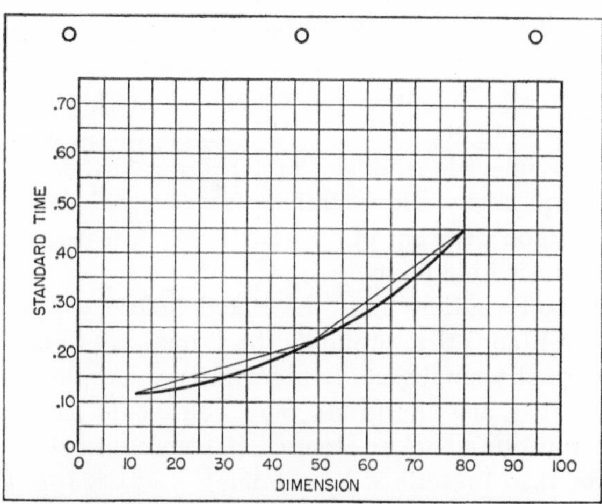

b Straight lines approximate a curve within reasonable limits of error. See Fig. 25 for the method to use.

FIG. 24. Examples showing the relations between straight and curved lines.

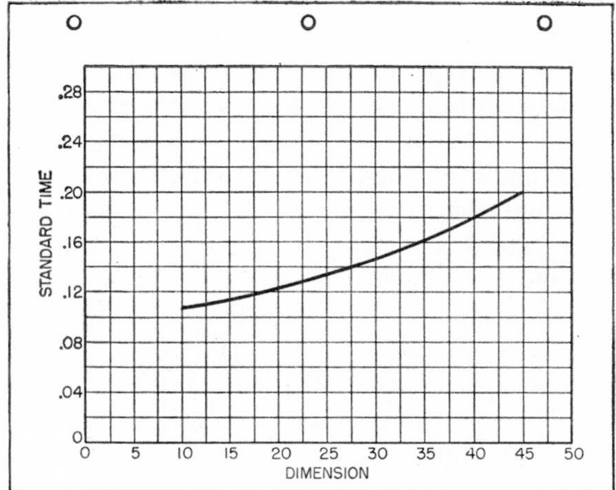

c Enlargement of lower section of Curve *b* shows a line that appears almost straight.

Fig. 24 (*Continued*).

As to the caution, you can see in Fig. 25 what is meant. The dotted curve illustrates the supposed true curve. It would have a constant of about .07 minute. On the other hand, the straight line projected would reveal the constant as a minus amount. This is contrary to the analytical point we are trying to make in this section. It should be self-evident that any extension in the low end of the range

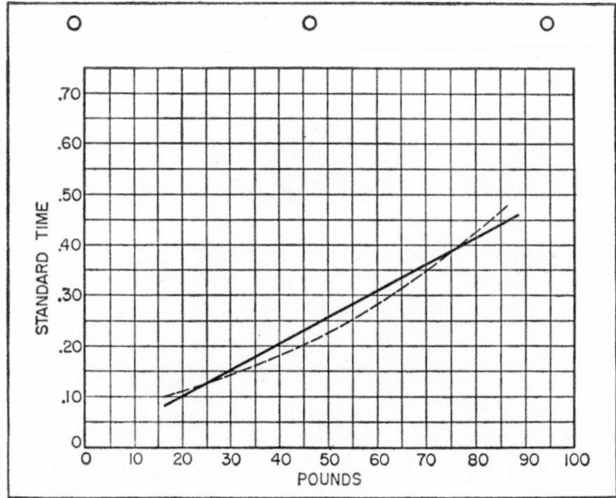

Fig. 25. A straight line used instead of a curve with small error. This example portrays why straight lines are so often drawn through a series of plotted points.

would require a change back to the curve. Only a slight change would bring a per cent of error greater than any reasonable tolerance. To reduce this to arithmetic, the spread between the true curve and the straight-line substitute is about 10 per cent at the lowest reading of around 17 pounds. At an extension to 13 pounds, the curve would read .09 minute and the straight line .06 minute. Now the spread is 33 per cent, calculated from .09 minute.

You can see from this example how extremely important the curve constant becomes in the lower ranges. It can have a large percentage influence on the standards in the small sizes. The effect is so important that I urge you to enlarge the lower part of a range when your small sizes approach 0 Dimension. You might make it a rule to blow up the lower 10 per cent when your data curve approaches 0.

Summarizing, we might set down a rule on the shape of curves as

7. *Expect curves of your variables to take the concave upward shape with a definite constant time indicated for 0 Dimension.*

The "Per Each" Error

Next comes a detail in standard data preparation that misleads some timestudy men. Maybe you have tripped over it. The difficulty comes about largely because of the constant previously discussed. It shows up when you seek a common denominator to a variable, usually of number. So you divide your element standards by the quantity to get a "per each" answer. This is the mistake. You cannot get a correct analysis then, because the constant has been prorated. Only after you have made the most careful kind of timestudy and excluded all constant time can you get away with this slide-rule leveling process.

The mistake is one of over-simplification. We attempt to make a constant "per value" out of a variable. Suppose, to illustrate, that we had computed some standards per nail for coremaking or molding.

Study Number....	1	2	3	4	5	6	7
Set one nail........	.120	.080	.065	.055	.050	.047	.045

Several of these answers come out reasonably close together. At this point, the easy step is to pick a value, or what is worse, to take an average. Both are wrong. Our inconsistent answers would look like Fig. 26*a* if we knew enough to plot them.

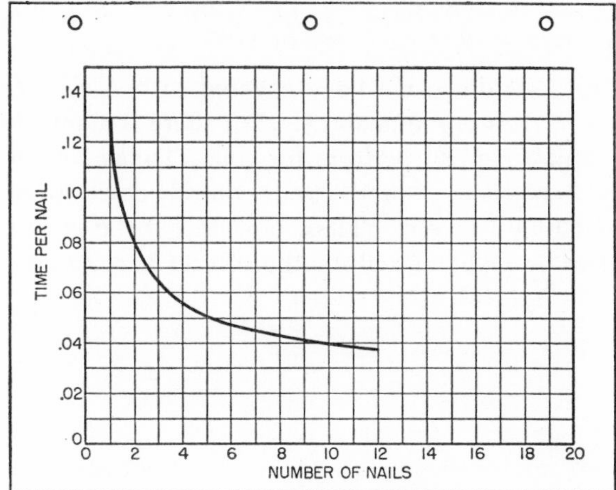

a A reciprocal curve results from prorating a Constant.

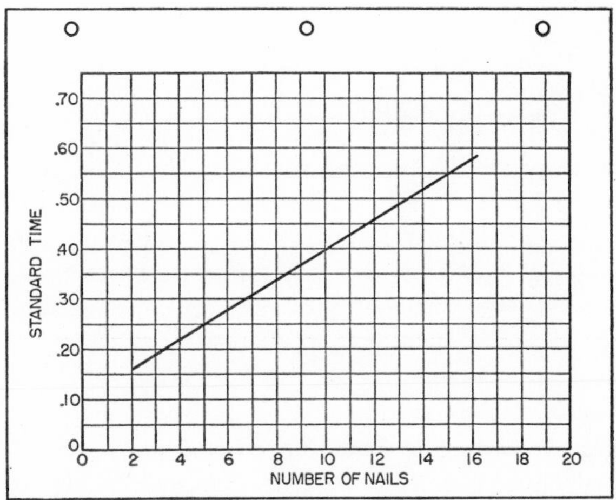

b A better and easier method is to plot against Number.

FIG. 26. Curves showing the correct way to analyze Standard Time elements that seemingly should have a constant per unit value.

My recommendation is to avoid the clerical effort of dividing and the error of trying to arrive at a uniform time "per each." Instead, plot your data against Number. See Fig. 26*b*. This is better practice, in my opinion, even if the constant does wash out because quantity is large relatively. This approach is better engineering and the final analysis is right, not wrong.

8. *Plot curves for elements that appear to have per unit values using Number as the dimensional factor.*

With this rule set down we have covered in two chapters the important points of data curve analysis. But there is another important function curve plotting can perform for you. To my way of thinking, it is a very constructive production control device. You should utilize it to its fullest extent. Thus, how to get the most from your timestudy effort by planning will be the subject of our next chapter.

CHAPTER 6

Curves as Planning Controls

"How many points are necessary to determine a straight line?" You answer, "Two." "How many for a circle?" You say "Three." "How many points are necessary to establish a curve in standard time data?" Your reply may be, "That depends." It does. The number should be related to the measurements we must have. And yet, I find that usually we waste time on timestudies at points in a range even when our data is poorly supported by insufficient studies at other points.

The paradox is the same one we see in the shop every day. We go out to take a study of an assembly. We find that the assemblies cannot be completed because all the pieces are not there. We have too many of some and not enough of other parts. Planning has fallen down. Yet in timestudy, since we are not controlled by physical limitations, such as the absence of nuts, bolts, and washers, we may "complete" our data because the boss says to start the installation next Monday. It isn't any more complete than the assembly. But—we may not know it. At the same time, we have too many studies of certain operations. The reason is that we did not plan any better than Production Control scheduled the parts for assembly, if as well.

The Variables Control

Look at it this way. If you worked like a "rate setter" from individual studies, you would handle every element as if it were a constant. If, later, you decided to build data, you would not need very many studies if all the elements actually were constants. But as soon as variables must be considered, the data solution really becomes the solution of the variables. The constants are relatively easy to determine. Actually, you get more studies of them than you need. Obviously, then, we make our efforts productive according to how well we control the studies of the variables.

Returning to the opening question about a straight line, we remember that only two points are required. However, that has only the slightest bearing on our approach because variable element lines are curved, as a rule. But it serves as a ridiculous extreme to emphasize the point. Let's put it another way. Suppose you were plotting the solution to a formula. You would spot points at intervals. You would plot more points where the curve changed rapidly. You would skip more space where the curve was relatively flat. The points might be about an inch apart. You would need only a few points because you had the shape of the curve expressed in a formula. In contrast, you are seeking the timestudy curve. You do not know what its shape is. But is that any reason for getting 15 or 20 times as many studies as are required at some points on your curve and few or none at other places?

Theoretically, you do not need any more than a representative number of points spread out over the entire range. Surely that is all that would be needed if you could rely absolutely on each one to be correct, as with a known equation. Suppose you double that number to satisfy yourself. Then add in the extras you get "fer nuthin." The extras come from studies taken to get readings on some other variable you need to learn more about. All these together are not nearly as many points as you usually get. Why?

Careless Timestudy

We do a lot of indirect labor for two reasons. The first I will try to explain by using an incident. This happened in a training group. The trainees had each performed an operation designed to provide timestudy practice for data building. The studies taken were for a range of distances. At the conclusion, the instructor said, "Now compute your element standards. Plot them. Then draw in your curve."

After considerable time, one of the trainees said, "I think we need more studies." After some discussion, it was decided to repeat the sequence. That gave each man double the number of points. When these were plotted, the instructor asked, "Did the added studies help you?" The answer in chorus was, "No!"

Of course, these men were trainees. Their studies were rather poor. Yet, at least one man thought he could improve upon the results of his poor timestudies by taking more of the same kind. Whether you call it indecision or attempting to average errors, the result is the same. We take too many studies because they are not sufficiently correct. We try to bolster the weakness of the studies with a mass of observations. That wastes timestudy time. We should remove the causes, as described earlier in Chap. 4.

Duplication

The extra points resulting from poor timestudy are irrelevant to our theme of planning. But they all look alike to the unpracticed eye. I had to get them separated from our thinking. Now the second reason for the extra studies, the one I am trying to help you overcome by suggestions outlined in this chapter, is failure to plan. They just happen. Often they are "leaf raking," if you want to be blunt. The timestudy man runs out of work and asks, "What do you want me to do next?" You know, the way a person does in the office or shop. He is given work to do to keep him busy. What he does may accomplish no more than just that.

This sort of duplication and other studies taken intentionally can be saved by better planning. Here is where curves plotted for variable analysis can be made to perform a valuable by-product service. To do it, however, you must start them with your first studies.

Plotting and Planning

The anticipated curves should be laid out at the start of the project. They should provide for the ranges of the variables. The extremes of the range should be determined, perhaps, even before studies are started. In similar research projects the experts say, "Define the

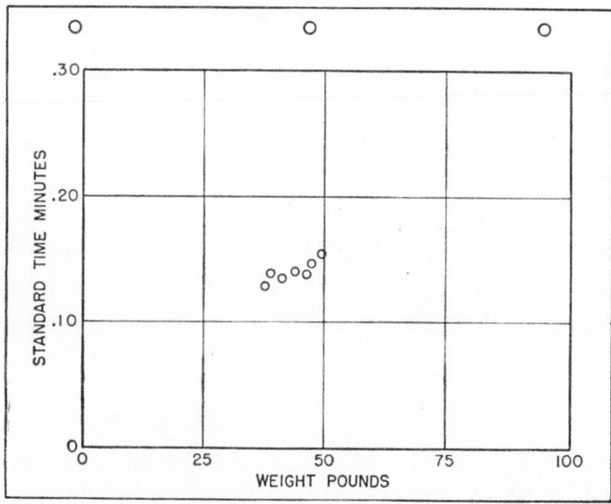

Fig. 27. Unplanned timestudy produces relatively too many studies of the "average job" and too few over the full range of the work.

problem." In defining yours, do not restrict yourself to studying only part of the range. Note again the fundamental on this phase of analysis described in Chap. 5. Set up to check, at least, the full ranges of your variables.

With curve sheets set up, the first few points you obtain can be plotted. Ordinarily, these will fall around the "average job" (Fig. 27). It is this easy-to-find study of the regular work that brings about most of the duplication. Right away, your production control should start. To save time and money, you want to stop further study of these "average jobs" as soon as you have a representative number. Place the emphasis on those studies you do not have.

If necessary, see what you can do to get the extremes produced so that you can get studies of these sizes (Fig. 28). Almost always these

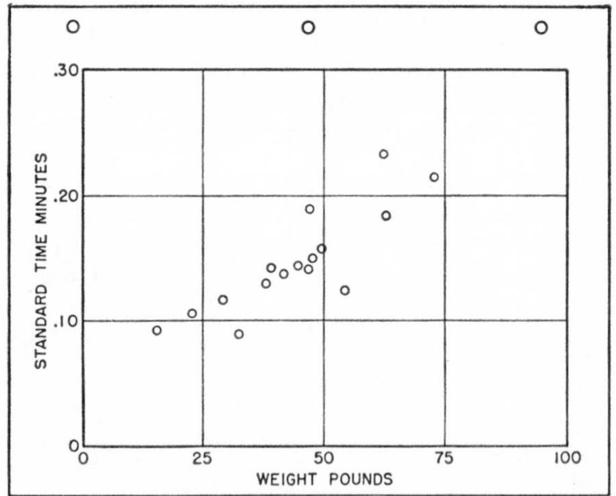

Fig. 28. With the full range of work portrayed by your curve layout, you should push to get studies at and near its extremes.

extremes hold up the concluding of your data. They are the jobs most unlikely to occur. If they come through once in 6 months, just to make an example, then the probabilities of timestudy might be about as follows:

Type of Job	*Probable Studies*
Extremes	Studies every 6 months
Next to extremes	Studies every 3 months
In between	Studies every month
Near average	Studies every week
Regular	Studies every day

You should not want to be restricted to only one study of either extreme. You would try to get several. Suppose you were unable to get more than three studies of each extreme. Then to emphasize my point, and refer again to the straight-line question, let me ask, "Do you need more than three of those between the extremes?" Before you say, "Yes," let me ask, "Would you set a "rate" for an operation from one timestudy?"

Please do not be misled. Far from trying to skimp on timestudy, I am insistent upon building sound data. I personally refuse to set standards from single studies. I try to get three or more before reaching a conclusion, for example, when making a check study of a "rate" that is in arbitration. But the point here is that some timestudy men will draw in a curve with a study or two of the extremes. Yet they will have dozens around the average. Many studies of the regular work are unnecessary waste. The time might better have been spent studying some type of work not yet on incentive. That is where you can improve timestudy efficiency by planning. You can control the number of studies. You should limit them to the jobs you need in order to get representative curves for the variables.

Up-to-date Plotting

Beside controlling production, the immediate plotting of studies gives two other values. We discussed one in Chap. 4, the detection of errors. There we likened curve plotting to a go–no-go gauge. That measurement of timestudy results is important in saving wasted time. From my point of view, here concerning timestudy productivity, if a plotted point is wrong, the whole study is wasted. You may disagree. You can say as many have, "All the other element standards add to the data." Then I counter, "Yes, but come back to our exaggerated straight-line question again." You would not need to take another study of the variable at fault if the element time standard on the previous study had plotted correctly. So in the restudy, you get an added set of readings on all the other elements you would not have studied. There is the waste I am trying to help you reduce by better planning after your men are thoroughly trained.

Just the same, the curve plotting is extremely important to minimize the number of faulty studies. For instance, on Fig. 28 are four out-of-line points, two above the trend line and two below. These four points are the results of poor timestudy or faulty plotting. How did we get four of them before this question was asked? How many more out-of-line studies shall we accept before taking action? These questions bring us to the second reason for prompt plotting of your variable element curves. This one, in my experience, can save you more time than you can recover by reducing the number of duplicate timestudies.

Checking Dimension Factors

Make the utmost use of up-to-date plotting as a "quality control" device. We touched on this in Chap. 4. There we used two curves to illustrate one form of timestudy "quality." This related to correctness of analysis. One curve was plotted against Area. The other used Volume as a dimensional factor. Those are comparatively simple examples of possible errors in analysis. Even so, you want to find out as soon as you can if you are off on the wrong foot. You want to verify the correctness of your analysis. Therefore, you need to plot your study results to see that they do line up.

Another form of "quality" shows up more often in the variations of work content. Herein lies the reason for the out-of-line points shown on Fig. 28. Those above the trend line were put in to represent studies of pieces picked up from a skid. Those below are for pieces picked up from the table. All the other studies were of parts picked out of tote boxes. All were plotted in the same symbol to make the point I want to stress here.

Had you noted the three conditions I have just described, you would have used different symbols in plotting. According to Rule 1, Chap. 4, you should *plot every suspected difference in an identifying symbol or color.* But you didn't know. So the out-of-line points look like poor timestudy. Here then is the important sorting or quality control device available to you in up-to-the-minute plotting. Let me cite a case to emphasize.

The timestudy men in one plant asked the boss, "What do you want me to study next?" He was busy solving a problem. So he gave them some quick instructions and assigned them to a new type of work. He continued to be busy. Several weeks went by. Studies piled up until there were about 50 of them. Then when the boss did take a look, you know the result. He had guessed wrong on controlling dimensions. The necessary ones were not obtainable. The men had been wasting their time, as things turned out, because new studies had to be made.

That result may seem farfetched to you if you are accustomed to repetition work. If so, it is because you can almost always get, from repeating orders, the information you failed to record when the study was taken. But job shops are different. The work is often finished and gone shortly after your studies are made. In contrast, they are way back in product history where repetitive operations were started. And in nearly every plant, this same condition still exists with most setup operations, maintenance work, toolmaking, and the like. Remember that timestudy itself brings about considerable development of engineering detailing.

Consequently, if you have wrongly planned to use certain dimensions, your study may be worthless. You may be unable to get other dimensions you need. If you have failed to record all changes from normal work content, your studies *will be worthless.*

So don't get caught short. Don't let studies accumulate. Plan to control the results. Check your analysis and work content specifications by plotting the variable standards right up to the minute. See Fig. 29. Make sure that the dimensional factors you have chosen

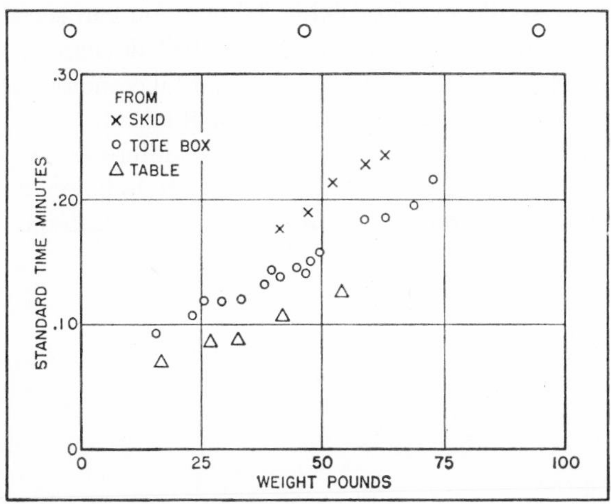

Fig. 29. Out-of-line points result from (1) faulty timestudy and (2) differences in work content. Therefore, you should plot results promptly to gauge the quality of your element standards.

are the right ones. Be certain that all variations from normal work content are recorded on all studies. Follow up day by day, as you must do with any planning or quality control that pays for itself. In summary, let me set down these two points very pertinent to gaining better timestudy results faster.

1. By plotting right up to the minute, you reduce the number of studies taken to get sound standard time data by eliminating the duplicates.
2. By plotting results promptly, you apply the go–no-go gauge of quality that sorts faulty timestudy from failure to record variations in element work content.

Making Hay

The suggestions given here are part of my effort to help you get more complete incentive coverage quickly and cheaply. They are not academic. They have grown out of experiences and observations of many mistakes made. Why not learn the easy way, for a change?

If you're reading this book with an industrial engineering viewpoint, one of your objectives may be to improve your timestudy methods. Your main purpose may be to get total coverage. To do so requires the use of methods you can afford. Note, I used the plural of methods because there is no one cure-all system. My suggestions are a lot of little items. Like Ben Franklin's, "Take care of the pence, and the pounds will take care of themselves."

If your interests lie in other fields, I hope you can see the applications of these production and quality control devices in your curve plotting. I believe you will see them if you take another look at Figs. 18 and 19 in Chap. 4. In all cases I can think of, out-of-line points will result from either faulty dimensions or differences in content, or both. So you can use the devices outlined here to help you dig deeper in your analysis when points you are plotting are scattered.

CHAPTER 7

Straight-line Equations

C. D. "Chief" Dyer taught me, "There are two times to make a profit—(1) "before you take the order" (right pricing) and (2) "after you get it" (cost reduction and control). His analysis fits here.

The before part of the "profit" in this book lies in making the most economically correct analysis of your data. The after part begins here. Now we move into chapters that explain how to make the most of the data you have by putting it together in convenient form. As you proceed, you should critically analyze each method for setting up your data. Each has certain advantages. Under some conditions, these outweigh the disadvantages. Remember, we try to use the most economical method of the several available when we produce articles for sale or for in-plant use. The same principle should be applied in our data preparation. We must strive to get the cheapest over-all cost per computation while holding its correctness within set limits.

To move from curves to charts you may need to use equations. Sometimes, these afford the best way to express the relationship between data and controlling dimensions. They may be best because they are convenient and simple. Once in a while, equations are your only good choice. But don't stop here. What follows will be an explanation of only those equations you should know about.

The Straight Line

The equation you may find the most useful is that for a straight-line curve. The line is like a road going uphill. We say a road has a certain "grade." A 5 per cent grade means that there is a rise of 5 feet in 100 feet. This grade in an equation is called the "slope." The slope is the rate of change. This is uniform with a straight line. In shop operations like painting, it may be expressed as so much time per square foot. In shoveling, the slope may be so much time per 100

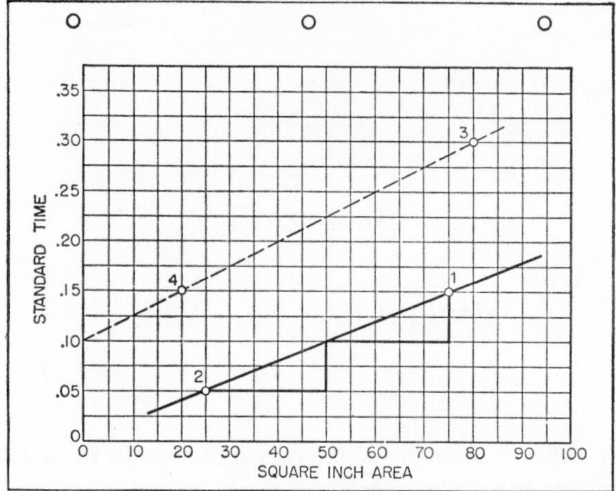

FIG. 30. *a* Note the heavy lines like steps that show how a curve rises so much for every so many units of Dimension. *b* To figure this slope, read two points as close to your curve extremes as you can correctly. *c* After you figure the slope and the constant of your curve, check the constant graphically and then your equation at a point not used in your computing.

cubic inches. The heavy line steps drawn on Fig. 30 attempt to show how a curve may go up 2 units of Standard Time for each 5 units of Dimension. This diagram is similar to steps leading up to a shrine like our Lincoln Memorial in Washington where the *rise* is two-fifths of the *tread.*

The slope of your straight-line curve may be anything. That is unimportant because you compute what it is. Let's find the slope in Fig. 30 as you can determine it for any straight line.

Step 1. Read the curve at the point of largest dimension you can determine. At point 1, this is .15 Minute for 75 Square Inches.

Step 2. Read the curve at the lowest point you can accurately. At point 2, you have .05 Minute for 25 Square Inches.

Step 3. Set these down in an orderly arrangement like this:

Point	*Square Inches*	*Standard Time*
1	75	.15
2	25	.05
Step 4. Subtracting:	50	.10

Step 5. Dividing the two differences: $\frac{.10 \text{ Min}}{50 \text{ Sq In.}} = .002$ Min/Sq In.

Step 6. Now, prove your solution by taking an example different from either one used in your computation. One in between is 50 Square Inches. At this point your curve should read .002 Minute × 50, or .10 Minute. It does, so the slope of .002 per Square Inch is correct. Your equation, then, is

$$\text{Standard} = .002 \times \text{Sq In.}$$

Constant at Zero

This example is of a straight-line curve that passes through 0–0. It was arranged that way on purpose. But most curves, if extended to your 0 Dimension axis, will have a constant amount. This fact was emphasized in my discussion leading up to Rule 7, Chap. 5. For this reason, we need to take the next step and consider the more usual type of straight-line curve.

There are two approaches you may use. One is to visually extend the curve to read the constant. The other is to calculate it. We will use the latter method as procedure and the graphical method as a check. To do so, let's work with the upper curve in Fig. 30. Figuring the slope as before, we have

	Point	*Square Inches*	*Standard Time*
	3	80	.30
	4	20	.15
Subtracting:		60	.15

Dividing: $$\frac{.15 \text{ Min}}{60 \text{ Sq In.}} = .0025 \text{ Min/Sq In.}$$

The slope in our equation is .0025 Minute per Square Inch. However, the total amounts on this upper curve are more. They contain the added amount of the Constant. So your equation reads

$$\text{Standard} = \text{Constant} + .0025 \text{ Min} \times \text{Sq In.}$$

At 80 Square Inches, we used .30 Minute. So if you put that curve reading in your equation, you can solve for our Constant.

$$.30 = \text{Constant} + .0025 \times 80 \text{ Sq In.}$$

Multiplying, you have

$$.30 = \text{Constant} + .20$$

Transposing, the result is

$$.30 - .20 = \text{Constant}$$
$$\text{Constant} = .10 \text{ min}$$

This checks closely with the reading you get after extending the upper curve in Fig. 30 until it crosses the vertical line at 0 Square Inch.

Now you can set up your final equation as

$$\text{Standard} = .10 + .0025 \text{ Min} \times \text{Sq In.}$$

Let's prove our equation at a different point, say 60 Square Inches

$$.25 = .10 + .0025 \text{ Min} \times 60$$
$$.25 = .10 + .15$$

Always double-check. You can make mistakes both in reading your curves and in making your calculations.

Combining Equations

When you have equations for several curves, you may want to combine them. One example would be where you want the total constant and slope for a Manufacturing Overhead Budget. Suppose you had worked out these two amounts for the simplified list of expenses shown in Fig. 31. You could add them in any combinations you needed to get total constants and slopes for the total budgets under the controls of your several responsible managers.

Expense Account	Curve Equations	
	Constant	Slope
Waiting time	$ 6,000	$ .220
Expense units	11,000	.395
Timestudy	20,000	.200
Production control	35,000	.325
Clerical	22,000	.490
Accounting	36,000	.620
Engineering	74,000	.730
Maintenance	42,000	.440
Toolroom	29,000	.755
Light, heat, power	25,000	.125
Depreciation	40,000	.000
Total shop overhead	$340,000	$4.300

FIG. 31. Combining Curves is easily done after you have worked out their equations.

In our budget example Fig. 31, we have a Constant but no slope for Depreciation. All other expenses shown have both Constants and Slopes.

The mix of both is common also in timestudy standard data. To bring this out, we might combine the curves in Fig. 30 with some constant element times. Suppose we had two element standards .06 and .05 that were Constants from our Comparison Sheet. Also, imagine we have another curve that has a Constant of .025 Minute and a slope of .012 Minute per Cubic Inch. Set down in form so we can see what we have, the starting figures would be

Source	*Min/Sq In.*	*Min/Cu In.*
(Comparison Sheet):	.0600	
(Comparison Sheet):	.0500	
Figure 31: lower	.0000 + .0020	
Figure 31: upper	.1000 + .0025	
A third equation:	.0250	+ .012

Adding, we have

Standard = .2350 + .0045 × Sq In. + .012 × Cu In.

This is a simple example, but it shows how to combine. Only one detail is important. Be sure to avoid trying to add "horses and apples." Add together only those terms that are alike. You will find that this step is easily made when you set down all like factors in column form as in this example. It shows a very convenient way to combine variables and constants.

Intersecting Lines

Another useful application of equations is in solving certain kinds of problems. One type is that of finding the intersection of two lines. Figuring the Breakeven Point on your company's profitgraph is one

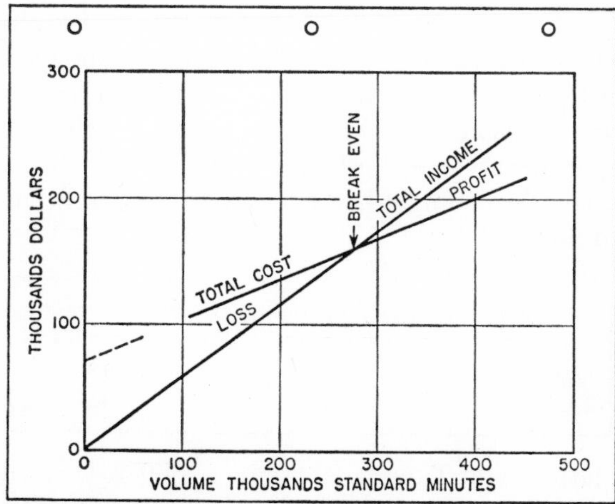

Fig. 32. Equations of two straight lines are equal at their point of intersection.

case. To do so, let's suppose Fig. 32 is your profitgraph and you have worked out equations for the two lines as

$$\begin{aligned}\text{Total Income} &= \text{Zero} + \$.5800 \times \text{Std. Min}\\ \text{Total Cost} &= \$75{,}000 + \$.3125 \times \text{Std. Min}\end{aligned}$$

To proceed, you will recall the fundamental rule that

Two straight-line equations are equal to each other at the point where their lines cross.

The Volume in Standard Minutes at your BE point is the same for both curves. So is the Dollar amount—the too-common way of expressing it. Thus, you can set down your two equations equal to each other

$$0 + \$.5800 \times \text{Std. Min} = \$75{,}000 + \$.3125 \times \text{Std. Min}$$

Collecting like factors together, you get

$$\begin{aligned}\$.5800 \times \text{Std. Min} - \$.3125 \times \text{Std. Min} &= \$75{,}000\\ \$.2675 \times \text{Std. Min} &= \$75{,}000\\ \text{Std. Min} &= \$75{,}000/\$.2675\\ \text{Std. Min} &= 280{,}000\end{aligned}$$

The dollar amount of your BE volume is easy to compute. The easier equation is that of Income = Zero + \$.5800 × Std Min Substituting, you get

$$\begin{aligned}\text{Break-even} &= \$.58 \times 280{,}000 \text{ Std. Min}\\ BE &= \$162{,}400\end{aligned}$$

The break-even point changes, as you realize, with every variation is product mix. For this reason its location might more readily be found by means of a multi-variable chart. The same is true of the quantity of pieces in the question, "When should we change methods?" This is a question that should come up every day in a well-run Production Control Department. It is illustrated by Fig. 33.

Here we have two straight-line equations resulting from the following standard times

Lathe	*Setup Minutes*	*Operation Minutes*
Engine.........	20.0	4.0
Turret.........	50.0	1.9

$$\begin{aligned}\text{Engine lathe Total Time} &= 20.0 \text{ min} + (4.0 \times \text{Quantity}) \text{ min}\\ \text{Turret lathe Total Time} &= 50.0 \text{ min} + (1.9 \times \text{Quantity}) \text{ min}\end{aligned}$$

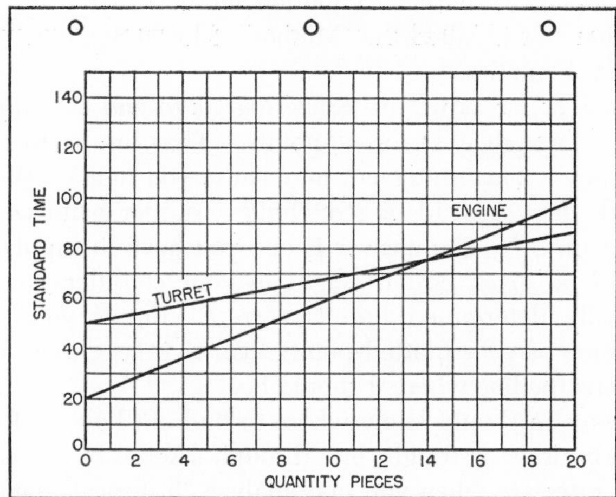

FIG. 33. The economical quantity where method should change is at the point of crossing of the two curves of total time.

The Quantity we want to determine is the number of pieces where we should change method. It is the Quantity where the two lines cross each other. At this point, the total Standard Time is the same for the lot produced either way. Then, as for finding the *BE* point, we can set these down equal to each other. With Q standing for the Quantity, we have

$$20.0 + 4.0Q = 50.0 + 1.9Q$$

Collecting like terms, we get

$$\begin{aligned} 4.0Q - 1.9Q &= 50.0 - 20.0 \\ 2.1Q &= 30 \\ Q &= 30/2.1 \\ Q &= 14.3 \text{ pieces} \end{aligned}$$

We purposely went through this solution of equations by mathematics to make a point. It should serve to demonstrate a method you can use many times in a variety of forms to solve all sorts of problems that stem from data compiled in curve form. My personal opinion is that sometimes we can analyze even better by setting down our problems in simple algebra.

Method of Least Squares

More equations will probably bore you to tears. But there are several more uses of them I want to get in before we sign off. At this point, let's work with an equation method that is often used in job evaluation. It is called the "Method of Least Squares." You may want to use it some time.

Its purpose, as far as we are concerned, is to find the equation of a straight line through a series of points. That line is to be located mathematically. That statement may cause you to ask, "Why not use this method, then, instead of stretching a rubber band as you illustrated in Chap. 3?" The answer is one you have to supply. If each point should be given equal weight in your consideration, then the mathematically determined line is correct. But if you have more "faith" in some of your plotted points than in others, then my suggestion is to draw the line where it should be.

Regardless, you should know where to find out how, as I express it, "to accurately draw a straight line through a series of errors." That's what wage rates are when you first analyze "historical" data to set up job evaluation. The same is true if you look upon our next example as the problem of trying to draw the proper line through historical, uncontrolled expenses to set up your first budget.

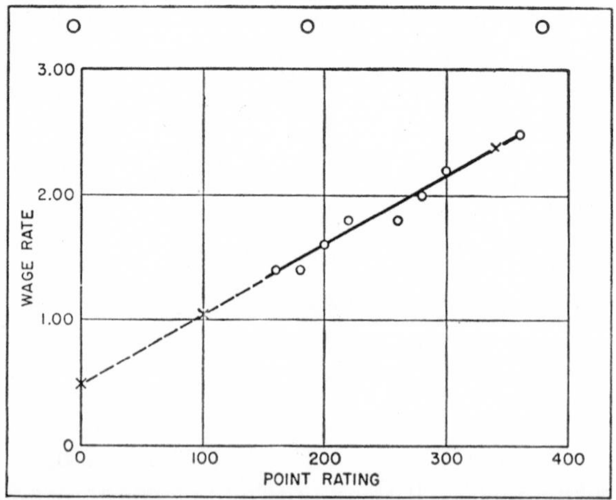

FIG. 34. A Straight line for a series of points may be located with mathematical exactness by the method of Least Squares. The Xs are three calculated points of location.

To make an example, let's use Fig. 34. There we have plotted eight points. Each one has two factors of location (the $10 word is "coordinates"). These we need to use in our equations. Setting them down in an orderly way, we have

Point	*Wage Rate*	*Point Rating*
1	1.40	160
2	1.40	180
3	1.60	200
4	1.80	210
5	1.80	260
6	2.00	280
7	2.20	300
8	2.50	360

Next, we set down these readings as though each were a factor in an individual equation of a straight line. You remember that in the early part of this chapter we came out with an equation for a straight line as

Amount = Constant + Dimension × Value per Unit Dimension

Using this form for each of the points, we get eight equations. In these we will use *P* as the Dimension to mean Point rating.

Point	*Equation*
1	$\$1.40 = C + 160P$
2	$1.40 = C + 180P$
3	$1.60 = C + 200P$
4	$1.80 = C + 210P$
5	$1.80 = C + 260P$
6	$2.00 = C + 280P$
7	$2.20 = C + 300P$
8	$2.50 = C + 360P$

These equations are not like the others we have been using. They are more like the trial type you may start with to solve some problem of your own. We simply wrote these arbitrarily. But the mathematical procedure will permit us to work these eight into two that we can handle.

The procedure requires that we do some multiplying. Two multipliers are used. With these we get two sets of equations. Our first multiplier is unity (1) for the *C* term in our equations. Thus, each of our equations in our first set will be the same as it is now.

Obtaining Two Equations

Our second multiplier is the factor with the *P* term. Here each one is different. Hence, our results in the second set will be quite unlike the present equations.

Equation Number	First Set		Second Set	
	Multiplier	Equation	Multiplier	Equation
1	1	$\$1.40 = C + 160P$	160	$\$224 = 160C + 25600P$
2	1	$1.40 = C + 180P$	180	$252 = 180C + 32400P$
3	1	$1.60 = C + 200P$	200	$320 = 200C + 40000P$
4	1	$1.80 = C + 210P$	210	$378 = 210C + 44100P$
5	1	$1.80 = C + 260P$	260	$468 = 260C + 67600P$
6	1	$2.00 = C + 280P$	280	$560 = 280C + 78400P$
7	1	$2.20 = C + 300P$	300	$660 = 300C + 90000P$
8	1	$2.50 = C + 360P$	360	$900 = 360C + 129600P$

Adding all the equations in the first set, we get

$$\text{Eq. (9)}\ \$14.70 = 8C + 1950P$$

The total of all those in the second set is

$$\text{Eq. (10)}\ \$3762 = 1950C + 507700P$$

To solve these two resulting equations simultaneously, let's first cancel the *C* Term. So multiply Eq. (9) by 1950 and Eq. (10) by 8:

$$\begin{aligned}
\text{Eq. (10)} \times 8:&\quad \$30096 = 15600C + 4061600P\\
\text{Eq. (9)} \times 1950:&\quad \$28665 = 15600C + 3802500P\\
\text{Subtracting}&\quad \$\ 1431 = \qquad 259100P\\
&\quad P = \$1431/259100\\
&\quad P = \$.005523P
\end{aligned}$$

Using our answer for *P* in Eq. (9), we can determine *C*

$$\begin{aligned}
\$14.70 &= 8C + 1950 \times \$.005523\\
\$14.70 &= 8C + \$10.76985\\
8C &= \$3.93\\
C &= \$\ .49
\end{aligned}$$

Drawing the Line

The value of *C* is our Constant for 0 Points. And the answer for *P* is the slope of our wage line. This is \$.005523 per Point. Putting these together in equation form, our end result is

$$\text{Wage Rate} = \$.49 + \$.005523 \times \text{Point Rating}$$

Now, after all this figuring, we are set to draw in the "accurately" placed line. To do so, we should compute some points. Of course, we already have one—our Constant of \$.49. But to check, let's figure two more.

At 100 Points, the solution to our equation becomes

$$\begin{aligned}\text{Wage Rate} &= \$\ .49 + \$.005523 \times 100 \\ &= \$\ .49 + \$.55 \\ &= \$1.04\end{aligned}$$

Then, at 340 Points, the answer is \$2.37. This with our other two computed rates are shown as *X*s on Fig. 34 and mark the location of the line we sought.

So much for the straight-line equation and how to find it. It has many uses that can be helpful to you in solving problems that involve variables. Keep in mind these uses when they can best serve you for making combinations.

Now let's turn to some uses for equations when you want to take apart variables that are combined.

CHAPTER 8

Equations for Separating Variables

Equations can be used to help you "take apart" variables you seem unable to get at any other way. One problem I recall vividly. My job was to divide a plant inventory among four products as a first step in determining where the profits were made or lost. I spent what I thought were the hottest Saturday and Sunday they ever had in Cincinnati, in my hotel room when I wanted to be home, juggling simultaneous "equations." It seemed to me the only way I could get the answers I had to find. And this approach is one you should know because it may be the only way you can use to solve a problem you may have some day.

Dividing Overlap

The problem I have met more often is that of dividing the overlap in timestudy elements for building basic data. One case will serve to illustrate—filling, sanding filler, or brush painting of small castings. In actual timestudy, I could get only partial breakdowns of the elements by dimensional causes. The painters would overlap the work done on bosses, areas, and edges—the divisions of data I was trying to make. Naturally, the painter I was studying did not know what I wanted. It wouldn't have made any difference if he had. He was busy working on the castings. In so doing, he filled, sanded, or painted around one side of a boss while doing some work on the area. Then he would overlap some of the area work by getting over on the edges of the castings.

This kind of mixed observation requires some clever timestudy. And when all is done, you still have to take apart readings by solving equations. One break in solving this sort of problem often occurs when, for example, certain castings have no bosses. Of course, all have area and edges. Hence, part of the planning is to get studies of pieces that have no bosses. This gives you readings that eliminate one or more of the unknowns in the equations you want to set up.

Studies of such work result in equations something like the following, where A means minutes per square inch of area of side, E is minutes per inch of perimeter edge, and B is minutes per boss:

$$33A + 28E = .58 \text{ min} \quad (a)$$
$$28A + 32E = .58 \text{ min} \quad (b)$$
$$16A + 20E + 2B = .47 \text{ min} \quad (c)$$

To solve, you can begin with Eqs. (a) and (b). Your first step is to cancel out one term. To do this, you make that term equal in your two equations. To cancel the A terms, multiply Eq. (a) by 28 and Eq. (b) by 33.

$$924A + 1056E = 19.14 \text{ min} \quad (b)$$
$$924A + 784E = 16.24 \text{ min} \quad (a)$$

Subtracting:

$$272E = 2.90 \text{ min}$$
$$E = 2.90/272 \text{ min}$$
$$E = .0107 \text{ min/in. of edge}$$

Going back to (a) and substituting the value of E, you get

$$33A + .30 = .58 \text{ min}$$
$$33A = .58 - .30 \text{ min}$$
$$33A = .28 \text{ min}$$
$$A = .28/33 \text{ min}$$
$$A = .0085 \text{ min/sq in. of area}$$

With values for A and E, you can tackle Eq. (c), to find the time per boss.

$$(16 \times .0107) + (20 \times .0085) + 2B = .47$$
$$.17 + .17 + 2B = .47$$
$$2B = .47 - .34$$
$$B = .13/2$$
$$B = .065 \text{ min/boss}$$

In these steps, you break down your timestudy readings into .0107 minute per inch of edge, .0085 minute per square inch of area, and .065 minute per boss.

You can see that this problem has been made simple. That was done purposely. I am trying here only to show a method. It is one you should know because, chances are, you will get certain problems that you can solve in no other way.

Paint Spraying

I had another problem of this type, I think interesting enough to relate. Three men were spray-painting automobile frames hung on a monorail. The first man painted until the second man pushed the frame he was painting on to the third man. Each did about a third. But each third was indefinite.

The frames had two long side rails. These were fairly uniform. The cross-members differed according to customers' specifications. And some frames had brackets riveted to the side rails.

My first step was to follow through a number of different frame types. These studies were to get the total work done, without part duplications. From these studies, I set complete standards. Then I made element breakdowns as closely as I could. And like the omitted bosses in the casting problems, I could take some studies on frames that had no brackets. With total standards and the breakdowns available, I set up some equations. From distinctly separate parts shown on some studies, I substituted to eliminate certain terms. It was quite a struggle. But like most problems, I solved it in time by using lots of patience. I stress patience because you must recognize that "equations" are not always equations just because you write them that way. Consequently, you have to make many trials before you can get all your terms solved and proved.

Three Unknowns

Here is another practical problem. This one came up in the study of mail delivery routes. It is typical of certain problems that, in my opinion, require the use of equations. You may skip over this example if you are expert with equations. My advice is to wade through it if you are not sure.

We will start off with four equations. Actually, the rule says that you need only as many equations as you have unknowns. Hence, three would be enough in this case.

Mail Delivery—Starting Equations	*Routes*
37 boxes + 40 doors + 2,200 ft = 12.30 min	(1)
33 boxes + 10 doors + 5,200 ft = 23.10 min	(2)
55 boxes + 50 doors + 2,600 ft = 15.30 min	(3)
115 boxes + 25 doors + 2,200 ft = 16.50 min	(4)

To determine the standard time for each of our three factors, we approach this problem similarly as in the previous castings example. Only here it is a bit more complicated.

Pairing to Cancel

If you are a timestudy man, you will look for an easy way. The easy way here is to cancel out the factor of "doors." So let's combine

Eqs. (1) and (2). Also we will simplify our work by using *b, d,* and *f* as symbols meaning the times for boxes, doors, and feet.

$$33b + 10d + 5{,}200f = 23.1 \text{ min} \qquad (2)$$
$$37b + 40d + 2{,}200f = 12.3 \text{ min} \qquad (1)$$

To cancel the *d* terms, we can multiply Eq. (2) by 4 ($40d/10d$).

$$132b + 40d + 20{,}800f = 92.4 \text{ min} \qquad (2)$$
$$37b + 40d + 2{,}200f = 12.3 \text{ min} \qquad (1)$$
$$\text{Subtracting:} \quad 95b + 18{,}600f = 80.1 \text{ min} \qquad (A)$$

Next we want to get the combination of Eqs. (3) and (4)

$$115b + 25d + 2{,}200f = 16.5 \text{ min} \qquad (4)$$
$$55b + 50d + 2{,}600f = 15.3 \text{ min} \qquad (3)$$

With this pair, we can cancel the *d* terms if we multiply Eq. (4) by 2, ($50d/25d$), and then subtract.

$$230b + 50d + 4{,}400f = 33.0 \text{ min} \qquad (4)$$
$$55b + 50d + 2{,}600f = 15.3 \text{ min} \qquad (3)$$
$$\text{Subtracting:} \quad 175b + 1{,}800f = 17.7 \text{ min} \qquad (B)$$

Reducing Further

Our next step is to combine the simplified equations (*A*) and (*B*). In so doing, the easiest way is to multiply (*A*) by 175 and (*B*) by 95. That will make the *b* terms the same. Then we can subtract and have left only *f*.

$$\text{Eq. } (A) \times 175: \quad 16{,}625b + 3{,}255{,}000f = 14{,}018 \text{ min}$$
$$\text{Eq. } (B) \times 95: \quad 16{,}625b + 171{,}000f = 1{,}682 \text{ min}$$
$$\text{Subtracting:} \quad 3{,}084{,}000f = 12{,}336 \text{ min}$$
$$f = \frac{12{,}336 \text{ min}}{3{,}084{,}000}$$
$$f = .0040 \text{ min}$$

With one factor known, we can go back and substitute. Equation (*B*) is the easier one to use.

$$175b + 1{,}800f = 17.7 \text{ min} \qquad (B)$$
$$175b + (1{,}800 \times .004) = 17.7 \text{ min}$$
$$175b + 7.2 \text{ min} = 17.7 \text{ min}$$
$$175b = 17.7 \text{ min} - 7.2 \text{ min}$$
$$175b = 10.5 \text{ min}$$
$$b = 10.5 \text{ min}/175$$
$$b = .06 \text{ min}$$

Getting the Standards

Since we have the standards for one foot and one mailbox, we can get that for one door. Let's substitute our two knowns in any of our starting equations, say the equation for Route 2. It looks like the easiest one to handle.

$$\begin{aligned} 33b + 10d + 5{,}200f &= 23.10 \text{ min} \qquad (2)\\ (33 \times .060) + 10d + (5{,}200 \times .004) &= 23.10 \text{ min}\\ 1.98 \text{ min} + 10d + 20.8 \text{ min} &= 23.10 \text{ min} \end{aligned}$$

Combining all the minute terms together, the sum of the two on the left side, $(1.98 + 20.8)$ or 22.78 minutes, is subtracted from the 23.10 minutes on the right side. The result is

$$\begin{aligned} 10d &= .32 \text{ min}\\ d &= .32 \text{ min}/10\\ d &= .032 \text{ min} \end{aligned}$$

From all these mathematical gyrations, we finally get our answers:

Time for Each	*Standard Minutes*
Mailbox	.060
Door	.032
Foot	.004

Correcting Overlap

Now, that wasn't so difficult, was it? And the method should be used in cases like this. You cannot get the right answer by simple timestudy without a great deal more work than this method takes. Here is the reason. You know what we mean by acceleration and deceleration. In this example, getting under way and slowing down take place with every door and every mailbox. For that reason, you cannot get the correct standard per foot for walking by ordinary methods. You would have to time separately the approach to and departure from each door and box. But to do that, you would have to "guesstimate" the points where those elements started and stopped.

To my way of thinking, it is more correct and easier to solve this type of element overlap problem as we have. By this equation method, we took the extra times belonging to boxes and doors out of the walking time. You must make this separation or you do not have correct standard data. Each of these factors must be right when standing alone. Otherwise, you cannot build up a fair time for a route that has not been studied. If you tried to study every change, you'd never get done. You know how often they rearrange your offices. So get the right answers. Then you can set the standard for a new mail route faster than they can rearrange the desks and offices.

Short-element Times

Finally, we come to the use of equations to sub-divide element watch readings that are too short to observe and to record. You may have run into this in fast punch-press operations. I have had two very extensive applications in recent years where equations were used.

My recommendation is to take your watch readings in several ways on each study. Maybe you will time 10 cycles one way, 10 another, and so on. In any case, you should get properly rated over-all readings also. Then repeat all sets of readings in several ways. The purpose is to reduce the errors in your assumptions. You cannot have true equations. There are the variations caused by both you and the person you are studying. He may vary his methods. You may be off slightly in rating, watch reading, and work content definitions. These are errors when you set down your "equations." The algebra you write down with an equal sign may not be an equation.

With that caution, we can take some watch readings to work out a sample problem. Suppose we have a study on an operation made up of four elements. We can call them *a*, *b*, *c*, and *d*. Our data requirements make it necessary to get separate element standards for each one.

Elements		*Minutes*	*Observations*
$a + b + c$	=	.045	(1)
$b + c + d$	=	.045	(2)
$c + d + a$	=	.035	(3)
$d + a + b$	=	.055	(4)
Total cycle	=	.060	(5)

Arranging the equations so we can add them, we get

$$
\begin{array}{rcl r}
a + b + c \phantom{{}+d} & = & .045 & (1) \\
b + c + d & = & .045 & (2) \\
a \phantom{{}+b} + c + d & = & .035 & (3) \\
a + b \phantom{{}+c} + d & = & .055 & (4) \\
\hline
3a + 3b + 3c + 3d & = & .180 &
\end{array}
$$

Dividing by 3, the result is

$$a + b + c + d = .060 \qquad (5)$$

This checks with our total cycle time. We must have the same total. That may seem silly for me to mention. But a learned man once sent me some actual cases to work out that had different totals.

You should check, then, for two reasons. First make sure you have totals that agree. Second, note that here all our starting observations include only three of the four elements.[1]

Moving on, we start to solve for our unknowns. One is omitted to ease our work.

$$
\begin{array}{lrl}
 & a + b + c + d = .060 & (5) \\
 & b + c + d = .045 & (2) \\
\text{Subtracting:} & a \qquad\qquad = .015 & \\
 & a + b + c + d = .060 & (5) \\
 & a \qquad + c + d = .035 & (3) \\
\text{Subtracting:} & b \qquad\qquad = .025 & \\
 & a + b + c + d = .060 & (5) \\
 & a + b \qquad + d = .055 & (4) \\
\text{Subtracting:} & c \qquad\qquad = .005 & \\
 & a + b + c + d = .060 & (5) \\
 & a + b + c \qquad = .045 & (1) \\
\text{Subtracting:} & d = .015 &
\end{array}
$$

In this way, we get standard time for each of our unknowns. Often, these are variables and our times are to be plotted on curves for trend and range analysis. That is how we got the element standards for several types of operations where element times were in the range of .005 to .015 mins.

Equations Are Tools

Before concluding our discussion of equations, there is one more use that deserves mention. It is the application for what I call a "formula." Figure 35 is an example. Even this one can be charted with advantages. This formula was figured backward from curves drawn for total standards. It was worked out because, as the drawing shows, the one-at-a-time method of setting standards was too costly. The solution was approached after what seemed to be a sufficient number of direct standards had been set. These were plotted. Additional ones were determined to fill in gaps and measure the extremes. The formula was then worked out from the lines drawn.

Such a formula has many adaptations as a variation of the usual

[1] Lichtner, W. O., "Timestudy and Job Analysis," p. 170, The Ronald Press Company, New York, 1921.

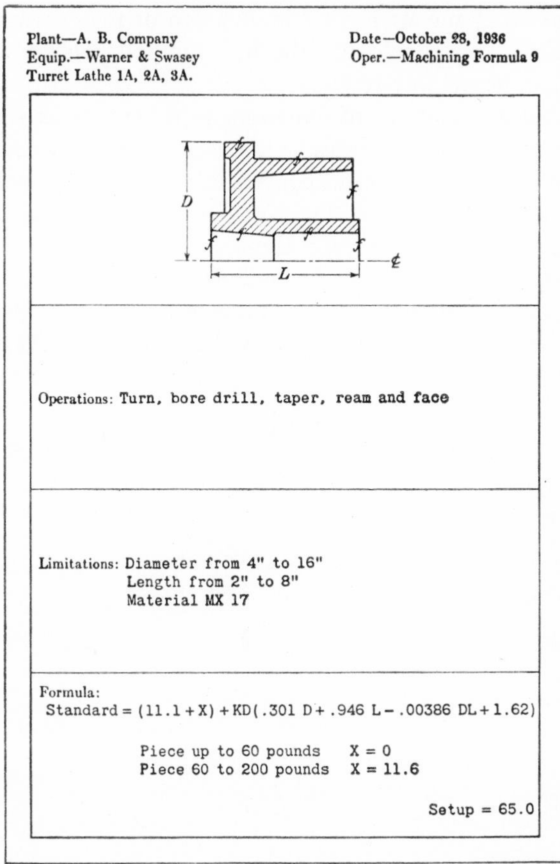

Plant—A. B. Company
Equip.—Warner & Swasey
Turret Lathe 1A, 2A, 3A.

Date—October 28, 1936
Oper.—Machining Formula 9

Operations: Turn, bore drill, taper, ream and face

Limitations: Diameter from 4" to 16"
Length from 2" to 8"
Material MX 17

Formula:
Standard = (11.1 + X) + KD(.301 D + .946 L − .00386 DL + 1.62)

Piece up to 60 pounds X = 0
Piece 60 to 200 pounds X = 11.6

Setup = 65.0

FIG. 35. Formula computed to set the standards for a very complex machining operation.

methods. It should be applied more frequently to make up special solutions. This is advisable when certain types of work occur regularly within an operation that is covered by general working data. Specialized applications are suggested to you by those parts and assemblies drawn by your Engineering Department as typical tracings with blank dimensions. One drawing applies to a whole line of products. Dimensions are filled in according to the sizes of a particular part or assembly. Whenever you can, you should adapt this idea to the problems of standard setting. It often pays to specialize within the general method by using a localized formula or chart for typified operations. Again let me repeat. You want to get the lowest cost possible for each calculation while maintaining accuracy within tolerances. To me that means having knowledge of many ways to solve problems. Then you should use the best method you know to work out the problem before you today.

These several applications of equations represent types you need to know for many kinds of analysis. Others are useful, of course. But for the higher forms, you should consult texts written about empirical equations.[1]

Knowledge of equations beyond those explained here is very useful in certain applications. Those beyond are not the simple algebraic array of constants plus variables. Practically all such equations are much more efficiently expressed and used in chart forms we will discuss in later chapters.

Selected References

Davis, D. S. "Empirical Equations and Nomography," McGraw-Hill Book Company, Inc., New York, 1943.

Running, Theodore R.: "Empirical Formulas," John Wiley & Sons, Inc., New York, 1914.

Worthing, A. G., and Joseph Geffner: "The Treatment of Experimental Data," John Wiley & Sons, Inc., New York, 1943.

[1] Carroll, Phil, "Timestudy for Cost Control," 3rd ed., pp. 215–216, McGraw-Hill Book Company, Inc., New York, 1954.

CHAPTER 9

Making Alignment Charts

To solve problems graphically, many folks use alignment charts or nomographs. They are used extensively in many engineering fields. They are especially good for solving complicated formulas. You can find hundreds of them illustrated in the reference texts listed at the end of this chapter. You see them used in timestudy work particularly to compute machine time using feed-speed data. These appear in texts and magazine articles with surprising frequency.

Nomographs are useful when you want to combine a number of additions and subtractions or multiplications and divisions. You can cross over and combine addition with multiplication. That is more difficult. But you will see many examples of combinations in the texts referred to. Here we will stick to the simpler ones.

Simple Addition

First, let's make up a nomograph to add. To start, you may use any piece of squared paper. Quarter-inch divisions are preferable. Then, along both sides of the page, lay out vertical scales. These should be uniform like 0, 1, 2, 3, 4, . . . , 10. Notice the 0. Both scales should be started with 0 on the same horizontal base line until you become fairly expert in constructing these charts. This is Step 1 (Fig. 36*a*).

Step 2 is to locate your line of sums. This is done graphically. Connect any number on the *A* scale with any number on the *B* scale. Draw a short line near the center. Remember the sum of the two numbers you connected. Write it alongside the short line you just drew. Then turn your straight edge to connect any other two numbers having the same sum. Draw in a short line to mark the intersection with your first line. Repeat this process to get three or more intersections (Fig. 36*b*). This repeating process is done for two reasons. One is to make sure the line you are determining is a straight

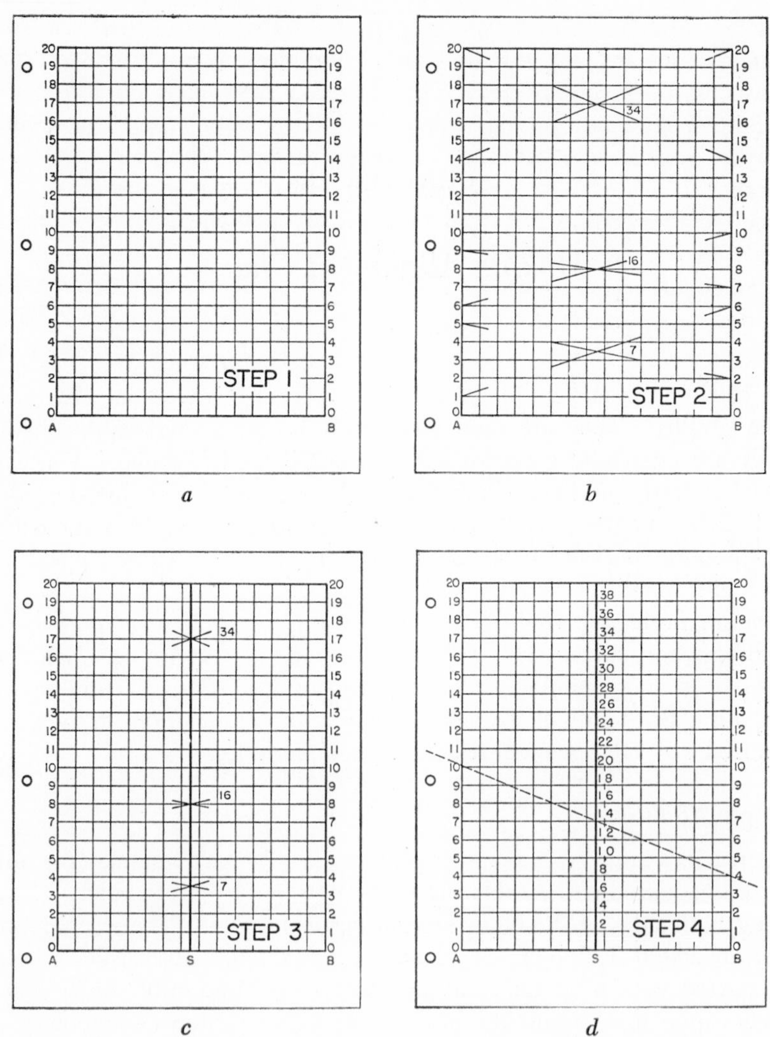

FIG. 36. *a* Lay out uniform vertical scales beginning with the same 0 line. *b* Locate the line of the sums. At the bottom, 6 + 1 equals 2 + 5. Near the center, 6 + 10 equals 7 + 9. At the top, 20 + 14 equals 14 + 20. Only the intersections need be drawn. *c* Three or more intersections should line up vertically. When they do, they locate the straight line of the sums. Draw in the line. *d* With the sum line located you may erase the intersection marks. Then you can lay out the sum scale.

line. The other is to make sure that your drawing has been done correctly. Men make mistakes in graphics sometimes. When all your intersections are on the same straight line, draw it in. Then you may erase the intersecting lines. This is Step 3 (Fig. 36*c*).

Step 4 is to lay out the Sum scale. This may be done in several ways. You know what three of the points are. In our example, we located 7, 16, and 34. We can locate other sums in the same way. One easy procedure is to spot the straight edge at one point on the *A* scale as a center. Then move the straight edge vertically along Scale *B*, one graduation at a time, to mark off divisions on the Sum scale. Naturally, you shift the center point on the *A* scale to more suitable locations as you progress upward. In this way, you can mark off every division on the Sum scale (Fig. 36*d*).

This method of layout is described first because it is an obvious continuation of the basic approach we used in the example. It is given in some detail, however, because you would have to use it under many conditions. Suppose, for example, that our paper were plain and unruled in both directions.

With or without cross-section paper, there is a simpler method often usable. Our example here is an instance. Why can't we take the sums horizontally on each cross line? To illustrate,

$$1 + 1 = 2, \qquad 2 + 2 = 4, \qquad 3 + 3 = 6$$

In this way, you need only write in the sums. When your two scales are equal, the Sum scale is twice either scale.

With the $4 + 10 = 14$ line drawn in on Fig. 36*d*, you see how a problem is solved. So we have completed a simple nomograph that correctly adds any pair of numbers in two ranges. But note. We can subtract with this chart. Reversing direction in our previous example, $14 - 10 = 4$. This is a step to remember. You may have problems to solve that require subtraction.

Dividing a Line

Another way to lay out your answer scale is to use simple proportion graphically. You may use it with both uniform and logarithmic scales. We shall show the uniform scale projection in some detail (Fig. 37), but only indicate the logarithmic dividing (Fig. 38).

In Fig. 37*a*, you will see a scale turned at an angle. This turning is to bring the number of divisions you have counted off on your scale within the range of the length of line you want to divide. In this

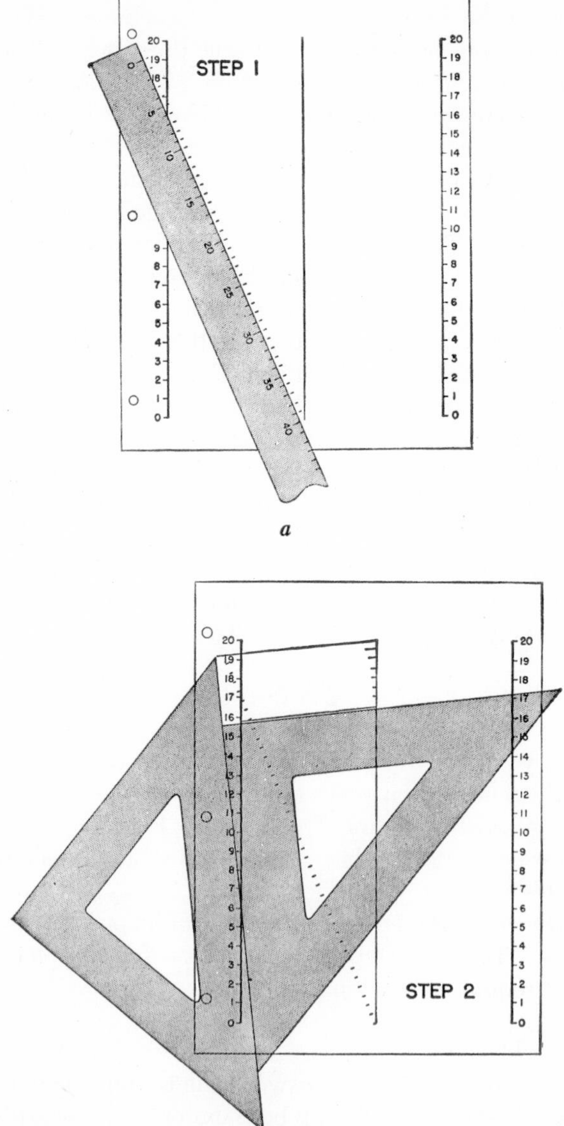

Fig. 37. *a* Turn a convenient scale to an angle sufficient to allow the required number of divisions to be marked off. *b* Set up triangles so as to connect the last mark with the corresponding division on your scale. Then, holding the parallel, mark off all the divisions.

position, mark off lightly the divisions. Connect the last one with the corresponding end point on the line to be divided. Carefully, holding this angle with another triangle, you mark off all the other divisions (Fig. 37*b*). If you have trouble with slipping, you can paste your aligning triangle and chart together with rubber cement.

The scale is only one aid to get your divisions laid out. In Fig. 38

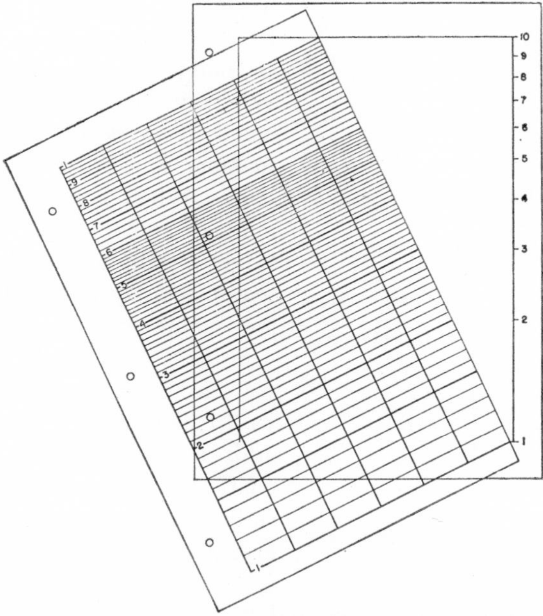

Fig. 38. To get logarithmic divisions, you can use cross-section paper with the desired scale. You will find it convenient to use if you will fold or cut the sheet to bring the scale to the edge of the paper.

you see another. This shows how to use graduated cross-section paper to get the same result. Here we turn a sheet of semi-logarithmic paper to obtain a logarithmic scale. In using such a scale, my preference is to cut off the border of the sheet. Then the scale is right at the edge of the paper. Of course, you can use your slide rule. But its scale is too far away from your paper for accurate marking.

You might want to get some special paper for this sort of layout. One such sheet published by Codex Book Company[1] has several logarithmic scales and a wide range of uniform scale divisions. The paper is No. 3160 Codex Scale Divider.

[1] Norwood, Mass.

Nomographs for Multiplying

Going on a step further with logarithmic paper, let's set up a chart for multiplying. To lay out this one, Fig. 39, I turned a piece of semi-logarithmic paper to an angle where the tenth division exactly coincided with a line connecting both 10s, while the 1 on the logarithmic paper rested on a line connecting the 1s of the scales. That made one layout of points correct for both scales. Then I marked off the main divisions. These dots show in a row on the angle. You would want to mark off all divisions in making a chart for solving problems. When the divisions are marked, you set your triangles so as to get a right angle with the vertical scales and lay out both scales from one set of points.

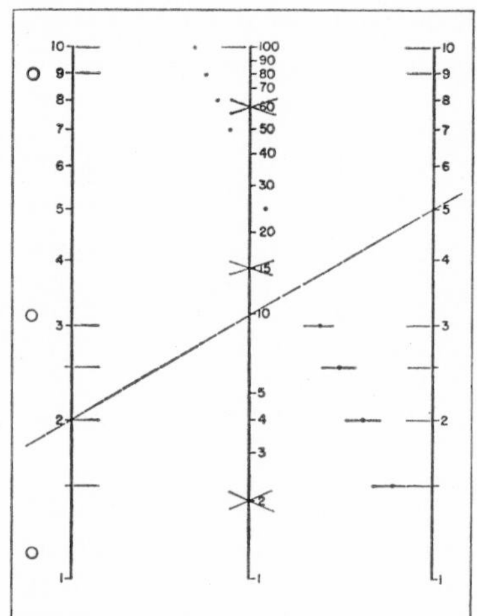

FIG. 39. You can multiply or divide with nomographs made with log scales.

Since these scales are logarithmic, you can use them to multiply. They work like your slide rule. That adds lengths together, as our first chart did. But here, as on your slide rule, the lengths represent logarithms. In other words, the figures 2, 4, 6, and so on are placed at distances from each other measured in logarithms. To illustrate, do a little measuring. On a 10-inch slide rule, the distance from 2 to 4 is about 3 inches. From 4 to 6, the distance is about 1¾ inches. The differences in logarithms correspond.

Number	*Log*	*Difference*	
		Log	*Inches*
2	301		
		301	3
4	602		
		176	1¾
6	778		

Thus, while on our scale we set numbers together, actually these are the first cousins appearing in place of their true dimensions—

the logarithms. In reality, you are adding logarithms when multiplying.[1] We need not worry about the mathematics mysteries, as long as our chart does the job. It will, when you lay it out correctly.

Performing Division

Before leaving this subject, we should recognize two similarities this chart bears to Fig. 36. First, products of the numbers horizontally opposite each other are found on the center scale. Second, division is accomplished by reversing procedure similarly as subtraction was demonstrated with the chart made for addition. For example,

$$10 \div 2 = 5$$

or $10 \div 5 = 2$. Thus, you can perform division when it may be necessary to solve a problem you have. Remember only that you must use log scales to multiply or divide.

Unequal Scales

You may realize that our examples have been very conveniently arranged. Your actual problems will not be so simple. For this reason, we should move on to add some complications. As we proceed, the explanations will be confined to addition. Generally speaking, however, you use the same approach for multiplying by substituting log scales for uniform scales. If you get lost, review the similarities between the uniform scale nomograph, Fig. 36, and the log-scale example like it, Fig. 39.

Perhaps the first inconvenience introduced by a practical problem is differences in scales. So let's tackle that one as a starter. In Fig. 40, one scale is twice the other. Without concerning ourselves about this difference, we proceed as in Fig. 36, to locate our line of Sums. Drawing three sets of intersections, we find that the location of the Sum line has moved. It is closer to the scale having the larger values per unit. If you check, you will see that it is located at one-third the distance between scales because of the 2 to 1 proportions of our scale values.

As before, you can proceed now with laying out the Sum scale (Fig. 40). You can write in the sums of the numbers that are horizontally opposite. This gives us a scale in 3s—0, 3, 6, 9, . . . , 60. Also you can plot the numbers in between. Remember, too, you can set a scale of the divisions you want at an angle (Fig. 37*a*). Then you can mark off your Sum scale by proportion.

[1] Harris, Charles O., "Slide Rule Simplified," American Technical Society, 1946.

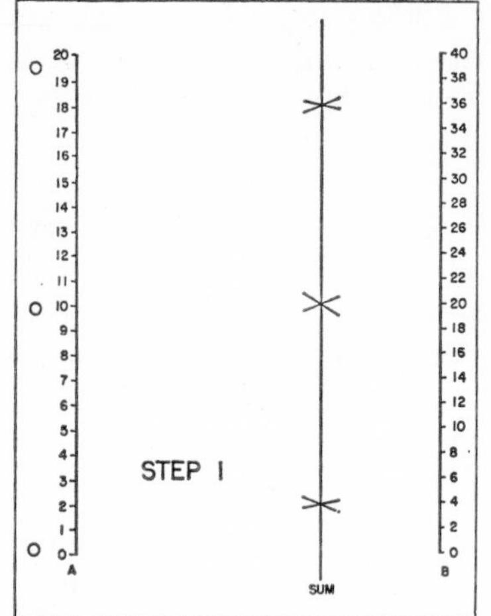

a The Sum line is located by intersections. It falls one-third of the distance from the double scale.

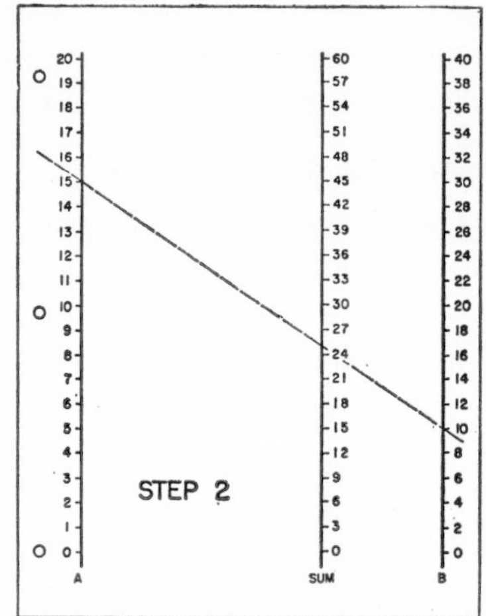

b The Sum scale is graduated to provide answers to our problems of adding two numbers.

FIG. 40. Nomographs may be used to add two variables having unlike ranges.

The Third Variable

To go further, as with a real problem, suppose we want to add another series of numbers to the sums of two variables. To carry out this step, we will continue on (Fig. 41*a*). This step of adding another term is simple if you will remember one thing. You are now starting a new problem. As for its solution, think nothing else is on the page but the Sum line completed in Fig. 40*b* and another line representing the third factor you want to add. This latter line can be a wholly new one, or another scale laid out on one of the lines already there. Using an existing line is better because it will allow the widest practical distance between the scales. Thus the maximum graphical accuracy is maintained.

With that explanation, let us lay out our third scale on line *A*. Call this one Scale *C* (Fig. 41*a*). When this is done, continue with Step 2 to find a new Sum line just as before. Using trial sums, make several intersections to locate the Sum line for $A + B + C$ (Fig. 41*b*). This will fall off center again. Its location is influenced by the ratio of the Sum $A + B$ scale of three values per unit to the *C* scale of two values per unit.

Then having drawn your final line, you can lay out its proper scale (Fig. 41*c*). The same three methods for graduating previously described are available to you.

a Lay out Scale *C* on the inside of the line of Scale *A*.

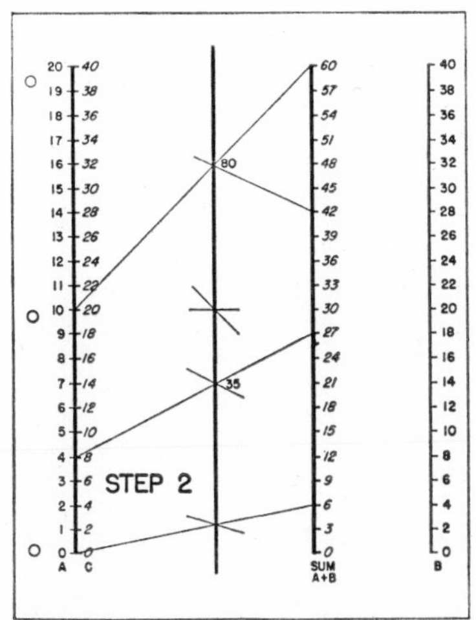

b Locate the new line of sums adding $A + B$ to C.

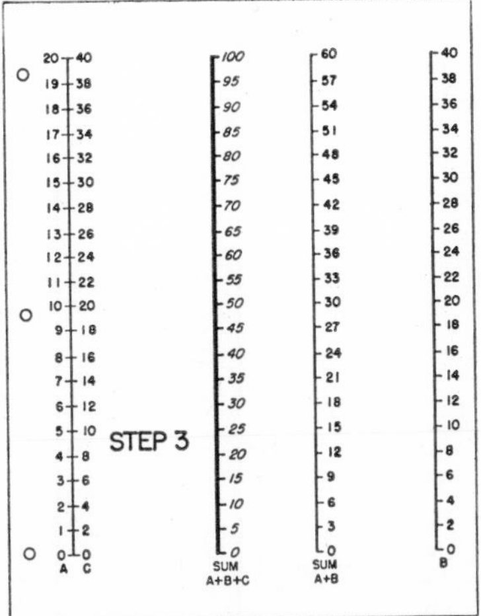

c Mark off the new scale showing the sum of $A + B + C$.

FIG. 41.

The Fourth Variable

It should be apparent, from our method of adding the third variable, that we can go on indefinitely. That is exactly so. Our only limitations are space and confusion. But to be sure this is understood, let's add one more before we call it quits.

Again, so we don't get lost, we will continue with the same ex-

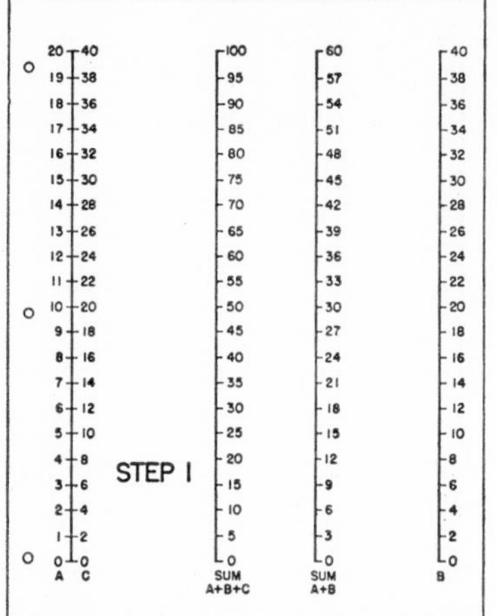

a We begin the addition of a fourth variable with a nomograph that combines three already located.

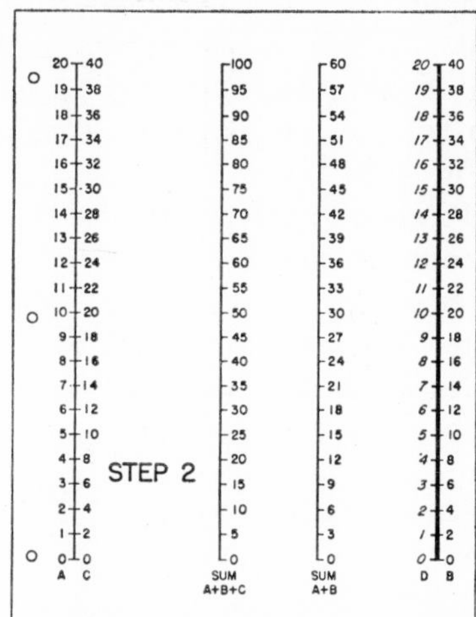

b The fourth scale *D* is added. Usually, this is laid out on a line available farthest away from the sum to be added to it.

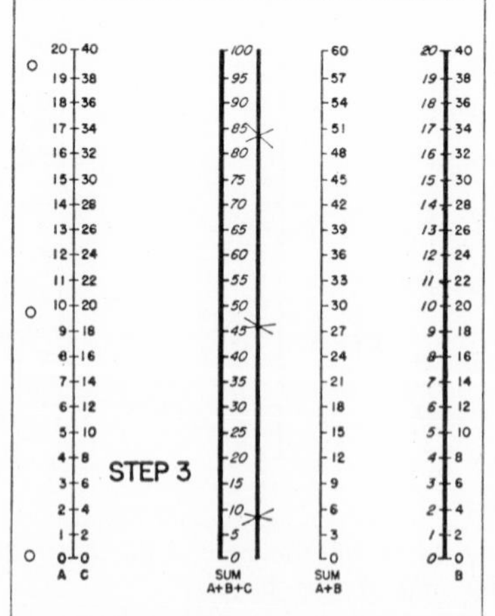

c The line of final Sum is located by intersections as described earlier in this chapter. Then it is graduated to provide the final Sums.

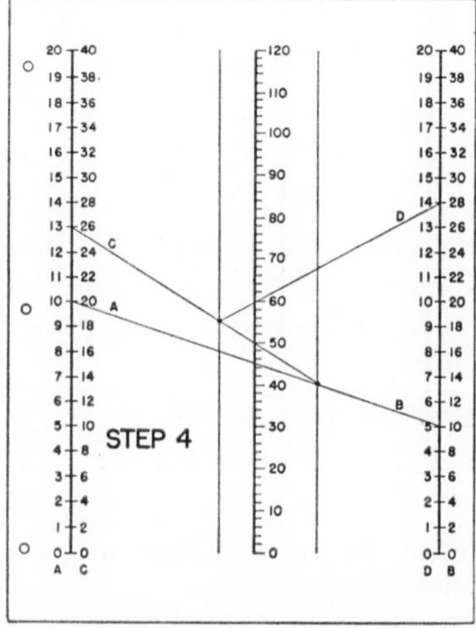

d With all lines located and scales laid out, we can erase construction details. The Sum lines for $A + B$ and $A + B + C$ become reference lines.

FIG. 42. Four variables are combined in a nomograph as shown by the example $A = 10$, $B = 10$, $C = 26$, $D = 14$ and the total is 60.

ample. We will start on Fig. 42*a* with three variables already laid out. As before, we will conserve space by placing our fourth scale on an available line. The one farthest away is the line of Scale *B*. So lay out the fourth scale alongside Scale *B* and mark it Scale *D* (Fig. 42*b*).

Proceed to locate the new line of sums. Forget all the other lines except the Sum $(A + B + C)$ and your new Scale *D*. Make several intersections to place the line correctly (Fig. 42*c*). Once it is located, you know how to lay out the final scale of sums.

Now you can erase the graduations on the sum lines for $(A + B)$ and $(A + B + C)$. They are only intermediate answers to your problem. They are construction scales only. We had to use them, however, to get our answer. Our final chart is shown as Fig. 42*d*. On it is drawn an example to show how the nomograph is used. This practice should be followed with all complex charts. Many like this one will apparently produce wrong answers if not used in the same sequence you followed to construct it. As a final step, check your chart, using a number of examples. Be sure to try it out with some extremes in your scales.

The Z Chart

We should briefly describe one more type of chart before concluding this chapter on nomograph construction. This one is known as "the Z Chart." It is one that will enable you to solve multiplication problems with uniform scales. It is particularly useful in cases where you want to spread out a short scale.

Figure 43*a* shows a simple layout of a Z chart. The scales are uniform but progress in opposite directions. The diagonal line is drawn in connecting the two 0's. But note: Scale *A* is one of our variables, while our other starting scale is our answer, $A \times B$. We must construct the scale for variable *B*. This is done graphically. An easy way is to pivot on one point of several on Scale A. Then, moving your straight edge to successive points on the $A \times B$ scale, mark off the answer scale you want to set up.

Carrying on, you will see in Fig. 43*b* a diagram of scales arranged to display my chief reason for including this explanation. Only the required portions of your scales are within the confines of the page. The completed chart is shown in Fig. 43*c* with finished scales. This is a form of solution to remember. It is the most convenient one to use under some circumstances.

With these examples limited to how to make nomographs, we will

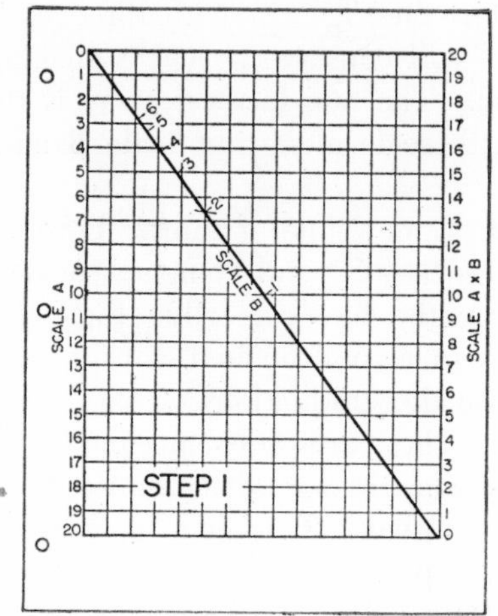

a Uniform scales are laid out in opposite directions. Scale ends are connected.

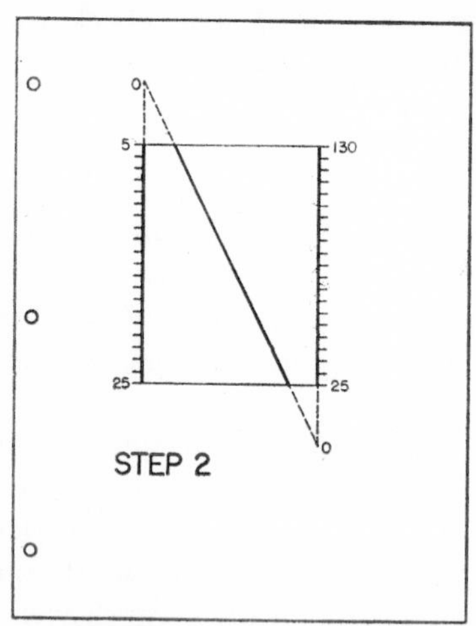

b Scale zeros need not be on the chart you want to use.

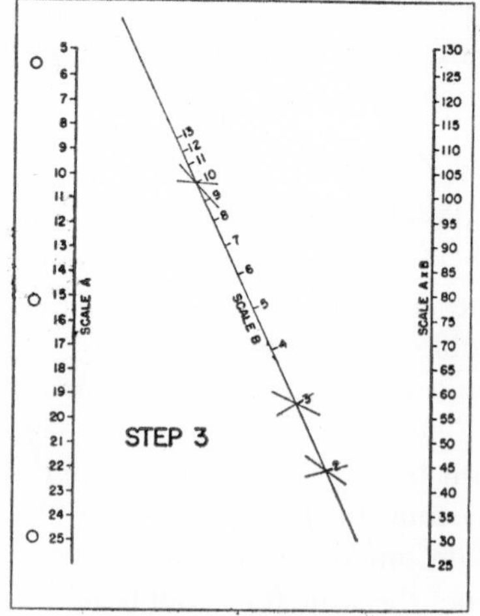

c Multiplying Z chart with scales spread out to suit the problem.

FIG. 43. Two charts may be used when the variables you want to combine are part only of a range.

see how to apply them in a few typical problems. These applications will be described and constructed in the following chapter.

Selected References

HASKELL, ALLAN C.: "How to Make and Use Graphic Charts," Codex Book Company, Norwood, Mass., 1920.

KRAITCHIK, MAURICE: "Alignment Charts—Construction and Use," D. Van Nostrand Company, Inc., New York, 1944.

Lehoczky, Paul N.: "Alignment Charts—Their Construction and Use," rev. ed., The Ohio State University Press, Columbus, Ohio, 1947.

Lipka, Joseph: "Graphical and Mechanical Computation," chap. 1, John Wiley & Sons, Inc., New York, 1918.

Peddle, John B.: "Construction of Graphical Charts," McGraw-Hill Book Company, Inc., New York, 1919.

Van Voorhis, Merrill G.: "How to Make Alignment Charts," McGraw-Hill Book Company, Inc., New York, 1937.

CHAPTER 10

Useful Alignment Charting

Knowing how to make an alignment chart is one thing. Putting your knowledge to practical use is something else. So let's see how we can apply what we learned from the previous chapter. To do so, we will work out three nomographs. One is to solve a common problem in Timestudy. The second is to compute Incentive Performance. The third is to answer the Inventory or Production Control question, "Was it the economical lot size?" We will take up the timestudy problem first because it is the least complex of these three.

Translating Variables

For our timestudy example, we will take two curves (Fig. 44). One shows Standard Times varying with Pounds. The other has Standard Times related to Inches.

To combine these, you must go one step further than in our previous examples. That step is to translate your scales into Inches and Pounds. But you start the same way. That is because Standard Times are what you want to add. The translation comes afterward.

The first step is to lay out scales as you did in Chap. 8. In this, you should utilize the maximum accuracy allowable by the size of paper you use. That should be apparent. You recognize that you get more accuracy on a 10-inch slide rule than on a 6-inch one. If you want more accuracy, you borrow somebody's 20-inch slide rule.

With a quick look-see at the curves, you note that Curve *a* (Fig. 44*a*) for Pounds has a range of Standard Times from .04 to .17 Minute. That range must be taken care of on one scale. You can lay out such a scale on either of two parallel vertical lines. In Fig. 44*c* it is placed on the right-hand line. It should be placed inside the line, to get it out of the way of your final translating step. The same applies to your other scale for Curve *b*. For this curve based on Inches, you need a scale ranging from .02 to .09 Minute (Fig. 44*b*). This is about

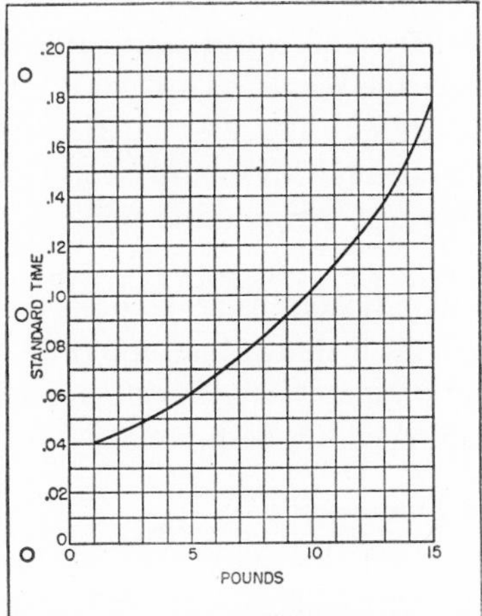

a A curve of Standard Time dependent upon Pounds.

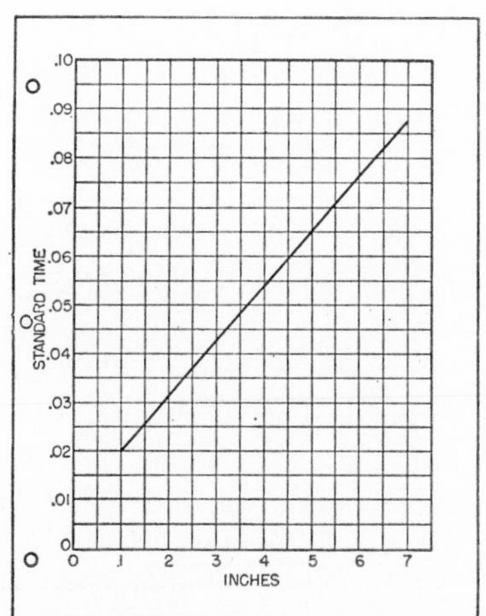

b Straight-line curve of Standard Time controlled by Inches.

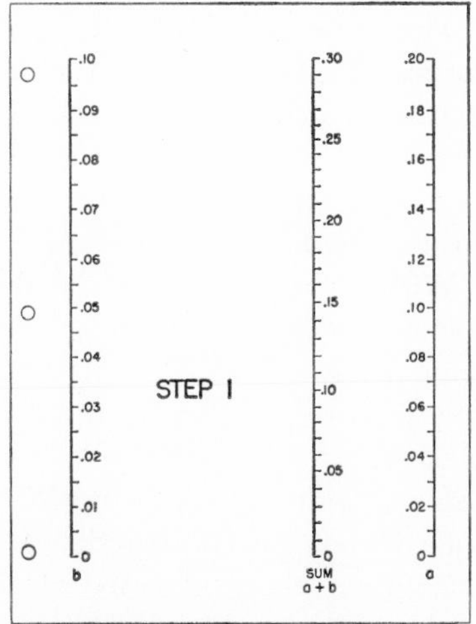

c Graduate the Sum line to provide maximum (.18 + .09) and minimum (.04 + .02) total standard times. *a* and *b*.

FIG. 44. Starting with two curves of variable element times, *a* and *b*, your first step is to make a nomograph that adds their time standards together *c*.

half the range of the Pounds curve, so you can double your scale divisions.

Considering how these look when finished, your question is, "Why not move the zeros off the page? That would expand the scales considerably." You are right. The .02 and .04 should be about where the scales start. The .09 and .18 should be as near the top as possible. This was not done because I wanted to make it easier to portray subsequent steps.

With scales completed, your next step is to locate the Sum line (Fig. 44*c*). Proceed by making some intersections. After you have fixed the line, then graduate it. Provide for all the sums you will need to set any standard within both ranges.

Translating Time to Dimensions

With your answer scale finished, you can begin the translation. You want scales in Pounds and Inches. Those are the dimensions that measure your times. For that reason, then, you want to make your chart into one that can be read directly in those terms. Let's start with Curve *a* and its corresponding scale *a*.

The scale was laid out purposely to correspond exactly with the curve. That means you can lay your curve alongside the scale and transfer readings. In placing it, be sure to locate it so your two scales of time standards correspond exactly. This operation is aided by folding under the margin of your curve paper. You can fix it in position with rubber cement.

With triangles, as shown (Fig. 44*d*), or, better still, a T square, you can make the transfers. Starting at the top, your maximum time standard is where the curve touches the vertical line of 15 Pounds. At the corresponding point on your Time scale, you mark a graduation. Make this mark on the outside of the time scale. Label it "15." Here you see why we laid out the Time scale on the inside. The Time scale is only for construction purposes. It will be erased later.

Continue the graduating of your Pound scale. Move your triangle to the point on the curve where the vertical line for 14 Pounds intersects. Do the same for 13, 12, 11, and so on down to your least number of Pounds. Mark each Pound division with its weight.

With your Pound scale completed, you can work out the second. The method is similar. With the Inch scale, however, you work from left to right. More care is necessary so double-check your locations. I would lay a straight edge across the curve and mark scale graduations on the right-hand edge. Then you can avoid making errors in location. With your curve placed correctly, you can transfer the Inch

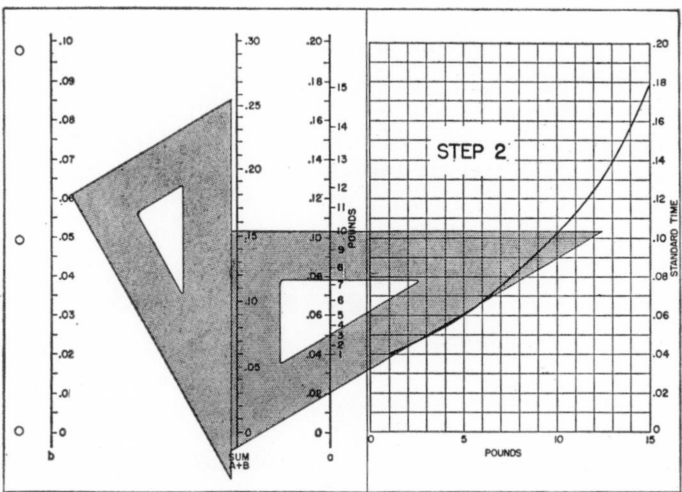

d Place the Pounds curve to exactly align with its time scale. Then transfer Pound equivalents by projecting from points where vertical weight lines cut the curve.

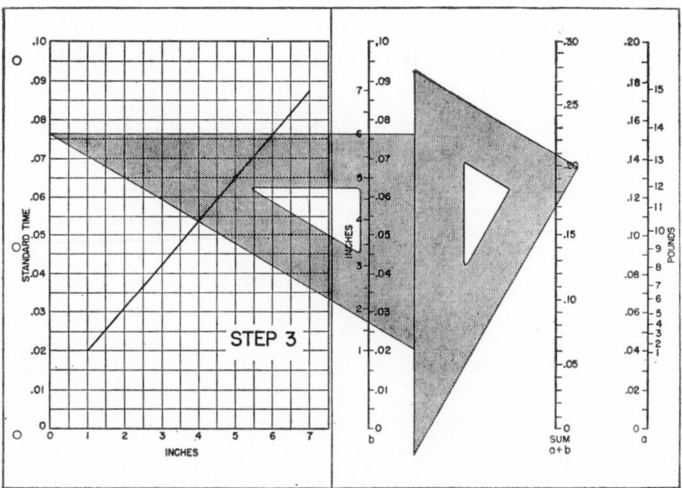

e Align Inches curve with its time scale and transfer dimensions as in *d*.

FIG. 44. (*Continued*). Nomograph that adds two variable standard times translated into terms of the dimensions that measure them.

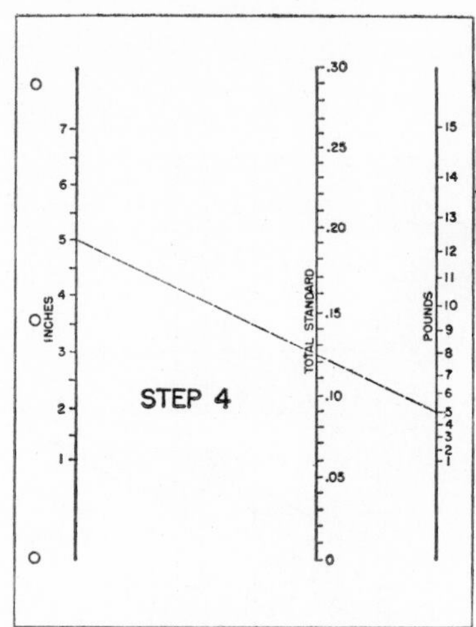

f Erase the time scales from the construction lines to complete your nomograph.

FIG. 44 (*Continued*).

divisions. Starting at the top, the first graduation is for 7 Inches. Next below that is 6.5 (Fig. 44*e*). Quarter-inch marks could be inserted if desired. They do not seem necessary because the time standards are so small. Hence, here we show only inches and halves.

With our transferring completed, we can erase the *a* and *b* Time scales. The finished chart will look like Fig. 44*f*, and we can draw in an example showing how to use the chart. Our example here is

Dimensions	*Readings, Minutes*	
	Curves	*Chart*
5 Inches	.065	
5 Pounds	.060	
	.125	.125

Charts to Divide

The second chart we shall make is to compute performance on incentive. In this, we divide Standard Minutes or Units Produced by Minutes on Standard. This example serves to set forth the method you can use to solve a problem that in algebra looks like

$$\text{Performance} = \frac{\text{Standard Minutes Produced}}{\text{Minutes on Standard}}$$

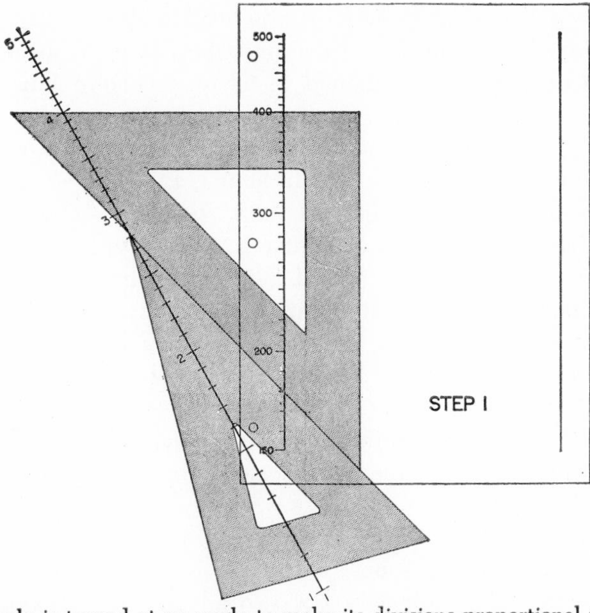

a Log scale is turned at an angle to make its divisions proportional to those we want. Notice that unity (1) is located on a base line below the chart.

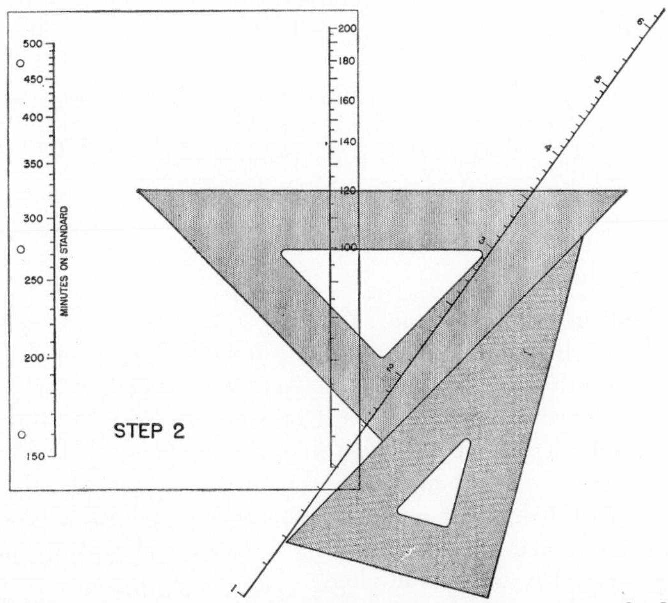

b The log scale is turned to a greater angle to get in more scale divisions. Notice that unity (1) is at the same base line.

FIG. 45. Computing performance on incentive.

Since this is a problem in division, you need to use log scales. These may be taken from your slide rule, log paper, or scale sheets like the No. 3160 Codex paper mentioned in Chap. 8. Here I used Codex paper.

To start, you draw two parallel lines as far apart as your paper will conveniently allow. Then, as in Step 1, Fig. 45*a*, you lay out the scale for your divisor. Either line may be used. Our illustration shows the left scale being laid out first. Notice also two details about the scale paper. One, it is turned at an angle to mark off our line into the dimensions we want. This step was explained in our previous chapter. Two, it has its base point outside the sheet of our drawing. The log scale was turned and shifted until it corresponded with the high and low points of the proposed scale. Note—the horizontal line of unity adopted for the first scale automatically determines the base line of unity for the other scale. That is why it is shown in the diagram.

When the desired location is found, the log scale should be positively fastened. My personal preference is to paste it down with rubber cement. That adhesive has two advantages. It permits you to slide the scale around and change your mind. Also, it allows you to pull off the scale when your work is done. You can clean up both scale and drawing with a clean rag. The rubber cement will roll up like artgum eraser. Besides, the pasted scale is free from the obstructions that you'd have if you used something like thumbtacks to fasten it.

When your scale is placed, your next step is to transfer the graduations to your line. I show triangles being used even though a T square is better.

Multiplying the Scale

One detail may perplex you. You may ask, "How do you get 500 on the chart when the scale has only 5 on it?" The answer is that these are log divisions like those on your slide rule. There are no decimal points you can use on most of your scales. One time you set 5 as 5,000. The next time, you may use the same 5 as .005. So with log scales, you can multiply or divide to suit your problems. You will notice a different multiplier was used in Step 2. There we wanted 100 to come near the center of the scale. This was brought about by using $^{10}\!/_3$ as the multiplier.

The Step 2 diagram in Fig. 45*b* shows the scale turned at a different angle. In effect, this, too, is actually using what amounts to a different multiplier. The angle was adjusted to obtain the graduations desired

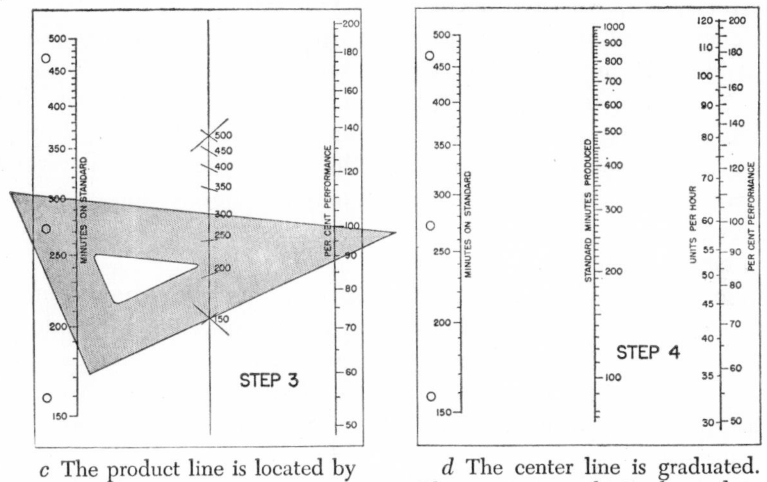

c The product line is located by intersections.

d The center line is graduated. The per cent scale is changed to read in Units per Hour.

FIG. 45. (*Continued*). Nomograph made to divide Minutes Produced by Minutes on Standard to obtain Units per Hour or "Efficiency."

within the extremes of the scale we want. Observe that the same base line was used for unity. Then the scale lines were marked off with triangles as indicated. Note that our divisor scale is finished and labeled "Minutes on Standard."

Dividend Scale

With the divisor and answer scales completed, we can locate the line for Standard Minutes produced. This line is the dividend of our fraction. It falls between the two scales already set. It is located by intersections. This is Step 3 (Fig. 45*c*). Here you see that our line does not fall exactly in the center. That is because one scale is slightly larger than the other as a result of turning our log-paper scale to different angles.

Our next move is to graduate the center scale. It can be done graphically. Many points can be located by using the 100 per cent point on the right-hand scale as a center. If you prefer, you may use any prepared log-scale papers like those I used in Steps 1 and 2. To use one for this center scale, you need to locate two points only. With these, you can turn and adjust your scale until you get a fit. That is the way I got the graduations. When they were completed, the intersections were erased and the line marked "Standard Minutes Produced."

At this point, we have a chart that will compute performance or "efficiency." But my preference is for the measure Units per Hour. So, in Step 4, I made another conversion by multiplying (Fig. 45*d*). With 60 Units per Hour being the equivalent of 100 per cent, this change-over was easy. You may prefer this same measure. If you do, then let's back up to Step 2. At this stage, you should put your per cent scale on the inside to be used only for construction purposes. You would erase it after you completed the Units per Hour scale on the outside of your chart.

These details are put in here because they describe a fundamental process. This is essentially the same type of conversion we made in our first example in this chapter. You will remember the conversion of two scales. They were laid out in standard times because we cannot add pounds and inches. After these were laid out, we converted the standard time scales respectively to Pounds and to Inches. Similarly here, we changed the per cent figures used in construction to Units per Hour to make our answer scale direct reading.

Economical Lot Size

Another typical application of the nomograph is for the solution of what we call the "economical manufacturing quantity." This problem needs to be solved in every firm that makes products for stock. The answer in simple terms depends upon balancing setup cost against carrying cost. For the solution, there are many formulas. The one we will use here is a simplified equation originally worked out by Bruce Wallace, retired Financial Vice President, Otis Elevator Company.

To make the logic apparent, we will develop the equation from its fundamentals. First, lets arrange the expression for setup costs.

$$\text{Setup cost per piece} = \frac{\text{Wage rate per minute} \times \text{Setup standard}}{\text{Quantity made per setup}}$$

Suppose we use a wage rate of \$1.80 per hour for ease of calculation. This will equal \$.03 per minute. Your setup rates may be more or less, depending upon who makes the setup. The rate used here should be reasonably close if the operator makes his own setups. For the other factors, let's use symbols. We can let S stand for setup and use Q to mean quantity made per setup. Then our first expression reduces to

$$\text{Setup cost per piece} = \frac{\$.03 \times S}{Q}$$

To balance against setup cost, we have certain carrying charges. These can include many details of cost. For our purposes, we will limit the factors to interest and obsolescence. Using 6 per cent for interest seems reasonable. The per cent for obsolescence is more a matter of good judgment than calculation. It should allow for the probable risks due to design changes—those made by our own engineers and those brought on by the advancing art of your industry. The greater the chance of making parts worthless or subject to rework, the higher should be the allowance. As a nominal figure in our solution, we will use 4 per cent. This added to the interest charge of 6 per cent makes a total of 10 per cent for carrying charges. In our equation, these will be divided by 2 because the full stock is carried for only half the time.

Total carrying costs are built up from our 10 per cent by taking into account factory cost, quantity run on each setup, and annual consumption. These several factors are arranged in equation form as follows:

$$\text{Carrying cost per piece} = \frac{\text{Carrying charge} \times \text{Factory cost} \times \text{Quantity per setup}}{2 \times \text{Annual consumption}}$$

Using the 10 per cent charge, *C* for Factory cost, *Q* as before to represent quantity per setup, and *A* for annual consumption, our equation becomes

$$\text{Carrying cost per piece} = \frac{.10 \times C \times Q}{2 \times A}$$

The carrying cost per piece should equal the setup cost per piece at the economical lot size. On that premise, our two equations are equal to each other.

$$\frac{\$.03 \times S}{Q} = \frac{.10 \times C \times Q}{2A}$$

Cross-multiplying to clear the denominators, we have

$$.03 \times S \times 2A = .10 \times C \times Q \times Q$$

Changing sides and combining terms, we get

$$Q^2 \times .10C = .06A \times S$$

$$Q^2 = \frac{.06AS}{.10C}$$

$$Q^2 = \frac{.6AS}{C}$$

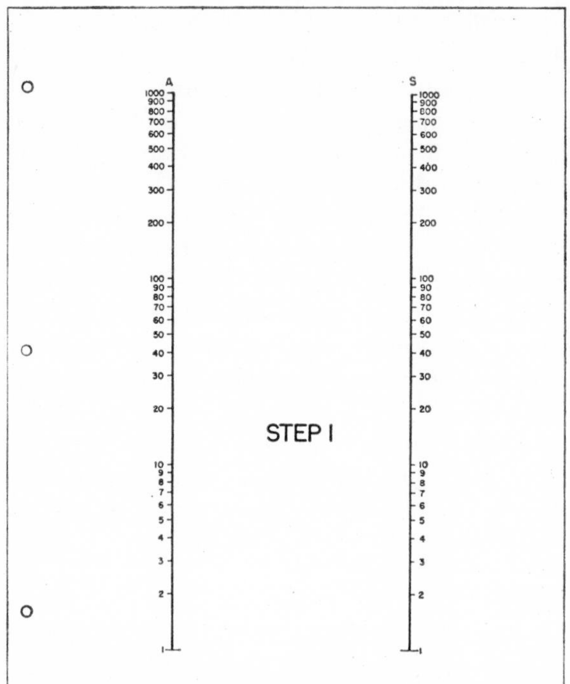

a Scales for Annual Consumption (A) and Setup Standard (S) are laid out exactly parallel and with three cycles of log divisions to cover a range from 1 to 1,000.

FIG. 46. Application of the nomograph for the solution of what we call the "economical manufacturing quantity."

To get our final answer for Q, we must extract the square root. But in working out this problem graphically, we are better off using the equation as it stands.

Step 1. Starting with the factors for Annual Consumption and Setup Units, we lay out a scale for each. These start with the same unity base line and have log divisions because we are multiplying $A \times S$. The ranges of both scales are taken as 1 to 1,000, being ordinary limits. This requires the use of a three-cycle log scale. When laid out, our scale will appear about as shown in Fig. 46*a*.

Our multiplier of .6 can be taken into account here or at any subsequent stage. In this case, it seems easier to apply it to the answer scale. The reason is that we have to convert the answer scale anyway, by extracting square root. Hence, we can make both conversions in the same step.

Step 2. Having laid out the two scales, we proceed to locate the

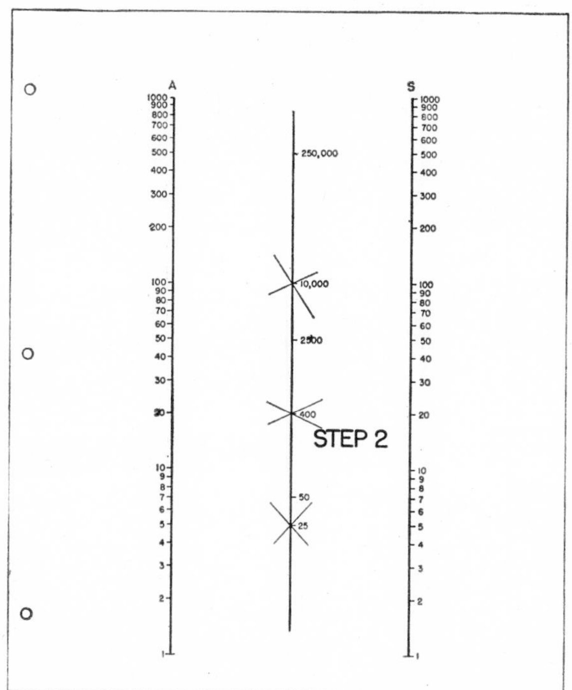

b The line of products of A × S is located. It falls exactly on center between them because they are equal. This is only a reference line and so you need locate only a few points for construction purposes.

FIG. 46 (*Continued*).

product line. This should lie exactly in the center between our scales. The reason, if you will remember, is because our two scales have equal graduations. With the product line located, it can be graduated lightly (Fig. 46*b*). Not all divisions need be made, however. This is only a reference line. Whatever divisions we do lay out will be erased later. All we need are a few points located and marked for use in the next calculation.

Step 3. Now we need a scale for Factory Cost. It can be located in any convenient place. It can be laid out on the opposite side of either of the existing scales. Either location would be equally accurate, because both lines are the same distance from the reference line. In Fig. 46*c* it has been set up separately. This makes the line stand out. Also, it permits us to place a title over it later to help reduce the risks of misinterpretations. With a location adopted, we can go ahead on the scale layout. This, too, will be logarithmic. The

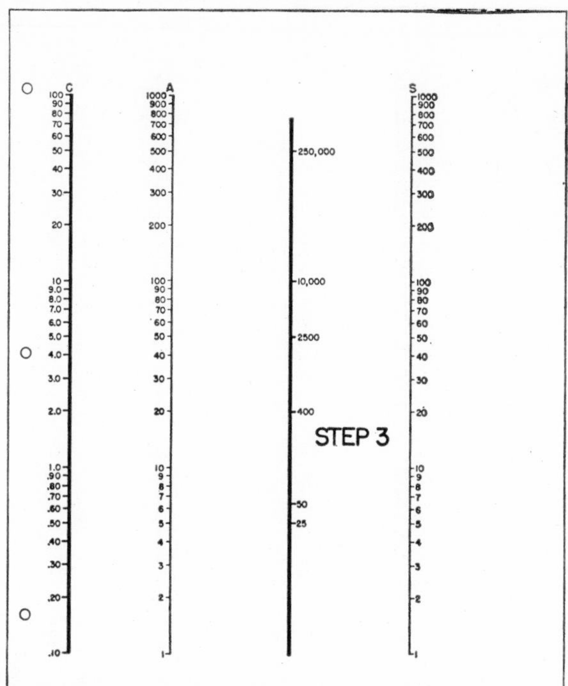

c A scale is added for Factory Cost. Its location can be most any place, including placement along either of the two scale lines already drawn. Here it is placed separately to have it show up clearly.

FIG. 46. (*Continued*) Application of the nomograph for the solution of what we call the "economical manufacturing quantity."

range chosen was \$.10 to \$100.00. The finished scale is shown in Fig. 46*c*.

Step 4. Having completed the scale for Factory Cost, we can use reference points on our product scale to locate the line of answers. This will fall as a separate line also. It will be near the scale for setup standards. Of course, it is found by intersections determined by dividing point values on the reference line by Factory Cost figures. When located, as with the product reference line, we need only a few answer points (Fig. 46*d*). The reason is that these answers have to be further modified.

Up to this point, we have worked with full values for Annual Consumption, Setup Units, and Factory Cost. At this stage, we have to make a conversion. It is to be somewhat like that made in the first example in this chapter where we changed time scales to Pounds and Inches. The difference is that here the conversion is mathematical.

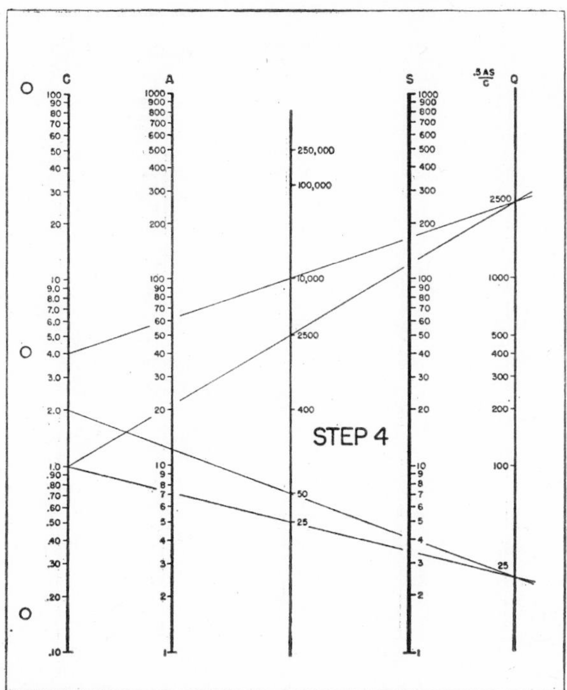

d Dividing reference-line values of A × S by Factory Cost values will locate the answer line. Points on this line are not final results. They must be converted by multiplying by .6 and taking the square root.

FIG. 46. (*Continued*) Application of the nomograph for the solution of what we call the "economical manufacturing quantity."

Our present construction scale values are .6 times the square of the economical lot-quantity answer we seek.

To accomplish this step, we can work out final conversions for the several answer points we have spotted on the line. These will show us what sort of a log scale to use in dividing the line. Placing it alongside, as in Fig. 45 early in this chapter, we can turn the scale to the proper angle. Once located exactly, the scale divisions are projected to our final answer line.

Step 5. In the final stage, we want to erase the construction details and letter the scales. Then we should check our chart in several places and draw in an example to show how it is used. In Fig. 46*e*, the factors assumed are

Annual Consumption	=	100 pieces
Factory Cost	=	$10.00
Setup Standard	=	20 min

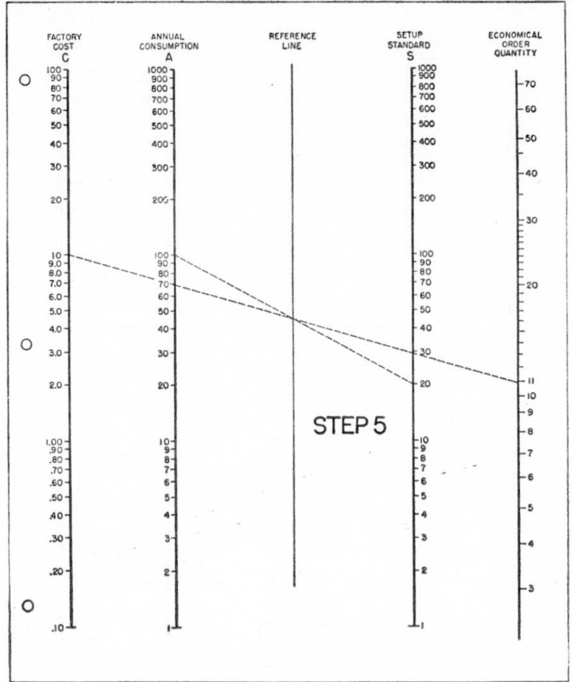

e The answer scale for Lot Size is graduated. All construction figures are erased. All scales are labeled and an example drawn to show how the chart is to be used.

FIG. 46. (*Continued*). Application of the nomograph for the solution of what we call the "economical manufacturing quantity."

The chart shows an answer of about 11 pieces as the proper lot size. We get almost 11 pieces by solving the equation, $Q = \sqrt{\frac{.6AS}{C}}$. Our solution is correct.

Solving Problems

The detailed explanations of the examples in this and the preceding chapter should give you a working knowledge of nomograph construction. They were chosen to show a range of application.

Nomographs are not difficult to make. They can help you get mathematical solutions through graphical methods. By their very nature, they cannot be as accurate as mathematics itself. In many instances, however—the last example is typical—only relative accuracy is necessary. And it can be increased, as with a slide rule, by enlargement.

The nomograph has special values, like other graphical methods. It can be used to get answers quickly. It has many uses, particularly when there are large numbers of computations to be made. These can be obtained at low cost by means of charts such as we have worked out in this chapter.

The nomograph is a working tool you should understand. You should be equipped to choose this method for problem solving when it best fits. In this respect, it is like any tool that should be part of a skilled man's kit. Only when his tool kit contains all the tools can he do his job most effectively.

CHAPTER 11

Multiple Curves

The family is the basic unit in our civilization. We are often reminded of this fact by seeing pictures of the clan gathered for some reunion. This family group shows up similarly as a quite common result of the analysis of compound variables. But families of curves may also be built up for computing answers to problems that involve multi-variables. In this chapter, we want to take up some of the ways to graphically combine both kinds.

Suppose you have a simple curve, as in Fig. 47, and you want to add

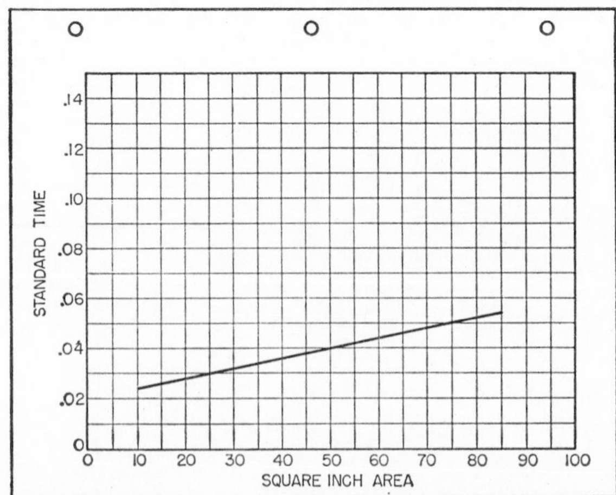

Fig. 47. A simple straight-line curve to be factored in several ways in subsequent illustrations.

a constant. We will start here just as you might if you had a problem involving one or more curves and one or more constants. The constants should be in your total. For this reason, you must add them in at some stage of chart construction. Here, let's add them to our starting curve because it is an easy way to portray how you can bring in factors other than simple addition.

Factored Curves

Figure 48*a* shows the addition of .02 Minute to our starting curve. To locate the new line, two points were plotted. Only two are necessary because the line is straight. At 25 Square Inches, our original

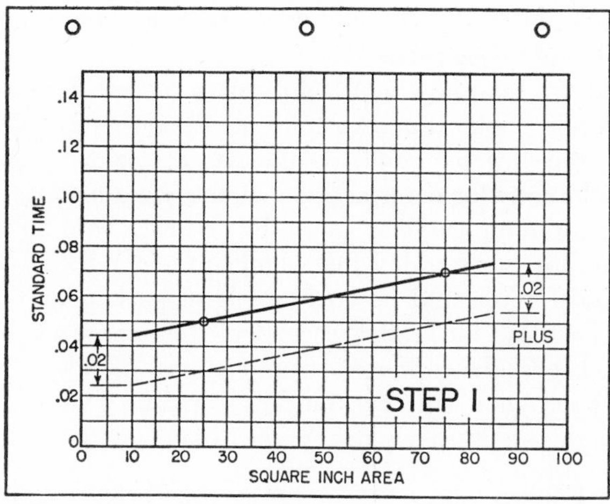

a The original curve with the constant .02 minute added.

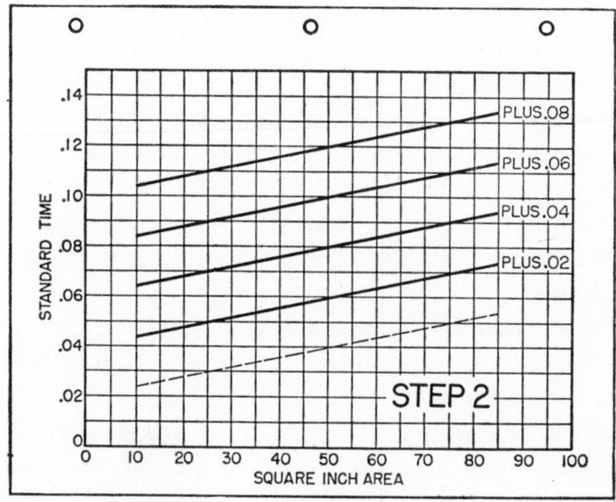

b The original curve with the four different constants, .02, .04, .06, .08 minute added.

FIG. 48. A problem made up of one variable plus several constants may be portrayed as a family of curves.

curve reads .03 Minute. To this we add our constant of .02 Minute and the sum .05 Minute is one point on our new curve. Likewise at 75 Square Inches, the .05-Minute curve reading plus the constant of .02 Minute equals .07 Minute, the other point. Through these two points, our new line is drawn.

In Fig. 48*b*, we have gone a step further. Including the first one just explained, we have added four different constants. Similarly, as in Fig. 48*a*, two points were obtained for plotting each new curve. As completed, we have a family of curves representing one variable plus four different constants.

You might see here how your solutions to several different types of problems would look. For example, in estimating simple molding-labor costs, the variable could be the size of mold. Then the constants are additions for cores added. If this were material costs, you could think of the top curve as your solid and each constant downward a subtraction for cores added that eliminate material.

In timestudy, this could be an example of packaging. The standards could be those for sealing cartons of different sizes plus writing on the packages the different combinations of identifying order numbers. I recognize that 2 × 5 inches would be a very small carton. You can laugh, and then we can go on to our next type of factoring.

Multiplying Factors

Quite often, you can have problems that require multiplication of a curve reading by one or more factors. To illustrate one form of solution, I have set up Fig. 49. In Fig. 49*a* our base curve is shown as a dotted line. The new line we want to locate is to have every base curve reading doubled. To plot our new curve, only two points need be located because our original line is straight. I took one point at 25 Square Inches. There the curve reads .03 Minute. Using .03 × 2, we get .06 Minute. This is plotted. The other point at 75 Square Inches is .05 Minute and .05 × 2 = .10 Minute is plotted. Then our new line is drawn.

In Fig. 49*b* I extended the multiplication and changed the scale to include several curves. The starting curve is dotted in Step 2 to contrast it with the results obtained by multiplying it by 2, 3, 4, and 5. Problems that this family represents occur frequently. In material costs, for example, you have both size and quantity as a variable. In such cases, the spread can be like the different costs of, say, steel, brass, aluminum, and stainless. In payroll, the variable can be hours and the factors of spread would be wage rates.

In timestudy, this problem appears in many operations where an

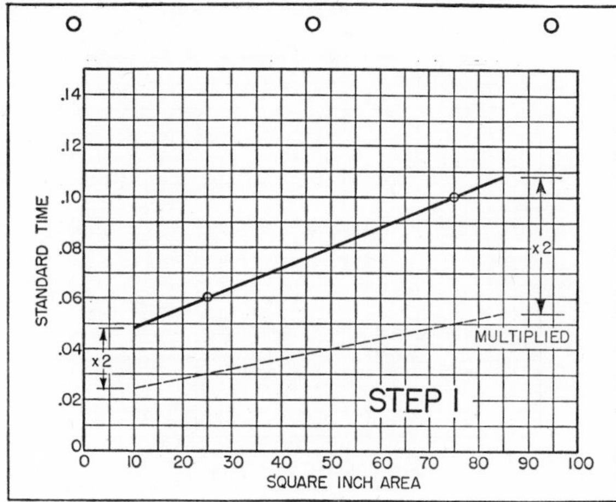

a. A Standard Time variable multiplied by two.

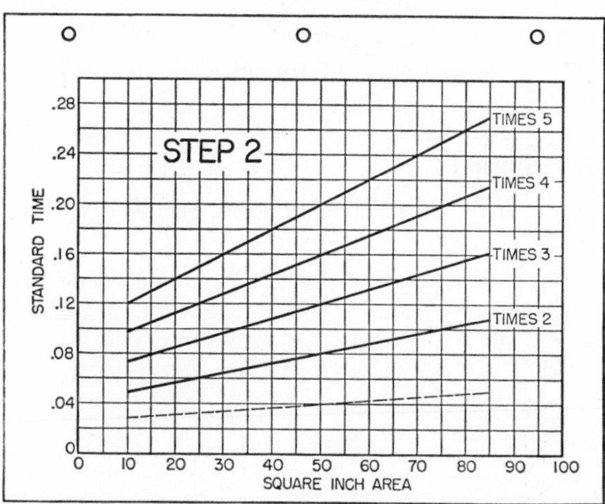

b. The same data variable multiplied by a series of factors.

FIG. 49. You can easily get answers to thousands of multiplications of one variable by a series of rates or factors.

element is repeated. Also, it happens when quantity comes in, provided, of course, that the time for each unit remains unchanged.

Occasionally, you may want to divide instead of multiply. That can be performed in a like manner. Figure 50, drawn to a larger scale, shows an example of one divisor. You might have several. One case I think of is the cost of an operation per piece where one or several may be made in that one operation. Foundry and plastic molding are examples.

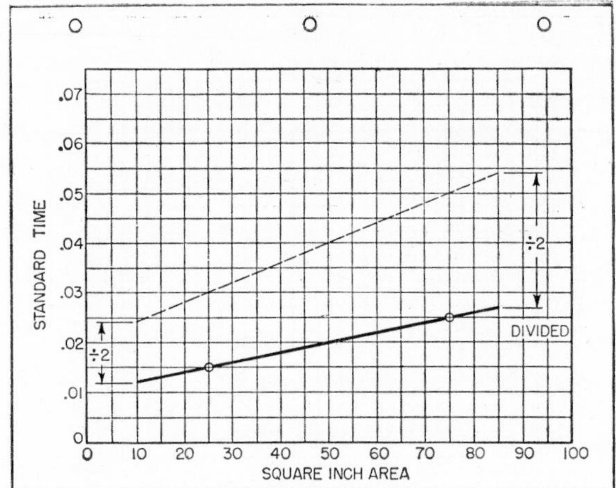

FIG. 50. A curve representing the cost or more factors to get the per piece amount.

Now, let's reflect a moment. We have set up several sets of new curves by plotting a couple of points for each one. Thus, we obtained dozens, hundreds, even thousands of answers to our combinations of variables. Isn't this a simple way to solve problems of this kind?

Two-variable Addition

Going in for a little more complication, suppose you have two sets of curves to be added. Those shown in Fig. 51 can be used as

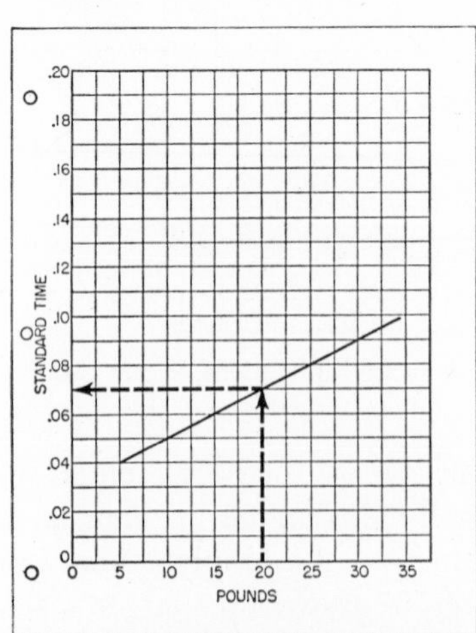

a. A curve for Standard Time based on Pounds that is only part of the operation standard.

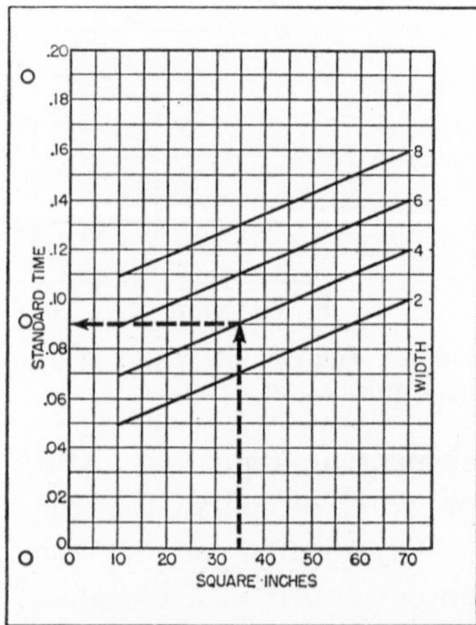

b. A family of curves related to Square Inches that shows part of total operation standard.

FIG. 51. Two different variables may have to be added to solve your problem.

examples of values from two curves that are to be added. If constants were to be included also, they could be treated as already outlined.

A reading for 35 Square Inches on Curve 4 is .09 Minute. And the value for 20 Pounds is .07 Minute. The total you want to get is .16 Minute. So let's go about obtaining that total by graphical addition. In starting, we will build around the more complicated variables for Square Inches. It has four curves already in place.

To read these curves, you select the Square Inch point on the base line that corresponds with your variable requirement. You move upward to the curve for the Width involved. Then you go left to the Standard. That means your problem of adding another variable can be solved by continuing to the left somewhere beyond your first curve sheet.

Let's place another sheet of cross-section paper alongside (Fig. 52*a*). On this, you can do some experimenting. Initially, you need a time scale because you seek a total time. Set that up along the bottom edge. Make it extensive enough to include the full range of possible totals. Your least one is .04 Minute (5 Pounds) plus .05 Minute (10 Square Inches on Curve 2). Your greatest is .10 Minute (35 Pounds) plus .16 Minute (70 Square Inches on Curve 8).

With your scale laid out, your next step is to get to the .16-Minute total time shown as two curve readings on Fig. 51. This you could

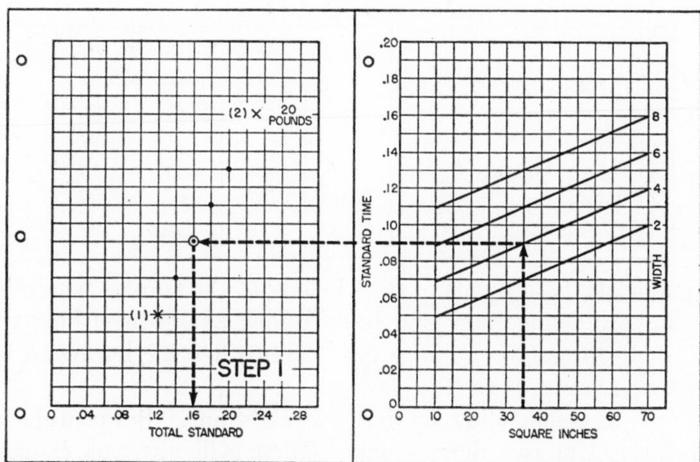

a. Place another sheet of cross-section paper alongside the chart so you can do some experimenting to get the total standard.

FIG. 52. You may add two variables to get a total answer for any combination over the complete range of both.

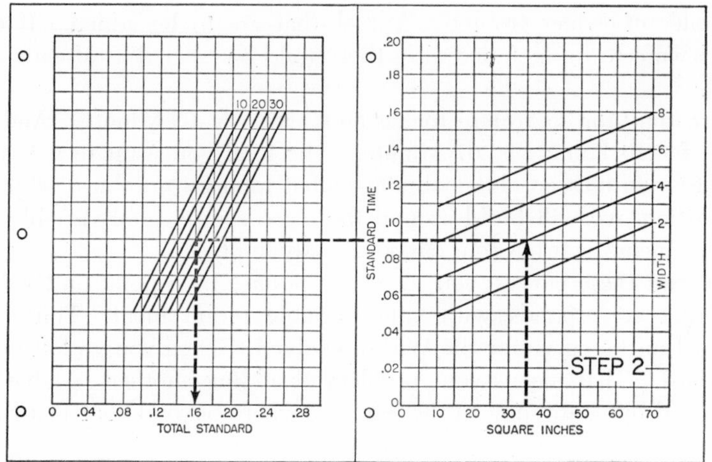

b. In the same way as you located the 20-Pound line in (a) you find the lines for other weights.

FIG. 52. (*Continued*).

do, if you interrrupted the east-west line of motion through your two charts at the point over your new scale reading of .16 minute. So set up a roadblock at that point. The circle shows where.

But one point is no solution. Let's see if you can find a line that gives us a complete road block. First, we know there are three more readings we can get for 25 Square Inches. They are for Curves 2, 6, and 8.

Dimensions	*Readings from Curves, Minutes*			
	2	4	6	8
35 Square Inches.........	.07	.09	.11	.13
20 Pounds...............	.07	.07	.07	.07
Total Standard...........	.14	.16	.18	.20

Let's spot all these points. They belong at the corners where horizontal lines extending from your base-curve readings meet lines vertically through the totals you must get. This is figuring backward from the answer, if you prefer.

These points should show up in one straight line. But continue one step further. Get two more points. These will give you an added check. Also they indicate the length of the line you must draw. The length must include the extremes in your totals. These are (1) the lowest reading for the 2-inch Width curve, and (2) the highest reading for the 8-inch Width curve. They show as Xs in the diagram.

With these points, you have located the line for 20 Pounds. There are many other weights in the range of Fig. 51*b*. So your next step is to find their lines. Proceeding in the same way you set up the line for 20 Pounds, and you locate the several you need. These will show up as a family like that drawn on the left of Fig. 52*b*. Looking at the result tells you that these curves could be spread out, and that more could be drawn, if desirable.

Conserving Space

As you look over your finished work, you might say, "Why so much paper?" You might then try to put both sets of lines on one page. One such attempt is illustrated in Fig. 53*a*. You will notice, however,

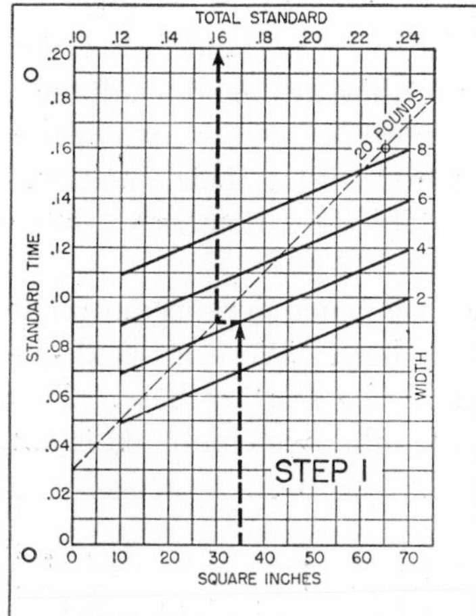

a. The first attempt at consolidation results in a line for 20 Pounds not too distinctive.

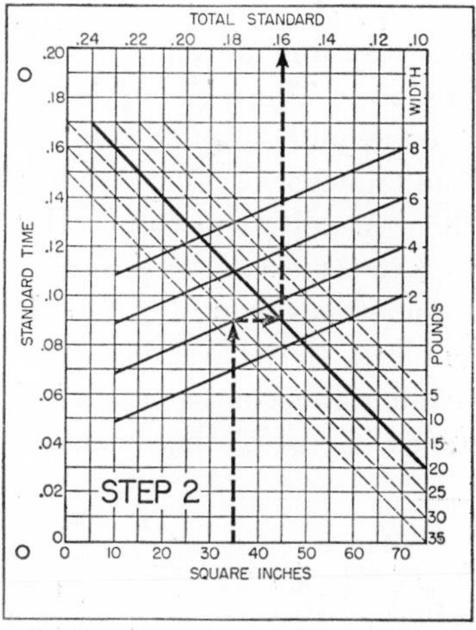

b. By reversing the scale of Total Standard you can get curves more nearly at right angles to each other.

FIG. 53. Two families of variables can be drawn on one sheet to simplify the problem of combining them.

that there is some confusion created, because the 20-Pound line is in the same general direction as the other lines. This can be remedied. Simply reverse the direction of your scale of Total Standard. This will cause the lines to fall in the opposite direction (Fig. 53*b*). So you have a point to remember:

1. *Reverse your scale when necessary to place families of curves at right angles to each other.*

In this same general way there is another rule to follow.

2. *Shift scale locations to minimize concentrations of curves.*

One other change was made in completing Fig. 53*b*. The closeness of the lines for weight in Fig. 52*b* was overcome. This was done by spreading out the scale for Total Standard. To clear up part of the confusion of multiple curves this way somewhat contradicts Rule 2 just stated. Hence, you must strike the best balance you can between it and the rule that follows. This third rule is a restatement in part of one given in Chap 3.

3. *Spread out scales to reasonable maximums for the purpose of separating curves of one family.*

Combining Families

Combining two or more families of curves can be a fairly simple task or a very difficult one. So much depends upon what kind of families they are. Those having interdependent variables are the difficult ones to cope with graphically. They require plotting against two scales simultaneously. They are best treated by first getting their equations. Then, usually, you can work with one variable at a time as we have done in the examples thus far.

Sometimes, you may be able to choose a sequence in procedure that simplifies the combining. That is the case here. We can avoid unraveling the complex family by using it as the starting base. This choice is possible because one of the two families we combined is not

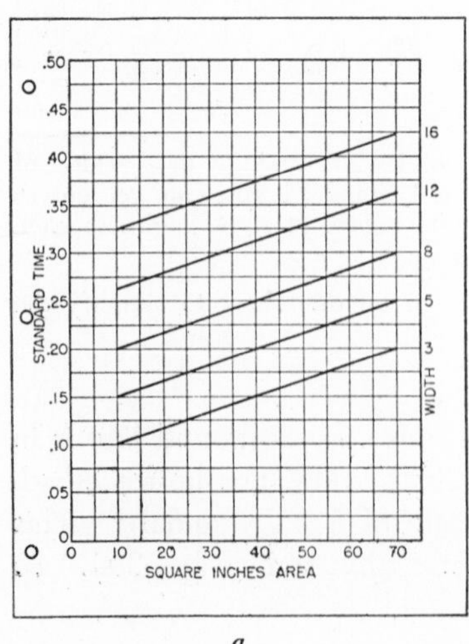

a

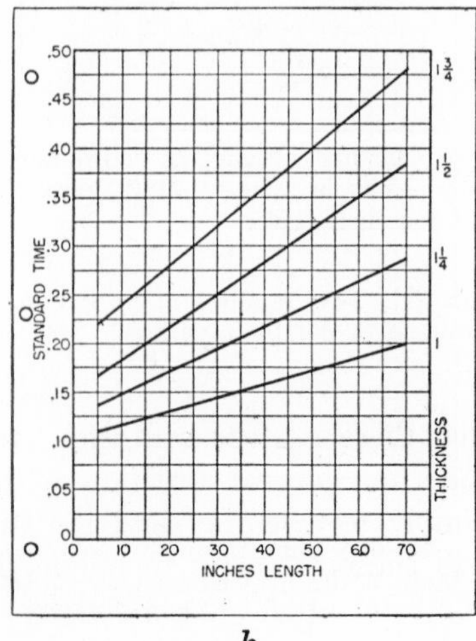

b

Fig. 54. Two families of curves to be combined in three steps shown on Fig. 55.

complex in its make-up. Therefore, right off, let me say that the explanation of how to combine two variables that follows is not to be taken as general. It will not apply to every two families you may want to combine. You will see what I mean by examining Fig. 54. Here, the curve family for Length is like our previous example. But the family for Area is simplified. Its lines are parallel.

Let us begin with Fig. 55*a*. It is like the chart completed in Fig.

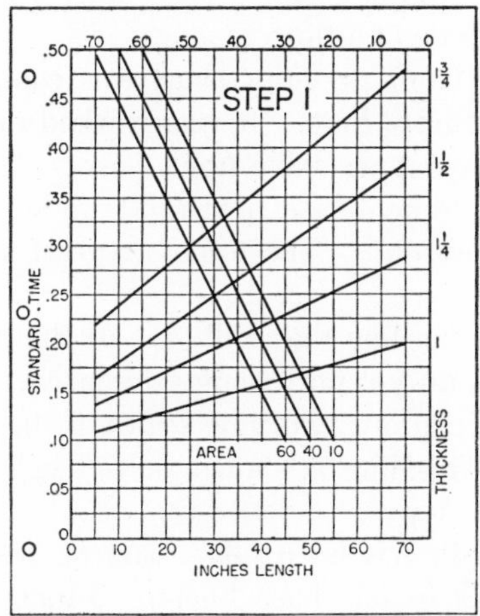

a. Area lines for the 3-Inch Width curve are located and drawn.

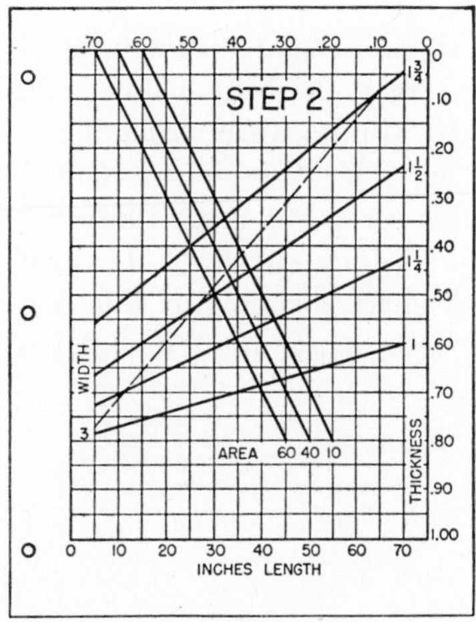

b. The base turning line for 3-Inch Width is located and drawn.

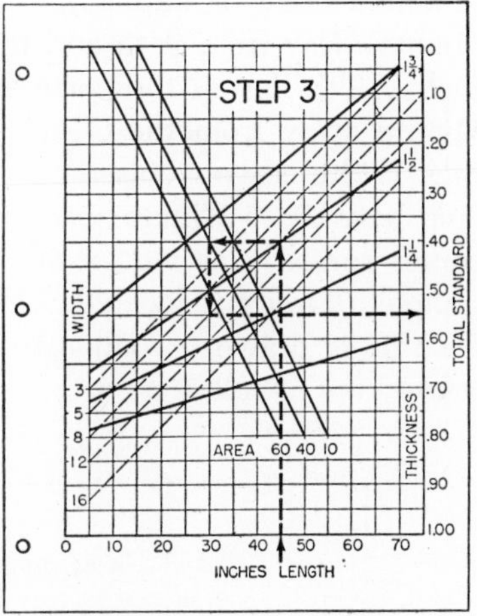

c. Increments for Width are added from the base line for 3-Inch Width.

Fig. 55. Two families of variables are combined and the heavy dotted road map line shows how to find the total answer.

53*b*. We have the sums of values from the Length curve added to readings from only the bottom curve in the Area family. Lines for 10, 40, and 60 show. More should be added. They are omitted to avoid confusion. These three lines were set up exactly like those in our previous example. They were laid out as though we had only one curve for Area. This was done to establish a foundation. It was a necessary step to separate the Square Inch variable from that of Width in Fig. 54*a*. That is because this family also has two variables and we can add only one at a time.

You will recall that our previous chart was complete at this point. It resembled this example here. It was worked out to add only one curve. That is just what we have now. To go to the next step, we must put in a line to indicate our next right-angle turn. But that line cannot add any to the total. The total is correct at this stage for the 3-Inch Width line.

So we want to draw a line that will give us the right place to make the right-angle turn and yet not change the answer. Such a line will bisect the angle between our two time scales, if they are equal. They are, in our setup. This line is shown dotted in Fig. 55*b*. It is the base line for our final step.

Since our Area factor has been taken care of, we need only to add for Width differences to our base line for 3-Inch Width. Take the first spread that is between the 3-Inch and 5-Inch Width curves of .05 Minute. Draw a line parallel to the 3-Inch Width curve and .05 Minute away from it to add that much time. That will place the 5-Inch Width line in the correct location. Next, the 8-Inch line is .05 Minute away from the 5-Inch line, or .10 Minute away from the 3-Inch Width curve we used as our base line. The 12-Inch and 16-Inch lines have .0625-Minute spacings. Use this spread to space these two curves similarly as we located the 5- and 8-Inch curves. Thus, the complete family is located. The finished chart is shown as Fig. 55*c*. On this is drawn a road map to show how to use it. The total is worked out as follows.

Dimensions	*Readings, Min*	
	Curves	*Chart*
45-In. Length × 1½-In. Thickness.........	.30	
40 Sq In. × 8-In. Width..................	.25	
	.55	.55

Applications

With these examples, I have tried to explain the general approach to use for combining lines representing variables and constants. Some more ideas will be developed in our next chapter. There, by means of some common problems, I will attempt to show ways to apply these principles.

The family-of-curves method is a good one to use in many instances. You can see how, with a little practice, it affords a fast method to solve some complex problems. That is its important advantage. It is quick. It is inexpensive. You should get better acquainted with this method of combining data. It can save time for you.

CHAPTER 12

How to Use the Curve Family

You will be interested in the solutions in this chapter. Some of them will intrigue you. I hope so, because this approach to problem solving is a good one to know. It is a very quick way to get answers to many types of complex problems.

The curve-family method, as I name it, appears to be not as well understood as it should be. Just think back into the previous chapter. Remember how you could get hundreds of answers by drawing just one line? All you had to do to get it was spot a couple of points. In most cases, that is all the time it takes. Thus in this curve-family method, you have an efficient way to get a large number of answers to multi-variable problems. True, it is not "accurate." But accuracy is relative in the solution of all problems where you must assume some factors.

For instance, to estimate, predict, or budget any kind of costs, you make assumptions. These may be of sales volume, price, usage, or scrap. All of these, and other variables could be built into your chart. All you need to take account of more variables after you understand the mechanics, are more time, paper, and patience.

The principles of the method were explained in our previous chapter. Here, we will carry on by applying them to some typical examples. The first will be the very common one of estimating. Every plant has the day-after-day question, "What will it cost?"

Material Cost

Estimating usually divides itself into two parts, (1) labor plus overhead and (2) material cost. I chose to compute material cost in this example because there seem to be very few illustrations of this application. It is an extension of Fig. 7, Chap. 2 where we worked out the profit or loss for product mixes of Shirts, Shorts, Sheets, and Shoes.

Once you forecast sales and compute likely profits, you need to "guesstimate" your costs. Material is one that you must think of first in order to get it in on time. Too, it's one you have to provide money for because its arrival precedes manufacturing. So computing material cost is a typical example.

We will work out answers to total material cost for quantities predicted in a sales forecast. As we do so, however, please look beyond the details I use. To see the general application try to think for instance, of Shirts as the basic unit of any one of your products with Shorts, Sheets, and Shoes as major variations or accessories you add to it as your customers may specify.

To begin, we will use the material costs shown in the table set up for easy reference. These are related to Sales Dollars for two reasons. One is that we are assuming we want to know the material cost we

Sales Dollars	*Material Costs*			
	Shirts	*Shorts*	*Sheets*	*Shoes*
$ 40,000	$10,000	$ 6,000	$18,000	$16,000
60,000	15,000	9,000	27,000	24,000
80,000	20,000	12,000	36,000	32,000
100,000	25,000	15,000	45,000	40,000
120,000	30,000	18,000	54,000	48,000

have in our Sales Forecast. The other is more basic. It is to repeat for emphasis the method I call "direct reading." That is to solve a problem in terms of its underlying causes (material cost) but then to translate your scales into dimensions more convenient or available (sales dollars).

Step 1. Following this fundamental, your first step is to set up an ordinary cross-section sheet with two scales in material cost dollars (Fig. 56*a*). These are the costs we want to add. Later, we will translate these into sales dollars. So across the horizontal, lay out a scale that covers the range you are using first. In this case, I picked Shirts. Our scale must include from $10,000 to $30,000.

Taking Shorts as our next variable, we lay out a vertical scale to cover the range of sums. The minimum is $10,000 plus $6,000 and the maximum is $30,000 plus $18,000. Now label this scale "Shirts + Shorts."

Step 2. Your next step is to locate the family of curves for Shorts (Fig. 56*b*). You can pick any points. Let's take the low point, material costs of Shirts $10,000 and Shorts $6,000. The total is $16,000 and locates point 1 vertically over $10,000 of Shirt Material and horizontally in line with $16,000 on your Shirts + Shorts scale.

Now be careful. Remember two details. First, most of us can correctly do only one thing at a time. Here that means work with only one curve of the family at one time. The second is to always plot extremes of your range.

With those two things in mind (1) let's find another point on the curve of $40,000 Short sales at (2) the extreme of Shirt cost. This is at $30,000 Shirt material cost and $6,000 Short material cost. The total is $36,000. Make a dot over $30,000 Shirts opposite $36,000 on your Shirts + Shorts scale.

The next step is to check (1) your arithmetic and your plotting. More important (2) is to see whether your line is straight or curved. So plot a third point, say $20,000 Shirt and $6,000 Short material costs. The total $26,000 is plotted over $20,000 Shirts opposite $26,000 of Shirts + Shorts. It falls in line so our arithmetic is correct and our line is straight. Draw it in. Label it "40" to mean $40,000 Short sales dollars.

Step 3. To complete the family for Shorts, you plot points on one curve at a time. Two points for each are enough because our curves are straight lines. They can all be for the extremes Shirts $10,000 and $30,000 material cost.

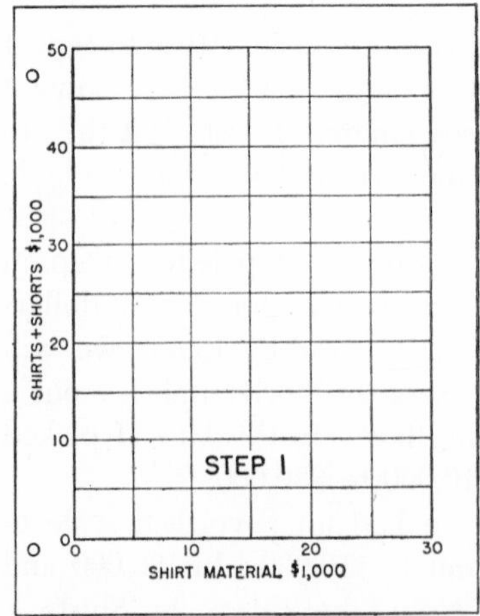

a. Begin as you would any curve plotting with a scale to suit your problem.

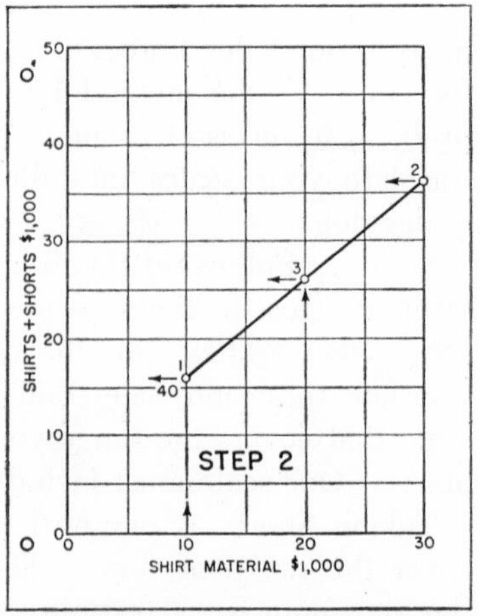

b. Plot any two points for one line of the Short family and check at a third.

FIG. 56.

Sales Dollars Shorts	Low Point Shirt Material $10,000		High Point Shirt Material $30,000	
	Short MC	Total S + S	Short MC	Total S + S
$ 40,000	$ 6,000	$16,000	$ 6,000	$36,000
60,000	9,000	19,000	9,000	39,000
80,000	12,000	22,000	12,000	42,000
100,000	15,000	25,000	15,000	45,000
120,000	18,000	28,000	18,000	48,000

When these points are plotted and your lines drawn, mark each one with its Short sales dollar identification. Then label this scale of legends "Short" to distinguish this family from others to follow.

Step 4. Your next step is important. At least, that's how it appears to me. I say that because it has been difficult for me to get trainees to go around this next corner. After they get by this hurdle, the rest seems easy. To help you overcome what I think is their problem, I have erased the bottom material cost scale for Shirt materials. In its place I have noted its translation into Shirt Sales Fig. 56*d*. By making this change, I hope to get you to forget the erased material cost scale. That step is completed. It is behind you so look instead at the next step you are to take.

If you will, turn your curve sheet so your Shirt + Sheet scale is

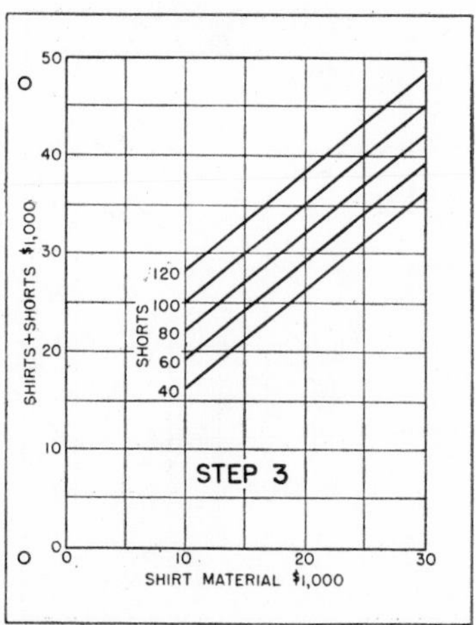

c. Plot points for all other curves, label each one and the family.

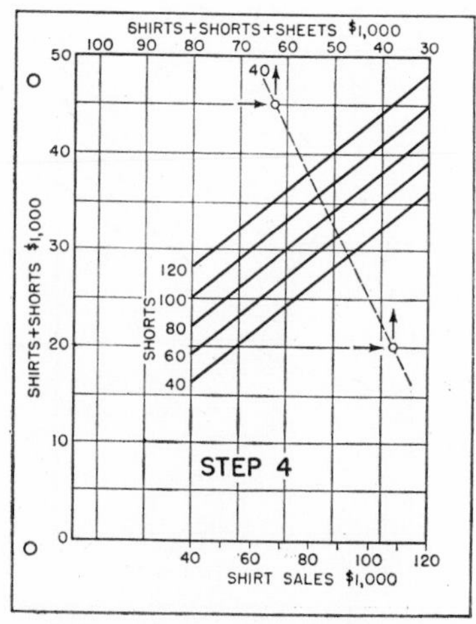

d. Set up a scale at 90° to include three variables and locate one curve of Sheet family.

FIG. 56. (*Continued*).

horizontal. Then you can think of plotting your first instead of your second family of curves. From this position, you want to follow your custom of laying out a vertical scale along what now is the left side of your cross-section paper. You want a scale that tells you how much more material cost you will have when Sheets are added to the total of Shirts plus Shorts. This will range from $34,000 material cost (Shirts $10,000, Shorts, $6,000, Sheets $18,000) to $102,000 (Shirts $30,000, Shorts 18,000, Sheets $54,000).

Following the rule for curve layout, you would start with 0 at the bottom and spread out your scale to include $102,000 at the top. Instead, you should experiment. One reason is that in this type of addition problem this usual scale will cause your next family of curves to fall in the same general direction as those for Shorts. To make this new family go more or less crosswise, you will want to reverse your new scale.

Another reason is seen by looking at the labels for the Short family (Fig. 56*c*). They are well inside the curve sheet when they might better have been at the edge. So again, you should break the rule of starting all scales at 0–0. Thus, at the top of Fig. 56*d* you see that the scale for Shirts + Shorts + Sheets is chosen (1) to just include the extremes of our totals and (2) is reversed to make this family for Sheets fall at roughly right angles to our first family for Shorts.

With this set, we can locate our line for $40,000 Sheets. One point

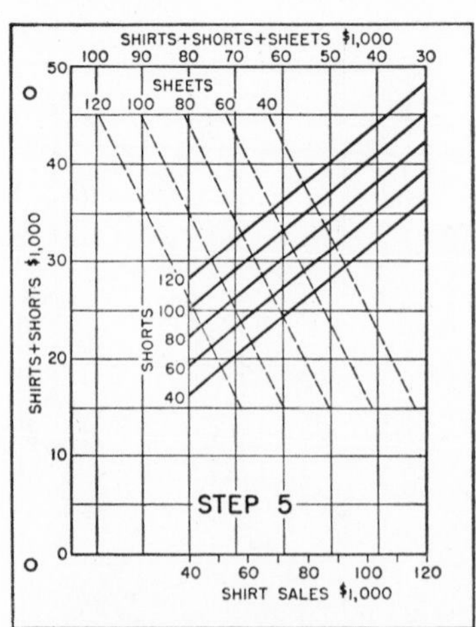

e. Complete family for Sheets and label it.

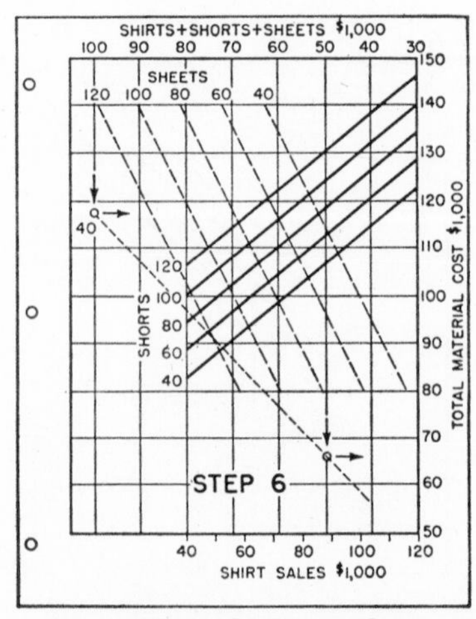

f. Locate scale for total material and plot points for one curve of Shoe family.

Fig. 56. (*Continued*).

can be on the line of $20,000 Shirts + Shorts after you have added $18,000 for Sheets. Plot this total of $20,000 + $18,000 under the location of $38,000 on your new scale for Shirts + Shorts + Sheets. A second point can be on the line of $45,000 Shirts + Shorts. Adding $18,000 for Sheet material, you get $63,000 total. Locate it on the $45,000 line opposite $63,000 on your scale for Shirts, Shorts, Sheets.

Draw in your line in dashes to distinguish it from your first family. Label it "40," meaning $40,000 Sheet sales dollars. Then before going on, you may save yourself some headaches by checking your line location using several more sums.

Step 5. If these all fall on your line, you can plot similar points for the other four curves (Fig. 56*e*). Each should be $9,000 from its neighbor—the difference between material costs for each $20,000 of Sheet sales dollars.

Mark each curve with its correct sales dollar equivalent. Then label these legends "Sheets" to designate the family.

Step 6. Now we turn another corner. As in Step 4, you want to try first to find out whether to run your scale up or down. The better choice appears to be low at the bottom and high at the top. It should include the low of $50,000 ($10,000 Shirts, $6,000 Shorts, $18,000 Sheets, $16,000 Shoes). The high is $150,000. So spread out such a scale and mark it "Total Material Cost."

Then to locate your $40,000 curve for Shoe sales, you will plot two points based on $16,000 for Shoe material cost. One can be on the

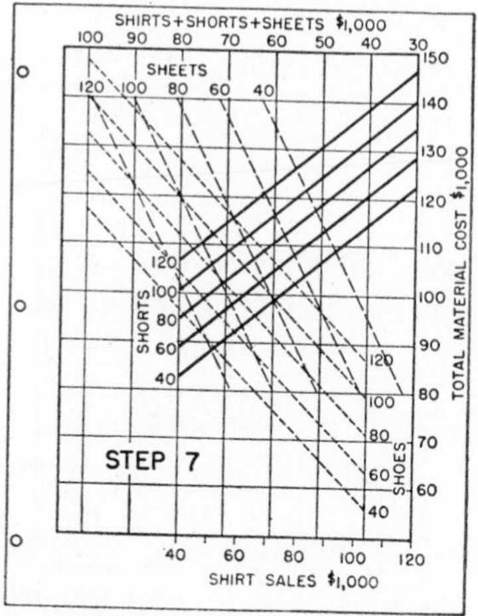

g. Complete the Shoe family of curves and label it.

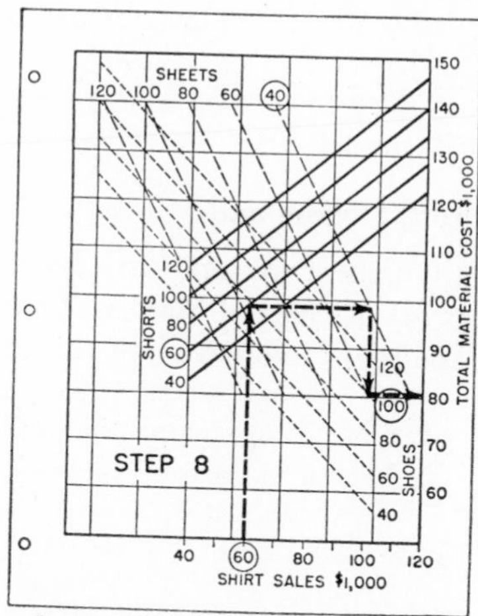

h. Check chart for several combinations and draw in one example.

FIG 56. (*Continued*).

line of $100,000 Shirts + Shorts + Sheets. Drop down to the point opposite $100,000 + $16,000 on your total scale and make a dot. A second point may be on the line of $50,000. Place your point on that line opposite $66,000 on your total scale. With these two located draw a dotted line and mark it "40" to denote $40,000 Shoe sales.

Step 7. Next locate the remaining lines of your Shoe family. These are parallel to your 40 line and $8,000 apart. Label each one in equivalent sales dollars. Then letter the description "Shoes" to set apart this family.

Step 8. With construction done, you can erase the scales you set up to build the chart. Then you should check it by working out several examples. Finally, draw in a road map showing how to read your

Sales Dollars		*Material Cost*	*Chart*
Shirts............	$ 60.000	$15,000	
Shorts...........	80,000	12,000	
Sheets...........	40,000	18,000	
Shoes............	100,000	40,000	
		$85,000	$85,000

chart. This is very important. Try it, to see why. Change the sequence of reading your chart, using variations of this example. You will get different answers. I tried one going from $60,000 Shirts to $100,000 Shoes to $40,000 Sheets to $80,000 Shorts and read $120,000 total material. Thus, we can set down a rule.

Multi-variable charts must be read in the same sequence they are set up.

Add, Divide, and Multiply

Our next example is a bit more complex. It goes beyond addition as in our chart of Material Costs to bring in multiplication and division. The four factors we will work with are

1. Length of carton (inches)
2. Width of carton (inches)
3. Number of Items in carton
4. Number of Bands on carton

These are combined in ways suggested by the following equation

$$\text{Standard time} = \frac{(\text{Width} + \text{Length}) \times 2 \times \text{Bands}}{\text{Number in Carton}}$$

Bands = 1, 2, or 3, and Number = 4, 6, 8, 12.

They are combinations such as you might have in a packaging operation.

Figure 57 shows curves for Length and Width time standards. The multiplier 2 is to change $L + W$ to perimeter. As carried out here, there can be 1, 2, or 3 Bands around the package. And in our problem, we may have 4, 6, 8, or 12 Items in a package. This factor for items is a divisor because we want to get the standard time per item.

Step 1. First, you lay out two scales (Fig. 58*a*). Length scale covers the range of standard times from .10 to .70 Minute on Curve *B*, Fig. 57. It must be in time units to start with because we cannot

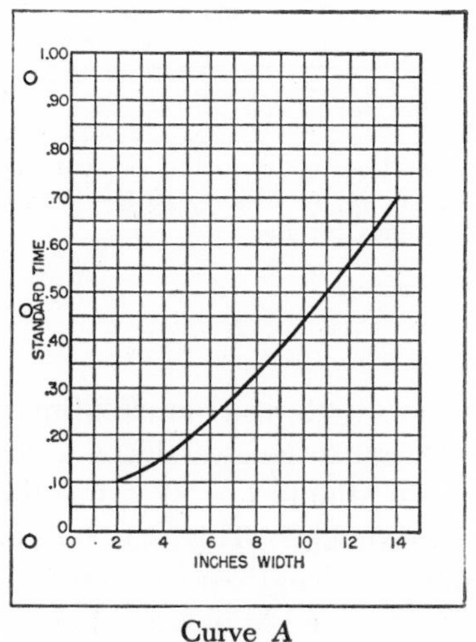

Curve *A*

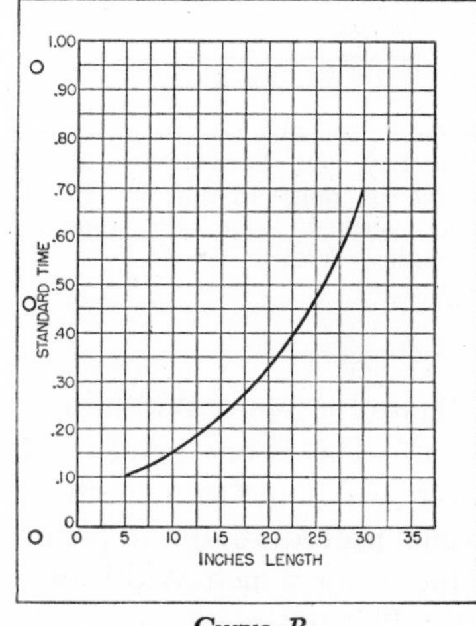

Curve *B*

FIG. 57. Our problem in standard setting involves the two variable element time curves shown above plus some factors.

add the unlike inches of Length and Width. Eventually, we will translate this time scale to equivalent units of Length.

Then, in order to add times for Length to those for Width, you set up a vertical scale to provide for the Sum. This has a maximum of .70 Minute from Curve *B* plus .70 Minute from Curve *A*. So you lay out a scale to include 1.40 Minutes at the high extreme. Label this scale $L + W$ so you won't get lost.

Step 2. With the two scales all set, your next step is to locate the first line (Fig. 58*b*). Any one of several will do. Let's start with the low one. The least reading on Curve *A* is .10 Minute for 2-inch Width. If our .10 Minute is added to values from Curve *B* for Length it will increase them by .10 Minute. Consequently, if you add .10

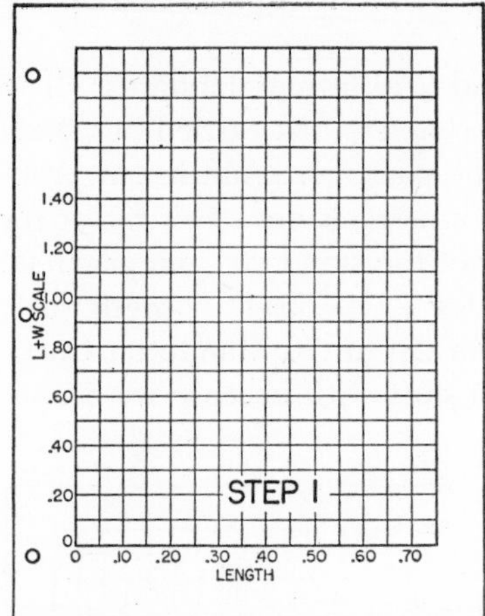

a. Lay out horizontal scale to cover the range in time for Length and vertical scale for time of Length + Width.

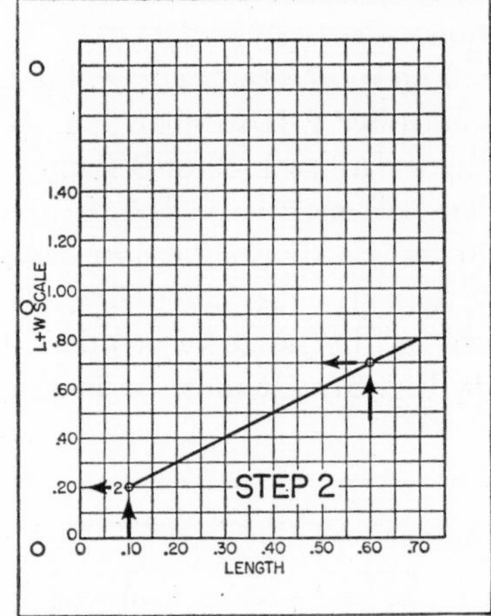

b. Locate two points on first line of family by adding .10 for W = 2 to times for L.

FIG. 58.

Minute for 2-inch Width to .10 Minute for Length, you get .20 Minute total. This is one point on the line you want to locate. Place a dot over .10 Minute for Length and opposite .20 Minute $L + W$. Use the same procedure for a point near the maximum. This can be .10 Minute for 2-inch Width plus .60 Minute for Length equals .70 $L + W$. Plot this point on the vertical line through .60 Minute for Length opposite .70 Minute on the $L + W$ scale. These two points locate the line. You can draw it through them. Mark it "2 inches" to distinguish it from other curves of the Width family to follow. Before you go on, check another point or two in order to make sure your plotting is correct and that your line is a straight one.

Step 3. In the same way you located the 2-inch Width line, you establish the others (Fig. 58*c*). The number of lines you draw depends upon the accuracy you want to maintain. For clarity, only a few are shown here. These were set up as readings from the labeled vertical in Curve *A*, Fig. 57. To illustrate, the reading for 4-inch Width is .15 Minute. Adding .15 to .10 Minute for Length you get .25 Minute as one point. This is plotted over .10 Minute for Length and opposite .25 Minute on $L + W$. Another point, .15 + .60 = .75 Minute is plotted over .60 Minute for Length and opposite .75 Minute on $L + W$. Then the line is drawn.

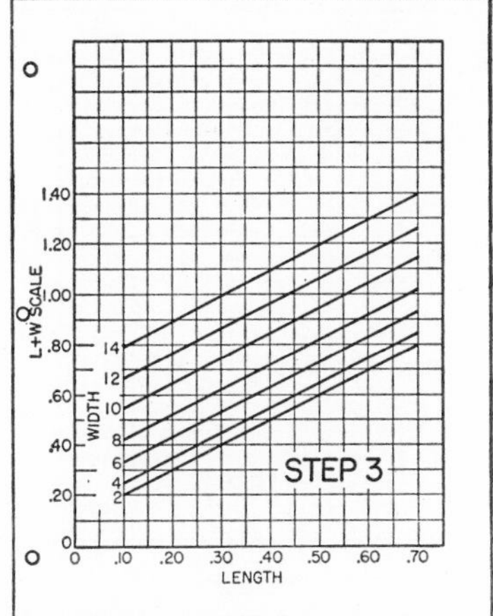

c. Locate other lines in the family, one at a time by adding times for specific Widths to conveniently located time for Lengths.

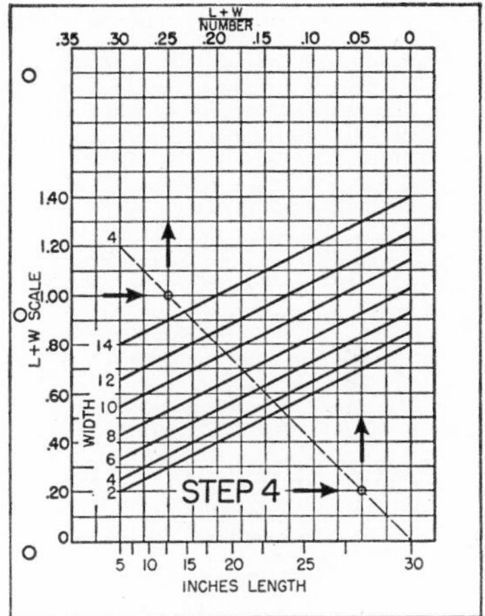

d. Arrange a scale for

$$\frac{\text{L + W}}{\text{Number}}$$

at top of chart, in reverse direction to throw new family across the one already drawn in.

Fig. 58. (*Continued*).

At the extreme, Curve *A* reads .70 Minute for 14-inch Width. Adding, .70 + .10 = .80 Minute, plot your first point, with .70 + .60 = .130 Minutes as the other. The line through these two is the top one. All the others are located in the same way. Each is labeled as it is drawn in, to avoid mistakes and back-checking.

Step 4. To move on, you turn 90 degrees and lay out a scale at the top for your next set of answers. These will be the results from *L* + *W* divided by Number. The factors of Number are 4, 6, 8, and 12. These will give you scale extremes of .20/12 and 1.30/4. Write in your scale backward to get a cross-trend to your new family lines. Label the scale "(*L* + *W*)/Number."

Starting with four items of Number, figure points for plotting your first line. Using 1.00 on *L* + *W* as the first one, you get 1.00/4 equals .25 Minute. Plot this opposite 1.00 Minute on *L* + *W* and under the .25-Minute on the (*L* + *W*)/Number scale. For a second point use .20 Minute divided by 4 to get .05 Minute. That locates a point opposite .20 Minute on *L* + *W* directly under .05 Minute on your top scale. Now you can draw in your line and mark it "4" for Number.

Step 5. Continue to divide and locate (Fig. 58*e*). Using 6 as your next Number, find two points. An easy one is 1.20/6, equaling .20

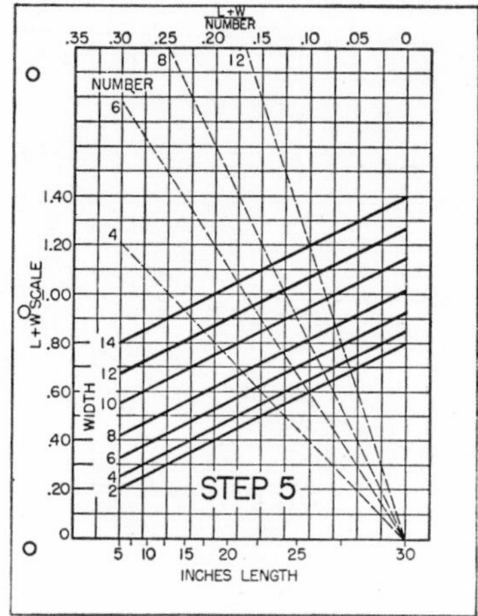

e. Locate family for Number by dividing convenient L + W Scale divisions by the several factors for Number.

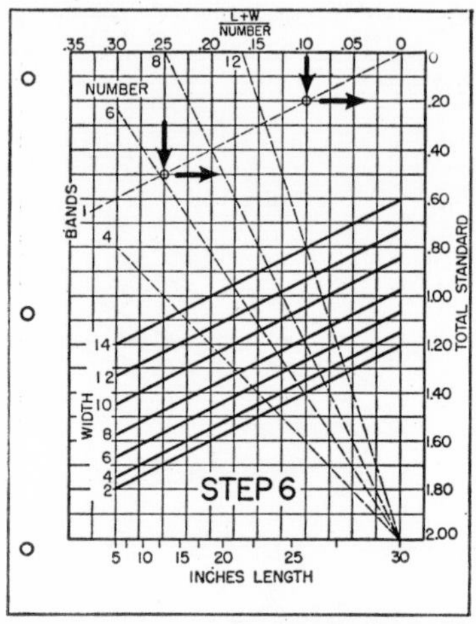

f. Lay out scale for final standard that includes full range at 90 degrees from previous scale.

FIG. 58. (*Continued*).

Minute. Another is .60/6 or .10 Minute. Make two dots. One is opposite 1.20 Minutes on $L + W$ and under .20 Minute on your top scale. The other is opposite .60 Minute and under .10 Minute. Draw in the line. This and other lines in the Number family will stand out better if you use long dashes to distinguish them. And you can complete the lines for Numbers 8 and 12 in the same way. Be sure to label each line correctly.

Notice that all these Number lines converge at 0–0. This is obvious when you think of it. Zero divided by 4 or any other number results in 0 as an answer. This simplification assists in plotting. It means that you need compute only one point for each of your lines. But be cautious. First, you do not always have 0–0 so conveniently located. Second, I advise two or more point locations to check. When they all fall on a common line you know two things:

a. You have a straight line.

b. You have made no mistakes.

Step 6. Your next step should be easier. This one involves multiplying. In it, you must provide time standards for 1, 2, or 3 Bands. Also, you must bring in your multiplier of 2 to change $L + W$ into perimeter. So you want to locate lines for the combined multipliers of 2×1, 2×2, and 2×3.

First, you can lay out the final scale, another 90 degrees from your

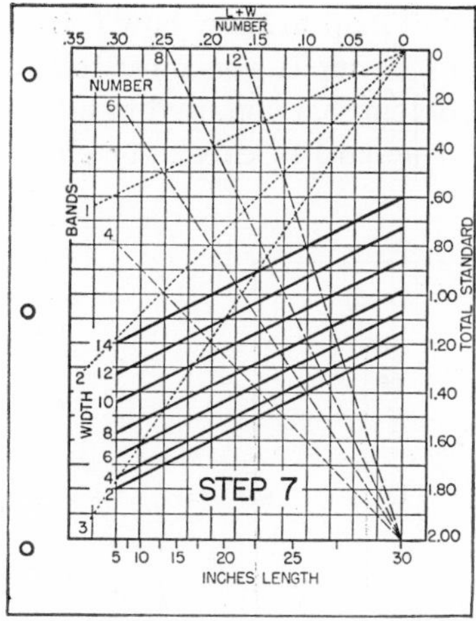

g. Locate lines for Band groups by multiplying constant 2 × Bands by scale readings for

$$\frac{L + W}{\text{Number}}.$$

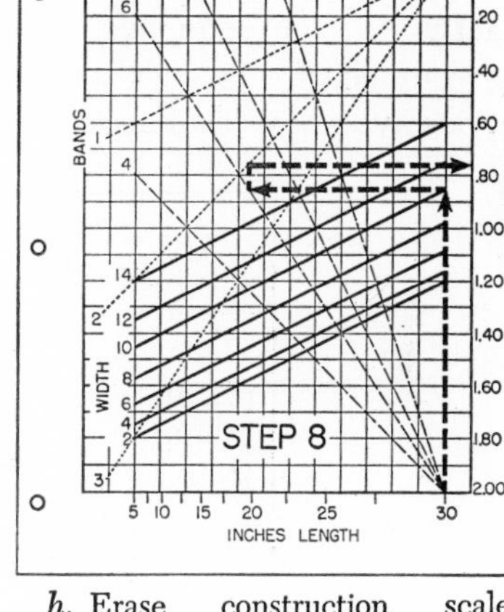

h. Erase construction scales. Check the chart in several extreme examples. Draw in a road map.

Fig. 58. (*Continued*).

top scale. Your new scale is to be the Total Time Standard. It will range from a low of (.20/12) × 2 × 1 to a high of (1.30/4) × 2 × 3. These are the extremes used in Step 4 multiplied by the constant factor of 2 to change $L + W$ to perimeter and the extremes of 1 and 3 Bands. Your low is .02 × 2 equals .04 Minute. High is .32 × 6 or 1.92 Minutes. Thus, a scale from 0 to 2.00 Minutes will be needed. Write that scale along the right margin and label it "Total Time Standard" (Fig. 58*f*).

Now you are ready to locate your first line in this last family. Let's start with the multiplier of 2 × 1. Using .25 Minute as one location, your answer is .25 × 2 or .50 Minute. Plot this under .25 Minute and opposite .50 Minute on your Total scale. Likewise, take .10 × 2 equals .20 Minute and locate it under .10 Minute and opposite .20 Minute Total Standard. Draw in your line. Label it "1 Band" so there will be no mistakes of wrong identity.

Step 7. Follow the same procedures for multipliers 2 × 2, and 2 × 3. When these lines are located, you can draw and label them (Fig. 58*g*). You might use dotted lines for this Band family. Again, notice that this group converges at 0–0.

Step 8. At this stage, your diagram is completed except for finishing touches (Fig. 58*h*). First, you should check it to see that it is correct. Second, you should draw in a road map to show how it is to be used. As I stressed with our previous example, you must follow exactly the same sequence in solving a problem that you used in building your chart. So let's set a total time standard to check our chart. Suppose you have these conditions.

Dimensions		*Reading*	
		Curves	*Chart*
Length............	30	.70	
Width.............	10	.44	
Bands.............	2		
Number............	6		
$\frac{(.44 + .70) \times 2 \times 2}{6}$	=	.76	.76

This is the example drawn in on the chart. Hurrah! It works.

Machine-time Chart

Before we conclude this subject of charting by the curve-family method we should try to solve the familiar problem, "What is the cutting time?" It's as old as the hills. But sometimes I think we get across an idea best with a familiar illustration. So here goes. Keep in mind that this chart is straight calculation. That may be just the kind of problem you want to solve. It is the type most often seen in curve-family form in our handbooks.

To show all the factors to be considered in the common machine-time problem, let's start with an equation.

$$\text{Time} = \frac{\pi}{12} \frac{\text{Diameter} \times \text{Length}}{\text{Surface Speed} \times \text{Feed}}$$

Everything in our equation is in inches except Surface Speed. The Speed is in surface feet per minute. That is how the 12 to convert feet to inches gets in our equation. The symbol π is equal to 3.1416 and is included because Diameter must be converted to circumference. Taken together, $\pi/12$ becomes .262 in number form.

Now, you can tackle the equation in several ways. You can work through the multiplication in the numerator. Then you can do each division in sequence. You can include the constant multiplier (.262) first, last, or in between. My preference is to alternate, as on a slide rule. I would divide after multiplying. It holds the scales to lower

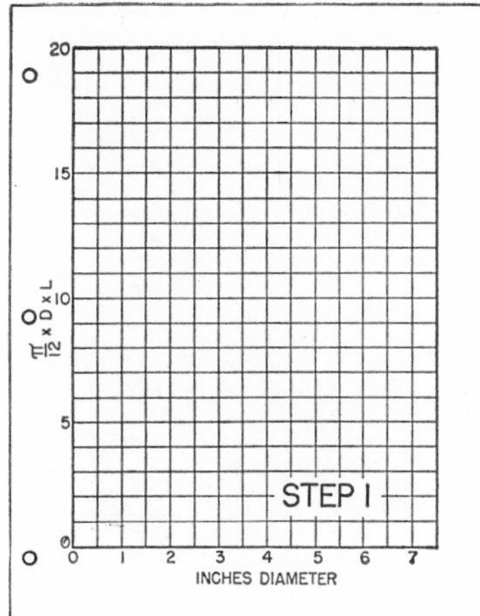

a. Lay out a bottom scale to include the range of Diameters. Then set up a vertical scale for $\frac{\pi}{12}$ (D $\times$ L).

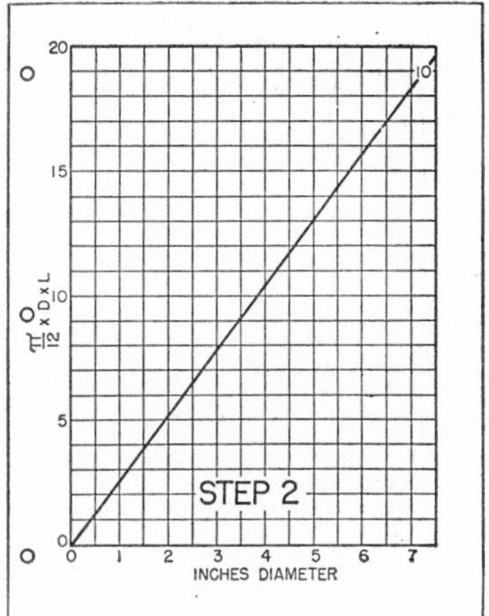

b. Multiply your maximum Diameter by maximum Length $\times \frac{\pi}{12}$ and spot the end of the line. Locate another point and draw the line.

FIG. 59.

ranges. In most cases, too, I am inclined to take care of the constant at the outset.

Step 1. With that explanation, let's lay out the first two scales (Fig. 59*a*). These are placed at right angles as before. The bottom scale is made to cover the range in Diameter you want to include. The vertical scale is worked out the same way, only here, you figure .262 $\times$ Maximum Diameter $\times$ Maximum Length you will need.

Step 2. In the example, I used 10 Inches as Maximum Length to get the extreme of the vertical scale (Fig. 59*b*). Proceed to locate one line. Using the extreme point just calculated for the 10-Inch Length gives you one point on that line. It is $.262 \times 7.5 \times 10$, or 19.65. At another point, $.262 \times 1.5 \times 10 = 3.93$. Of course, $.262 \times 0 \times 0 = 0$. But if you are no better mathematician than I am, you will not rely on this zero factor. It's all right, though, after you prove that it lies within your chart, and applies.

Step 3. Having located the line of maximum Length, you can spot the rest of the group (Fig. 59*c*). In doing so, I would use a constant multiplier. Set it up on your slide rule.

a. Divide $\pi/12$. The answer is .262.

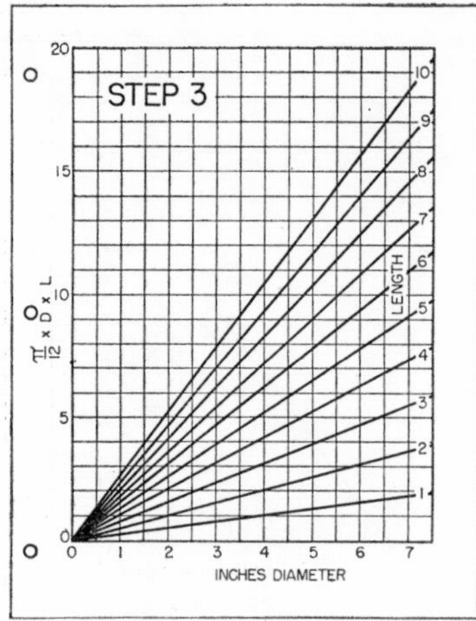

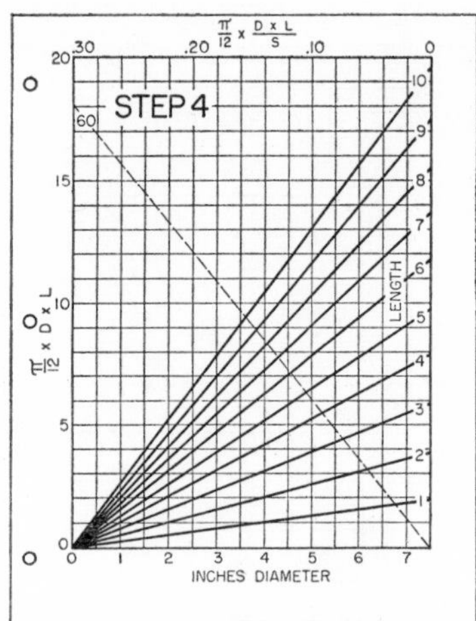

c. Using a constant of $\frac{\pi}{12} \times$ Maximum Diameter, multiply by all different lengths to locate ends of lines.

d. Set up a new scale at the top equal to left scale divided by Surface Speed. Locate the line of Minimum Speed.

FIG. 59. (*Continued*).

b. Multiply by 7.5, the maximum Diameter used here to get 1.96 constant factor.

c. Set 1 to 1.96 and read off the points for each Length.

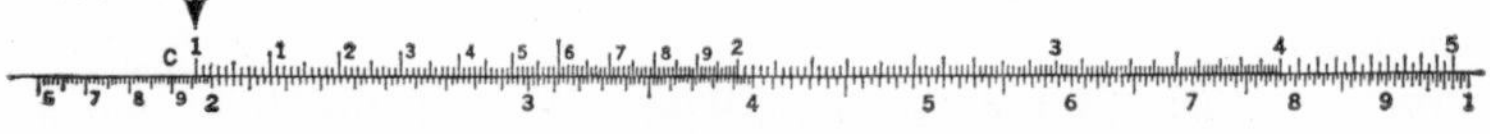

Diameter	*Point*	*Diameter*	*Point*
1	1.96	6	11.78
2	3.92	7	12.74
3	5.89	8	15.71
4	7.85	9	17.67
5	9.81	10	19.64

Plot these along your 7.5 Diameter vertical line because 7.5 was the multiplier. Then draw in each line and label it with its corresponding Length.

Step 4. Next you should divide to hold your scales to lower limits. So work with Surface Speed. Figure the limits of a scale you will need. The lowest Speed in the example gives us (Fig. 59*d*), 18/60 equals .30 as the extreme. Our scale is written backward to 0 because the lines should fall across those already drawn. Plotting the .30 re-

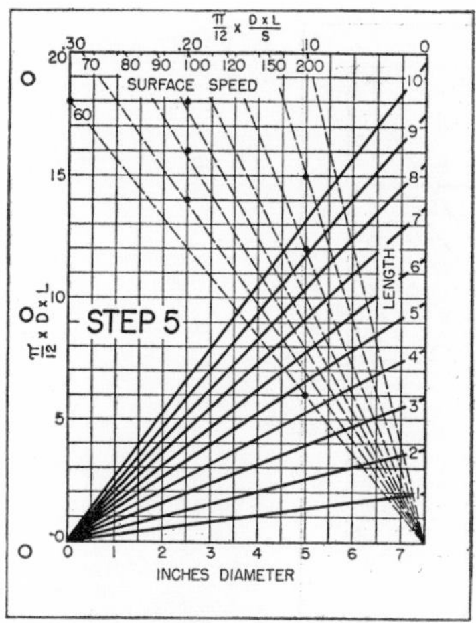

e. Divide Speeds into convenient divisions on left-hand scale to spot points on lines.

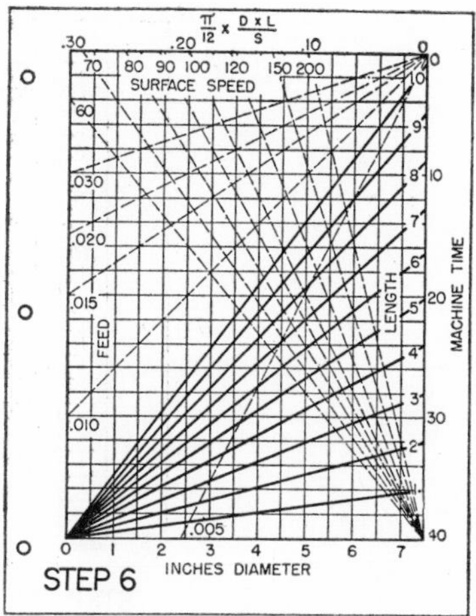

f. Lay out Time scale at 90 degrees and make it long enough to solve any problem in the range. Then divide top scale by Feeds to be located.

FIG. 59. (*Continued*).

sult gives one point on the line for 60 Speed. Dividing 6 on the $.262 \times D \times L$ scale by 60 gives .10 as another point. Drawing in the line, we see that it goes through 0-0.

Step 5. Again, you may set your slide rule. Use a red scale if you have one. Set the red 1 on 20 the top limit of your $\pi/12 \times D \times L$ scale and read off the points for all the speeds you need.

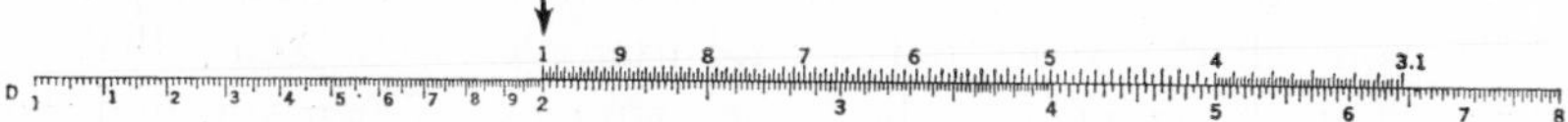

Plot these along the 20 line (Fig. 59*e*). These will be the upper ends of your Surface Speed family lines. The other end will be 0-0. Lacking a red scale, you can divide Speeds into any convenient divisions on the left scale—for example, 14/70, 16/80, 18/90, 20/100, 12/120, and 15/150. With these points, you can locate the lines and draw them. Label each Speed line and the family.

Step 6. Only the Feed family remains to be plotted. To start, you need another scale at 90 degrees that will be the answer in Time. If your lowest Feed is .010 Inches, then the maximum of your Time answer scale will be .30/.010 or 30 Minute. The .30 is the extreme determined in Step 4. The cross-section paper happens to work out for a limit of 40 Minutes. Dividing convenient steps on the top

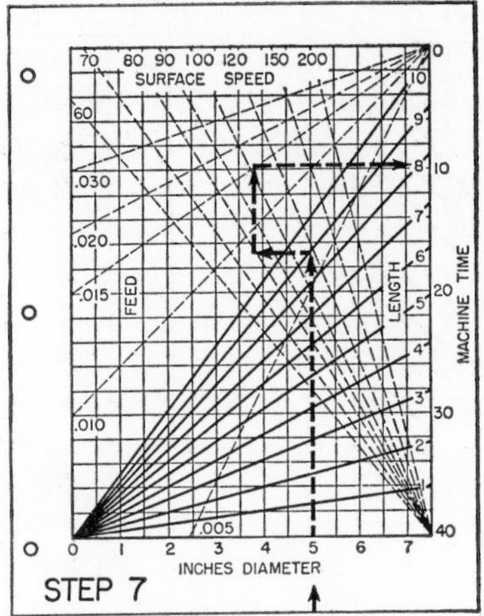

g. Check the chart by several extreme examples. Draw in one to show how to use it. Erase construction scales.

FIG. 59. (*Continued*).

scale by Feeds will locate the lines (Fig. 59*f*). On the .30 line, as an example, are spotted

.30/.010 In. = 30 Min	.30/.020 In. = 15 Min
.30/.015 In. = 20 Min	.30/.030 In. = 10 Min

All lines are then labeled. More Feed lines should be inserted in a solution you would work out for everyday use. These four serve only to illustrate.

Step 7. All our factors are now included. Your next step is to check your chart. Work out several examples. Use some that get away off in the corners to check the extremes. When you find that the chart is correct, then erase your construction scales (Fig. 59*g*). Use one of your check examples as the basis for a road map to show how the chart is used. The one shown is

$$\text{Time} = \frac{\pi}{12} \times \frac{\text{Diameter} \times \text{Length}}{\text{Surface Speed} \times \text{Feed}}$$
$$= .262 \times \frac{5 \times 9}{80 \times .015}$$
$$= 9.83 \text{ Min}$$

Usefulness of Family Method

These and the examples in the previous chapter should give you enough of the graphics so you can apply this curve-family method.

You will find a number of practical uses for it. It is a good method to have at your finger tips. It is easy to apply and it is efficient. Its particular value lies in its rapid way for getting answers to large-volume computations. You can build such charts often when you need quick solutions to current problems. I have made such charts to get answers in a hurry even when I never expected to use them again. Because of these advantages, my recommendation is that you acquire a working skill with the family-of-curves method of charting answers as a ready way to solve multi-variable problems.

CHAPTER 13

Numbers Preferred

To construct most of our charts in the preceding chapters we have used lines. Now we want to discuss the use of numbers to replace lines. "When?" is a question you will have to answer. One guidepost is frequency of use, just as quantity of parts to be made will influence machine setups and tooling. Changing line scales to numbers is an added cost that should be justified by savings.

Numbers have three advantages I should point out. First, and very important, is the advantage of understanding. Most of us who can think in technical terms forget that vice presidents trained in "broader subjects in business schools" may never have studied curve plotting or reading as an analytical tool. More likely, foremen and people in the shop we may be working with probably got out of school before the subject of "graphs" was being taught. For that reason, we should assume that curves and nomographs are unknown to them, and therefore are "mysterious." As a matter of fact, many graduate engineers are unacquainted with nomographs. But numbers in table form are understood by nearly everyone. Consequently, tables of numbers have decided advantages when we are explaining the answers we get.

Second, your answers are shown as definite numbers that people are in the habit of seeing as stock quotations, grocery prices, and baseball scores. In contrast, curves and nomographs show scales. Scales have to be interpreted before their readings can be set down as numbers. Reading the numbers directly from a table is faster and much less likely to result in error.

Third, numbers will usually include the decimal point. The positive recording of decimal points in a table reduces another possibility of error that exists with scales. When reading a scale, you must mentally create the number answer and then place the decimal point. This mental operation is necessary for 9 out of 10 uses when your scale has 10 divisions, or for 19 out of 20 with a 20-division scale.

Again, the chances for error are less when your answers are set up in tables as actual numbers.

When your answers are time standards for work measurement and incentive payment, this chance for error becomes a very important factor. You can affect either the employee's or the company's pocketbook. Should your error cut into the employee's pay, you can unnecessarily stir up a grievance, perhaps even an arbitration. You can get into similar problems when no error is made if your form for setting standards is not understood by those you are explaining it to. Therefore, my recommendation is that you convert your curves to table or chart form.

Curve Increments

To change curves to tables, you can use equations and compute your answers. Deriving the equation is easy when your curves are straight lines. It is more complicated when they are curved lines. Here you may refer to Chap. 7. In either case, you have to decide what interval spacing to use. As a rule, most men select uniform intervals of the dimension factors. They use increments like 10, 20, 30, 40, . . . , 100, or ¼, ½, ¾, 1, 1¼, . . . , 4. That's because we were taught to read curves, as we should, by starting with the independent variable, moving up to the curve, then going left to read the corresponding answer.

But, such increments have changing percentages. For example, 10 to 20 is 100 per cent change, 20 to 30 is 50 per cent change, and 30 to 40 is 33⅓ per cent change. Of course, the same per cent change may not be present in your answers. Dimensions are used here only to illustrate the point.

Uniform Increments

To overcome this variation, my approach is to use a constant per cent increment in the answers I read from curves. Naturally, this produces a variable increment in dimensions.

This idea came to me a number of years ago when I had built up a chart that was too big to use. I had set it up on the basis of uniform increments in dimensions. To cut down this chart was a new problem to me. As an experiment, I set my slide rule at 105 to get 5 per cent increments and compared time standards across the chart. The first few columns showed greater per cent spreads. As I went across the chart, alternate columns could be dropped out because the spread between columns of answers was about 2 per cent. Further on, two columns could be eliminated, then three, then four, and so on. Some at the extreme right of the chart had less than one-half of 1 per cent change from the adjoining column. Looking back I thought, "What a waste of time to build up all those time standards."

From my experience you can see how not to build a chart, if you agree that a uniform per cent increment is correct. You can start with proper increments. These can be any reasonable per cent. My recommendation with respect to incentive standards is 5 per cent for repetitive operations and 10 per cent for job shops. The increment is the difference between standards. But notice—in using 5 per cent, for instance, the spread does not create a 5 per cent error.

Let us use a few numbers to illustrate. Suppose we have the following portion of a chart. Decimal points have been omitted because per cent differences are the same regardless.

Dimension................	5	6	8	11	15	20
Standard Time............	100	105	110	115	120	126

For Dimension 5, the answer of 100 is correct. The same is true for Dimension 6 at 105. But whole-number Dimensions are not usual. We will have many different Dimensions between 5 and 6. As an example, the standard for 5¼ would still be 100. For 5¾, it would be 105. At 5½, we can have our maximum per cent error. If the correct standard for 5½ is 102.44, then our error is 2.44. This compared with 100 is an error of 2.44 per cent. Figured from 105, our error is 2.56 in time or 2.44 per cent. Thus the error is about half the spread between numbers read from our curves using constant per cent steps.

Reading Curves

Carrying this method to our everyday problems, it serves excellently for changing curves to tables. You begin backward from the way we were taught with Answers instead of Dimensions. Let's take Fig. 60*a* as the curve of a variable we want to change to table form.

Step 1 is to lay out a per cent scale along the Time axis. The per cent increment used should fit your problem. To convert this curve we will use an approximate 10 per cent increment scale. Its divisions show up better in the magnified Fig. 62*c*. These are laid out, starting with the least curve reading and progressing upward to the greatest standard (Fig. 60*b*).

Each graduation is then projected to the curve. This step shows in Fig. 60*c*. The intersections of the projections with the curve determine the locations of the corresponding Dimensions. By dropping verticals from these intersections, you read directly the Dimensions that correspond exactly with the Standard Times (Fig. 60). Our answers are shown in chart form in Fig. 60*e*.

This graphical layout depicts one method. But you would not want to clutter up your data curve with all the lines. You would

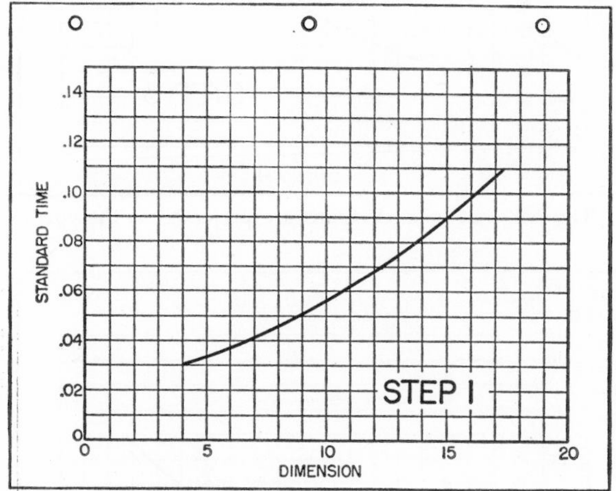

a. A curve of a variable to be converted to definite numbers.

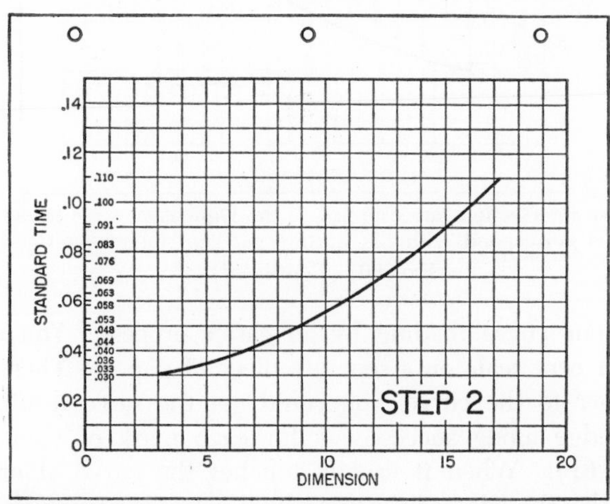

b. A per cent scale is laid out on the time axis. In the example, an approximate 10 per cent scale is used.

FIG. 60.

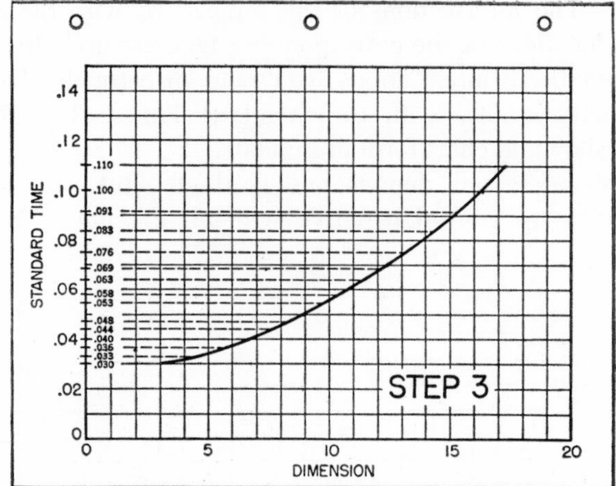

c. The per cent scale divisions are projected to the curve.

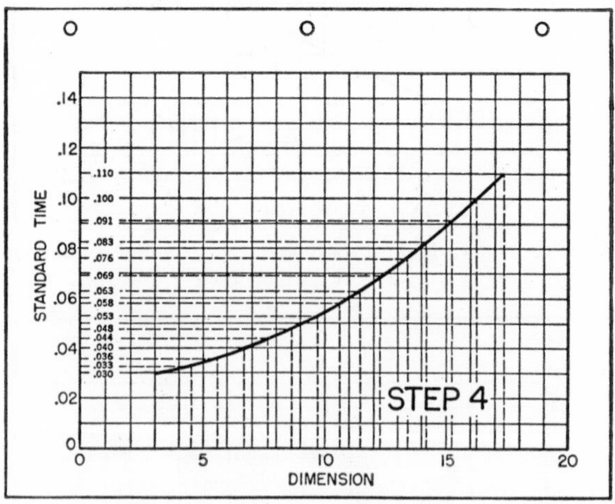

d. The curve intersections are dropped to the Dimension scale to determine the dimensions that correspond with the starting per cent increment standards.

FIG. 60. (*Continued*)

carry out your curve reading by an easier process. You could lay out your per cent scale on a separate piece of paper. Then, by moving the paper to the curve, you could get the same results. Move the paper edge along successively for each mark of your per cent scale (Fig. 61). When it exactly touches the curve at one of the division marks, the edge of the paper will act as the verticals we drew in Fig. 60*d*. You can save such scales for use later when you have similar curves to convert to tables.

DIMENSIONS	STANDARD
3.0	.030
4.4	.033
5.6	.036
6.7	.040
7.6	.044
8.6	.048
9.7	.053
10.6	.058
11.4	.063
12.3	.069
13.4	.076
14.2	.083
15.2	.091
16.2	.100
17.3	.110

STEP 5

e. The exact standards are those laid out on the Time scale with their corresponding Dimensions.

FIG. 60. (*Continued*).

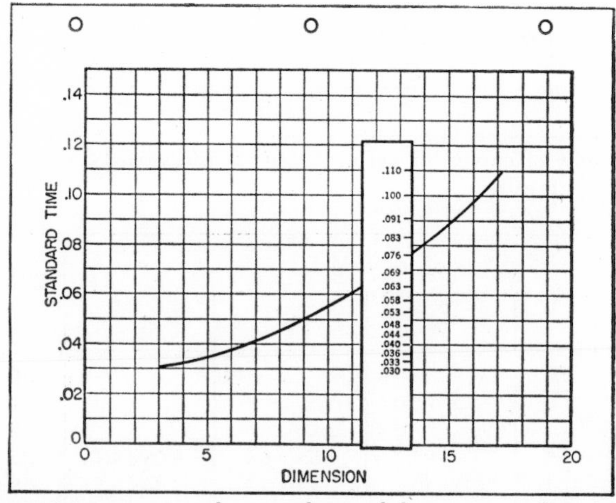

FIG. 61. Per cent increment scales may be used for curve reading instead of projections as in Fig. 60.

Change-point Curve Reading

Either method of increment reading can be used when you want to change several curves to numbers. Suppose you have a family of curves like that shown in Fig. 62*a*. With this, I want to bring out two methods of reading and recording your curve answers.

Notice the two per cent scales on Fig. 62*a*. The one next to the Standard Time scale is like that shown on Figs. 60 and 61. It is the

10 per cent increment markings used to gain uniform per cent spread in curve readings.

The added scale just to the right is also 10 per cent but marks off the in-between points. These are used to mark off the range of dimension that goes with the curve answers—Standard Time in this example.

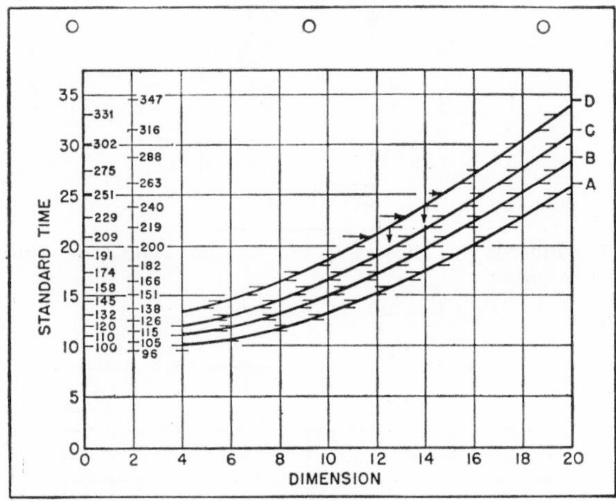

a. Read a family of curves for per cent steps as you would a single curve using two scales. See Fig. 62*c*.

CURVE				STD. MIN.
A	B	C	D	
4.0– 5.6				.10
5.7– 7.2	4.0– 5.0			.11
7.3– 9.0	5.1 – 7.0	4.0– 5.1		.12
9.1 – 10.5	7.1– 8.7	5.2– 6.9	4.0– 4.7	.13
10.6– 11.7	8.8 – 10.0	7.0– 8.4	4.8– 6.5	.15
11.8– 13.2	10.1 – 11.5	8.5– 10.0	6.6– 8.1	.16
13.3– 14.4	11.6 – 12.7	10.1 – 11.3	8.2– 9.5	.17
14.5– 15.8	12.8– 14.2	11.4– 12.7	9.6 – 10.1	.19
15.9– 17.2	14.3– 15.7	12.8– 14.1	10.2– 12.5	.21
17.3– 18.7	15.8 – 17.0	14.2– 15.5	12.6– 13.9	.23
18.8–20.1	17.1 – 18.5	15.6– 17.1	14.0– 15.4	.25
	18.6–20.1	17.2– 18.5	15.5– 16.9	.28
		18.6–20.2	17.0– 18.5	.30
			18.6–20.2	.33

b. Curve readings are answers that apply over the range of variable dimensions from mid-point to mid-point of the in-between dimensions.

FIG. 62.

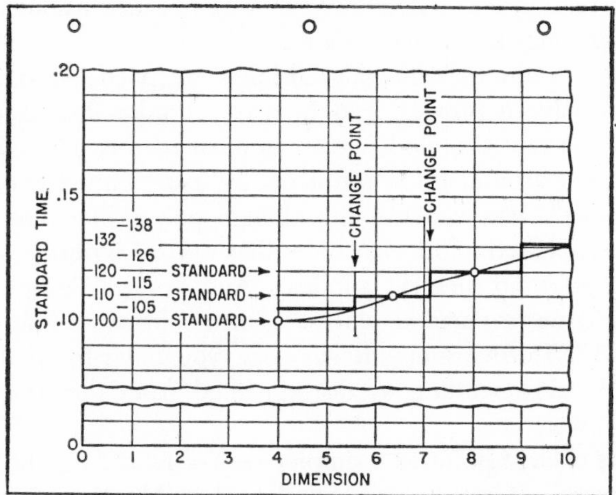

c. A part of Curve (enlarged) to portray range in dimension variable that each reading applies to or dimension points where change over takes place from one curve reading to the next higher.

CURVE				STD. MIN.
A	B	C	D	
4.0				.10
5.6	4.0			.11
7.2	5.0	4.0		.12
9.0	7.0	5.1	4.0	.13
10.5	8.7	6.9	4.7	.15
11.7	10.0	8.4	6.5	.16
13.2	11.5	10.0	8.1	.17
14.4	12.7	11.3	9.5	.19
15.8	14.2	12.7	10.1	.21
17.2	15.7	14.1	12.5	.23
18.7	17.0	15.5	13.9	.25
	18.5	17.1	15.4	.28
		18.5	16.9	.30
			18.5	.33

d. Space can be saved by using dimensions that are the change over points in curve reading.

FIG. 62. (*Continued*).

Your reaction may be, "That's an unnecessary complication." You're right, in many instances. But remember with a variable, you have an infinite number of answers and corresponding dimensions. You must discard some of them for practical reasons. Right away, you must think of any one reading you retain as applying to a range in dimension. You can see this in the enlarged part of Curve A, Fig. 62*c*.

For that reason, Fig. 62*b* shows the range of dimensions that govern the curve readings in Standard Time.

Showing two numbers like 4.0–5.6 takes up space. Too, such charts are more costly to prepare and to use. It takes longer to locate a dimension you have in mind when you must read two sets of numbers.

You can get around these problems by using only one of each pair of dimensions. You can use the change points like those shown in Fig. 62*c*. This method means .10 applies up to 5.6 dimension. When your size passes 5.6 then .11 applies. And so on. To be more exact, you can add more decimal places. You could say .10 applies up to 5.5999 or 5.555 dimension. Regardless, you have to spell out when to use one curve reading as distinguished from the next one to it, higher or lower.

I use this change point as a simpler way of recording and then using curve answers. It results in a smaller chart like that shown on Fig. 62*d*. Less space and simpler recordings have marked advantages that will become apparent later when we put together several variables to make combined charts.

Preferred Numbers

The per cent numbers we have just used for curve readings are similar to those often called "preferred numbers." Those used here were specially devised. Initially, I selected them to overcome the problem I described earlier in this chapter of building up a chart with unnecessary columns and later erasing them. That method caused too much wasted work. So I reasoned, "Why not start with the numbers I will select after I have done all that work?"

With some scale of "preferred numbers" chosen, and I believe they should have a uniform per cent progression, you can apply it directly in chart making. The advantage of space saving is suggested by Fig. 63. Here we start with a common table made up directly from a family of curves. Observe that such a table contains the same answer in several places. That is to be expected. But you will notice also that the per cent increment is greater at the top than at the bottom of the table. This condition exists even though certain Lengths have been omitted.

Now by listing all the different answers in chart Fig. 63*a*, we get the left-hand column of numbers on Fig. 63*b*. Such a list includes a wide range of per cent differences. For example, between the first and second numbers, 11 and 12, the increment is 9 per cent. At the other extreme, between 47 and 48, it is 2 per cent.

Listed alongside the original numbers are those from my preferred

HANDLING STANDARDS

LENGTH	DIAMETER						
	1	$1\frac{1}{8}$	$1\frac{1}{4}$	$1\frac{3}{8}$	$1\frac{1}{2}$	$1\frac{5}{8}$	$1\frac{3}{4}$
1	11	12	14	16	18	20	22
2	11	13	14	16	18	20	23
4	12	13	15	17	19	22	24
6	12	14	16	18	21	23	26
8	13	15	17	19	22	24	27
10	13	15	18	20	23	26	29
12	14	16	18	21	24	27	30
14	15	17	19	22	25	28	32
16	15	17	20	23	26	30	33
18	16	18	21	24	27	31	35
20	16	19	22	25	28	32	36
22	17	19	23	26	30	34	38
24	17	20	23	27	31	35	39
26	18	21	24	28	32	36	41
28	18	22	25	29	33	38	42
30	19	22	26	30	34	39	44
32	20	23	27	31	35	40	45
34	20	24	27	32	36	41	47
36	21	24	28	33	38	42	48

HANDLING STANDARDS

DIFFERENT ONES IN CHART	TEN PER CENT STEPS
11	11
12	12
13	13
14	
15	15
16	16
17	17
18	
19	19
20	
21	21
22	
23	23
24	
25	25
26	
27	
28	28
29	
30	30
31	
32	
33	33
34	
35	
36	36
38	
39	
40	40
41	
42	
44	44
45	
47	
48	48
TOTAL NUMBER STANDARDS - 35	17

b

a. A chart made up from curves with some dimensions omitted.

b. Compare the number of different standards recorded in (b) with the number needed when 10 per cent increment is used.

Fig. 63.

number list. These have approximately 10 per cent increments between numbers. The total count of numbers shrinks from the 35 shown in the left-hand list to the 17 noted alongside.

Three Reasons

There are other advantages in using the special set of preferred numbers I devised. Some of these will be brought out in our next chapter. Before concluding this one, however, let's make sure we are together on three points important to efficient charting.

The first is perhaps a little difficult to grasp because of the habits we were trained to follow. Logically, we read a curve by starting with the dimension that controls the variable we are measuring. That process is all right for the occasional curve reading. Here, we are doing a wholesale translation of all curve readings into table form.

Even so, we could still follow our habits and start with dimensions. But in multi-variable charting, it's the answers we must combine—not dimensions. We can't add Shirts, Shorts, Sheets, and Shoes together. To get their material costs or the probable profits from their mixed sales volumes, we must use the dollar equivalents of their quantities. You call this fact the use of a "common denominator."

Now take the next step. The easier way to work from the common denominator for a wholesale translation is to read your curve backward. That means pick some basis. Then you reason, "Accuracy is dependent upon per cent differences between answers." Thus you decide what answers you start with according to the degree of accuracy you need in your results.

> *Choose a scale of per cent answers to translate a curve to numbers that provides the degree of accuracy required.*

Second is the matter of space. How big your final chart will be depends upon many factors. At this stage in our book, all I can say is that extra numbers set up in your starting charts will multiply the space required for their combinations.

The number of answers you could have is unlimited. For example, think how many more we could have put in our chart Fig. 63*a*. Suppose we had read our curves at ½ lengths and $\frac{1}{16}$ diameters.

For that reason, we can't say that our comparison of 35 to 17 numbers in Fig. 63*b* is typical. But we can reverse our approach and make a rule.

> *The per cent scale for curve translation that has the degree of accuracy required will produce the minimum number of answers needed.*

Third is the importance of eliminating rework. You can't use the chart shown as Fig. 63*a*, to combine it with that for another variable. It must be "turned inside out" as I will describe when we begin to combine charts. You can see what I mean, however, if you will look back at tables Figs. 62*b* and *d*. All I need stress at this point is, "Let's not waste time making our usual type charts when we want to combine them. They can't be used in that form anyway." This extra operation can be avoided.

You can start with a list of preferred numbers and write down only those you want to use. The first number would be the lowest in your range of answers. The others would be written in sequence and end with the highest in your range. This is the approach we used to read our curves in this chapter. Thus, you can use preferred numbers to translate curves and to set up tables directly while attaining constant per cent increments in your answers.

Further uses of preferred numbers will be explained in several chapters to follow. These will be brought out as they apply in methods for combining charts. For example, in Chap. 14 I will describe, in more detail, the use of constant per cent numbers in charting. There are so many time- and space-saving advantages to be gained that it seems well worth your further study.

CHAPTER 14

Constant Per Cent Charts

You must choose some intervals of spacing to translate your curves to tables. Suppose you have a curve drawn on regular cross-section paper having 20 squares per inch. Assume your answer scale has a spread of .10 minute for each major division of 20 squares. Then, one square equals .005 minute. Also, unfortunately, one square is nearly $\frac{1}{16}$ inch long. Now, $\frac{1}{16}$ is a long distance on your slide rule. If you were to interpolate curve readings as you do your slide rule, you could set up such easily obtained different answers as .005 and .005025 minute. Why do so when no good can come from it and complaints are more likely to be the result? Let me suggest what I mean with a story.

Ben wrote down ".5 minutes" as the time for the mechanic who asked what his standard was. Later, a different man asked how many minutes were allowed for the operation. This time my friend wrote ".50 minutes." In nothing flat, the first man was at Ben's desk vigorously complaining. "You cheated me," he shouted. "You gave me only .5 minutes but you gave my buddy .50 minutes."

Simple, I know. But serious problems of industrial relations can stem from false notions of "accuracy" or amount. Different degrees of interpolation will cause inconsistencies. Interpolation can occur whether curves or tables are used. Besides, this notion of trying for an answer within a gnat's eyebrow is too costly.

What Intervals?

The question then is, "What spacing should I pick?" If you want to translate a curve of variable dollars, for instance, steps like $100, $200, $300, . . . , $1,000 with constant amount differences of $100 have varying per cent relations to each other. Note, $200 is 100 per cent more than $100 while $300 is 50 per cent more than $200. Using $1,000 as the top limit of our scale, it is only 11 per cent more than $900, the next step below.

Per cents between steps change the same way when you use Standard Times like .04, .05, .06, . . . , 20 with steps of .01 minutes. Reducing the amount of step will, of course, change the amount of actual per cent but not the fact of variable per cent. This is true, even when you read the smallest increments of your curve drawn on 20-squares-to-the-inch paper. Whatever interval you select will, in effect, cause an error. Your interval is like an average that applies between certain limits. The wider the spread of your average, the greater will be the error between its mid-point and its extremes.

You can liken the error caused by the interval you choose to the tolerances we have for drawing dimensions. Properly set according to fit required, these are per cents even though expressed as amounts. They are calculated from the cube root of the diameter in the ASME tables of standard tolerances for fits.

Per Cent Steps

"What to do?" has come up many times in my long experience with setting Standard Times for incentives. So my approach is by way of per cent, but for a different reason. Here's why. The Standard Time and the production are reciprocals of each other. For example, 1.0 minute represents 60 pieces per hour, 10.0 minutes mean 6 per hour. Thus quantities turned out on incentive become multipliers of whatever errors are set up. In turn, these affect the pay check. Thus long ago, I concluded that intervals selected for reading curves and building charts should be in constant per cents. It works out this way. Suppose, to illustrate, we use a 10 per cent interval. Then 1.0 or 1.1 could apply for 1.05-minute change-point standard. Similarly, 10.0 or 11.0 for 10.5 minutes. Then if we take as an expected 10 hours earned in 8 hours on incentive, we have

Production	*Stand. C.P.*		*Output C.P.*	*Error*
	1.00	=	600	− 5%
600 pieces ×	1.05	=	630	—
	1.10	=	660	+ 5%
	10.0	=	600	− 5%
60 pieces ×	10.5	=	630	—
	11.0	=	660	+ 5%

What Per Cent?

The per cent interval you should choose depends upon the use you will make of your answers. For time standards, I recommend 10 per cent in job shop operations and 5 per cent in repetitive work. My reasoning is this. When a person has several jobs per day, the probabilities are that the plus and minus per cents will offset each other.

Greater intervals than 10 per cent can be used to translate your basic curves when combinations are to be made. To illustrate, when you add two sets of 10 per cent numbers together you reduce the intervals in your sums to 5 per cent. So select the per cent that will

NOMINAL PER CENT SCALE EXAMPLES

$2\frac{1}{2}$	5	$7\frac{1}{2}$	10	$12\frac{1}{2}$	15	20
1 000	1 000	1000	1 000	100	100	100
1 023	1 047	1068	1096	112	117	126
1 047	1 096	1 141	1 202	126	136	159
1 071	1 148	1218	1 318	141	159	200
1096	1 202	1301	1 445	158	185	251
1 122	1 259	1389	1 585	178	215	316
1 148	1318	1484	1738	199	251	398
1 175	1 380	1 585	1 905	224	293	501
1 202	1 445	1 693	2 089	251	342	631
1 230	1 503	1 808	2 291	282	398	794

Fig. 64. Comparisons of part scales of different per cent increment.

give you the answers you need. Note the several ranges set up in Fig. 64.

Unit Cards

Numbers like these were evolved. After building charts and erasing columns, as I mentioned in our previous chapter, it finally dawned on me how to save work. Why not select a set of numbers that could be used directly in chart building? Later, these were modified to do multiplication and division. Subsequently, I worked up these numbers into special arrangements and I was granted a patent (2,295,497) covering their use. These specially arranged numbers are in logarithmic progression. That makes them differ somewhat from selected numbers.

The intent of my patent was to save first the writing and then the typing of numbers that repeated in many charts. Out of this came what I call a "unit card." These are printed in both 5 per cent and 10 per cent approximate increments. In this form, they can be used to perform any operations of multiplication and division in any combinations.

Space savings are made also as shown in Fig. 65. Some of the

100	110	120	132	145
110	120	132	145	158
120	132	145	158	174
132	145	158	174	191
145	158	174	191	209

(a) PRINTED

100	110	120	132	145
110	120	132	145	158
120	132	145	158	174
132	145	158	174	191
145	158	174	191	209

(b) ELITE, 12/INCH

100	110	120	132	145
110	120	132	145	158
120	132	145	158	174
132	145	158	174	191
145	158	174	191	209

(c) PICA, 10/INCH

FIG. 65. Comparative samples of size of the same set of numbers reproduced.

difference in space results from separations in the printed form that are unlike those required in typing. But observe, too, that printed numbers are easily read even though only about half-size.

Short Cuts

The numbers in these chart sections are logarithmic in progression. Logarithmic scales are like those on our slide rules. They can be used to perform all types of multiplication and division. To illustrate, let's do a few problems with a section of such numbers.

The problems occur regularly in timestudy. For that reason, prepared numbers can be used to save computing tables of certain types. For instance, suppose you wanted the products of two series of numbers. Area figures are a common requirement. You will find that kind of answers on Fig. 66. On this section of my 5 per cent chart, select two figures. Take one in the left-hand vertical column, say 200. Choose another in the top row, perhaps 126. Now, at the intersection of a horizontal line through 200 with a vertical through 126 is the approximate answer of 251. (See Fig. 66.) The reason the answer is not exact is that all these numbers have been rounded to three digits.

You can divide by reversing this procedure. An example of this use of constant per cent charts is shown in connection with making "direct reading charts" (Chap. 18, Fig. 93).

For another application, suppose you want a chart of standards multiplied by quantity. Assume the standard is .19 minute per square foot. Again, think of the left-hand column as the multiplier. Scan the right-hand column headed 191 as the product. If the least area you need to consider is 120 square feet, then part of your chart will look like Fig. 66*c*. As a matter of fact, you may simply make marks

100	105	110	115	120	126	132	138	145	151	158	166	174	182	191
105	110	115	120	126	132	138	145	151	158	166	174	182	191	200
110	115	120	126	132	138	145	151	158	166	174	182	191	200	209
115	120	126	132	138	145	151	158	166	174	182	191	200	209	219
120	126	132	138	145	151	158	166	174	182	191	200	209	219	229
126	132	138	145	151	158	166	174	182	191	200	209	219	229	240
132	138	145	151	158	166	174	182	191	200	209	219	229	240	251
138	145	151	158	166	174	182	191	200	209	219	229	240	251	263
145	151	158	166	174	182	191	200	209	219	229	240	251	263	275
151	158	166	174	182	191	200	209	219	229	240	251	263	275	288
158	166	174	182	191	200	209	219	229	240	251	263	275	288	302
166	174	182	191	200	209	219	229	240	251	263	275	288	302	316
174	182	191	200	209	219	229	240	251	263	275	288	302	316	331
182	191	200	209	219	229	240	251	263	275	288	302	316	331	347
191	200	209	219	229	240	251	263	275	288	302	316	331	347	363
200	209	219	229	240	251	263	275	288	302	316	331	347	363	380
209	219	229	240	251	263	275	288	302	316	331	347	363	380	398
219	229	240	251	263	275	288	302	316	331	347	363	380	398	417
229	240	251	263	275	288	302	316	331	347	363	380	398	417	437
240	251	263	275	288	302	316	331	347	363	380	398	417	437	457

a. Section of a unit card of approximate 5 per cent numbers.

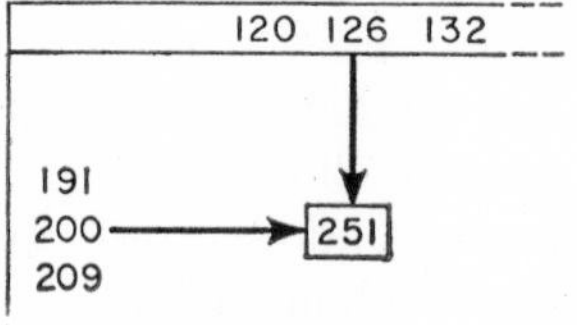

AREA	STANDARD
120	22.9
126	24.0
132	25.1
138	26.3
145	27.5

b *c*

b. A line diagram to illustrate one use of (a). Products are found at the intersections of two number lines.

c. Charts for quantity standards may be copied directly.

FIG. 66.

at the tops of the columns involved, hand the chart to your stenographer, and ask her to copy those two columns side by side.

Multiple References

Sometimes, you need several such charts to solve one problem. These may be superimposed on each other, if there are appreciable savings to be made. This is an idea I first saw used by Bruce Wallace.

A greatly abbreviated chart that portrays the idea is shown in Fig.

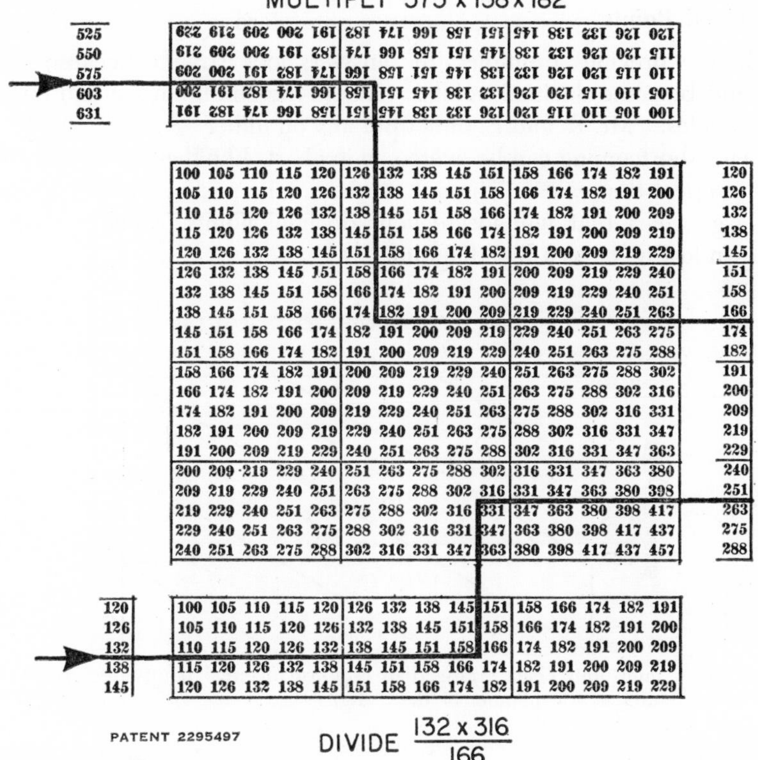

FIG. 67. Chart arranged to utilize portions of one chart body in two different solutions.

67. I arranged this one to perform two different types of computations, disregarding decimal places.

$$\text{Multiply:} \quad 575 \times 158 \times 182 = 166$$

$$\text{Divide:} \quad \frac{132 \times 316}{166} = 251$$

Only five variables are set up at the entry at the top. These are placed upside down to show how pre-arranged numbers are used. They are the same numbers as appear both in the body of the chart and below it. But they must progress backward because of the nature of the problem. You would have them lettered or typed in an upright position. Five are located for the bottom section. These are enough to show how you can utilize portions of a chart for multiple references.

Decimal Points

In the previous examples, the answers look strange because there should be some decimal points. This is the condition we find on our slide rules. Mr. K. and E. didn't put any on mine.

This shortcoming can be overcome in charts like these. The method is to repeat the scales. The unit cards may be pasted together to form a large chart that will locate your decimal points. Such a chart is shown in Fig. 68 as a line diagram.

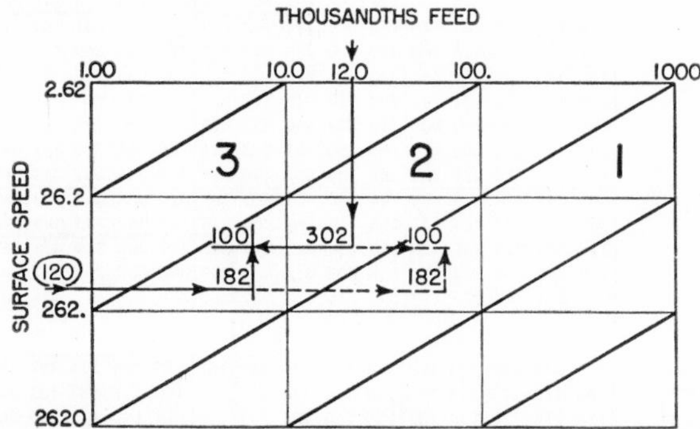

FIG. 68. A multi-unit chart arranged to establish decimal points, represented by the large figures as the number of the 3 digits shown that are to the right of the decimal point.

Across the top is a repeated scale for Feed in Thousandths of an Inch. Decimal points were added to the pre-printed rows of numbers. Down the side is a repeated scale for Surface Speed in Feet per Minute. It is pointed off.

Diagonal lines pass through the chart to divide it into decimal-point bands. The ghost letters indicate how many of the three numbers shown must come after the decimal point. In one plant, these bands were lightly washed with different pale colors and then protected by a coat of lacquer.

To see how this multi-chart arrangement works, let's solve two problems of machine time. For this, the basic machine-operation time equation is

$$\text{Time} = \frac{\pi}{12} \times \frac{\text{Diameter} \times \text{Length}}{\text{Feed} \times \text{Speed}}$$

For our first problem, we will use Diameter $1^{13}/_{16}''$, Feed .012″, Length 3″, Speed 120 fpm.

1.
$$\text{Time} = \frac{\pi}{12} \times \frac{1^{13}\!/\!_{16} \times 3}{.012 \times 120}$$
$$= \frac{.262 \times 1.82 \times 3}{1.44}$$
$$= 1.00 \text{ Min}$$

Our answer is in band 2 and therefore has two of the three figures to the right of the decimal point.

In our second problem, we will erroneously hold all factors the same except to use 10 times the Diameter or 18¼″.

2.
$$\text{Time} = \frac{.262 \times 18.2 \times 3}{1.44}$$
$$= 10.0 \text{ Min}$$

This time of 10.0 minutes falls in band 1 so only one of the three figures becomes a decimal place.

These two answers, and the factors, look alike. They change in magnitude by their locations similarly as on multi-cycle log paper or on your slide rule. Also, as on your slide rule, the 182 and 302 could be either Diameter or Length. Just the same, my preference is to use such charts only one way. My suggestion is to relate Diameter to Surface Speed and Length to Feed. When you use a chart only one way, there is less chance for error.

Mounting Drums

A method of controlling the choice just mentioned is built into another useful gadget. I will describe it first, then come back to the control features.

Big charts are unhandy to use. When they get beyond a convenient size, they seem to be under the papers you want to write on. If you have a big drawing to wrestle with also, then you do have your hands full.

One escape is to mount such charts on drums. A picture of one application is shown in "Timestudy for Cost Control."[1] Another very handy one was a big drum suspended horizontally over the desk. It was located about where the pigeonholes were above the old-fashioned roll-top desk.

A third variety is sketched in Fig. 69. Such a drum can be made by inserting circular wood plugs in the ends of a short length of large diameter pipe. Six- to ten-inch diameter is a good size range. In

[1] Carroll, Phil, "Timestudy for Cost Control," 3rd ed., p. 209, McGraw-Hill Book Company, Inc., New York, 1943.

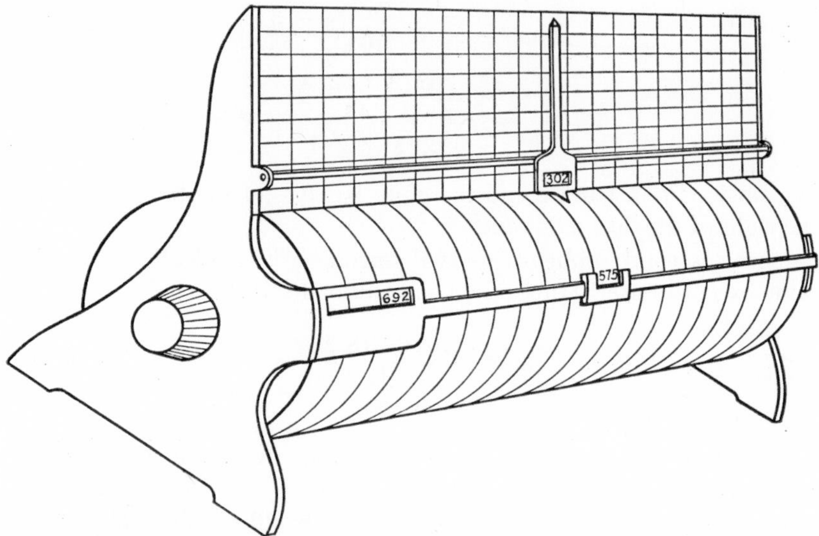

FIG. 69. Sketch of a drum for chart mounting. The vertical fixed chart is filled in with conditions and so are the bands at the left end of the drum.

my opinion, it is better to choose a diameter large enough so that the chart goes about halfway around it.

In the sketch, the body of the chart and the surface speeds are around the drum. The Feeds and conditions that control them are placed on the stationary backboard. Then a slide moved horizontally across the drum is set for Diameter. The drum is turned until the Length comes to the slide rod. Then the time answer will appear in the slide opening. This action accomplishes the same results as tracing horizontally and vertically in the chart drawn on Fig. 68. In an arrangement like this, you can set up clear distinctions between Length and Diameter. Thus, you can control their interchange. This would be very important where, for example, Feed changed with increases in Length as the work became springy.

There are many uses for number charts like those explained here. They are easy to prepare. The values are expressed in numbers. They can be made to perform any of the operations of multiplication and division in any number of factors. Few charts have all these advantages combined.

These constant per cent numbers were discussed here because of their unique application in solving problems of multiplication and division. Primarily, however, the foregoing explanations of their why and how were to prepare for their uses in charting. You can use them in many ways. Some of these will be shown in Chaps. 17 and 18.

CHAPTER 15

Space Factors in Charting

Charts made up of numbers have many advantages. Several were emphasized in our two previous chapters. Primarily, numbers are more readily understood by most people than are line scales on curves and charts.

Now, to go from lines having unlimited numbers of answers to relatively few specific figures brings up the question, "How many curve readings should we use?" One ready answer, "Use constant per cent numbers," was explained in our previous chapter.

These special numbers were shown in threes. The third number is recorded as an aid in rounding to two digits. Two digits are enough to maintain practical accuracy in most charts.

Why Cause Work?

You may object, as one man did, "But the Accounting Department insists on five decimal places." His concern was brought on by the plant's use for a "standard hour" incentive plan. That was not reason enough for me. Why we should confuse 1,000 people in the shop with five decimal places for the pseudoconvenience of a half dozen in Accounting was beyond me.

So I recommended he use 0's in the meaningless decimal places. For example, he should express .53626 as .54000 decimal hours. In this way, he would avoid the problems being emphasized here. Besides, he would help the accountants save some money. To illustrate, if the standard were the multiplier in Pieces × Standard, the calculation would take 9 instead of 22 strokes on a comptometer. This detail seems important to me. The real cost of repeated calculations is in the upkeep—not in the first cost. Many people disregard this fact. They know better. They know that their automobiles, their homes, their plant machines have to be maintained.

If you write down 2 digits or 10, the probabilities are that Accounting will go on unquestioningly multiplying out exactly whatever figures you set down. Therefore, this detail is one I want to stress as one starting point in number charting. Here we are discussing the *source* of the figures to be used. The numbers you set down may be used thousands of times in the future.

Here is the point to control and to minimize one element of clerical cost. My recommendation is to hold the digits to two significant numbers. The maximum error does not exceed 4 per cent. Such an error occurs around the number 1 or unity. At 2, it is halved.

Saving Space

Using two digits whenever you can, instead of three or more, relates to number charting also because of the space saved. This factor will become more apparent when we begin to combine several variables.

As we proceed toward that goal, we should look at other factors of space as they influence chart layout. Think first of the fact that the

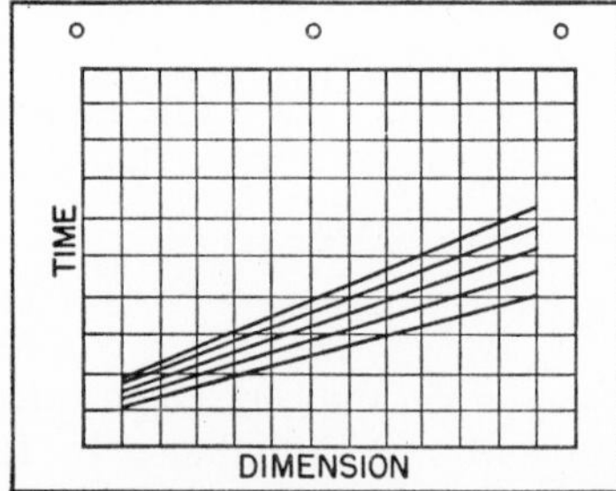

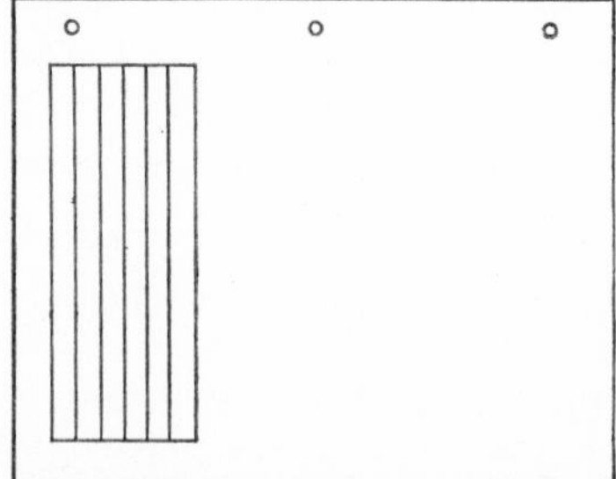

FIG. 70. Readings for each curve will require some part of one column. The columns as shown full length and four typewriter spaces wide relatively, but this amount of space may not be needed.

space required for two digits is much more inflexible than that necessary to show those same two digits as a line. A scale line could be almost any length, so short you could hardly see it.

Even so, if you look at the whole form instead of the lines, there appears to be a contradiction. This results from the fact that much space is lost between curves on line diagrams. To portray this detail, one example has been made up. In Fig. 70, five curves are shown in both forms drawn proportionally. You can readily see that about 30 per cent of the space is occupied by the five columns of figures. One column is needed for Dimensions. The others are used for chart readings. Both are shown full length. But all this space may not be required. As you will recall from the discussion of preferred numbers, some lists shrink considerably when constant per cent increments are used.

This simple illustration is just the beginning. It shows only the first stage of multi-variable chart construction. It is a necessary step, of course, to get from curves of variables to equivalent numbers.

Space consumed begins to multiply as we combine more and more variables. You can do little about minimum size. Yet, you can do a great deal to reduce sizes below those you may have accepted as minimum. To that end, I want to suggest several pointers that will be useful in preparing for chart combinations.

Why Bother?

Looking ahead, consider what is usually done when you work with complex data. One section is completed and typed for appearance and legibility. Then another section is finished and typed. Continuing, you wind up with a number of pages. Each set is spread out on its page to make it attractive-looking. But what is the result? Consolidation within a specified size like 8½ by 11 inches seems impossible. "It can't be done," is the first reaction. At this point desire becomes a necessary motive force.

Without desire and resolution, your data remains spread out. Maybe there are two or three times as many pages as need be. Each has to be handled. If, for example, these pages are to be used for setting work time standards, each extra page may be the cause of higher cost per standard by reference and writing.

Layout Device

To condense pages of typed data, you may cause your stenographer to say, "I can't get all that on one sheet." Maybe she is right. Can you tell? Do you take "No" for an answer? There is an easy way to get the fact. Besides, it will save much cost of retyping that is quite often wasted in the cut-and-try process.

Get yourself some cross-section paper especially designed for layout to be typed. It should have 10 spaces per inch across the page if you use Pica type, and 12 if you use Elite. Spacing down the page is ordinarily six lines per inch. These types of papers may be found on the market, because some firms specializing in form design do use them.

SAMPLE TYPEWRITER CROSS-SECTION DESIGN

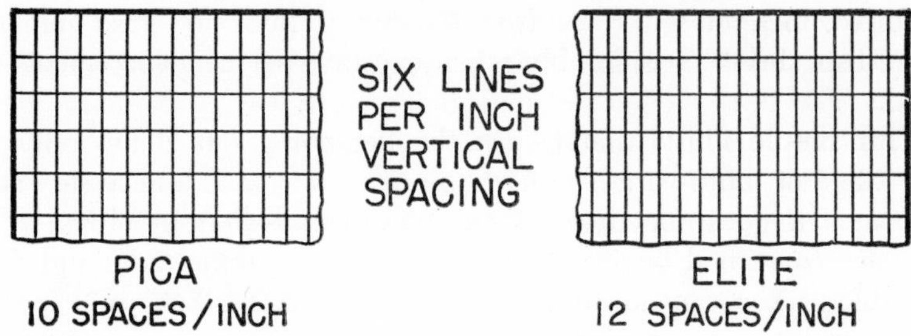

This detail of layout may be very useful at times. To illustrate, we find out, in the shop, before we cut into a plate or a casting. We lay out in the Engineering Department, if we are smart, because it is cheaper to change our minds on paper. And if we use a gadget like this special cross-section paper, and find that the page is not big enough, we may decide to adopt printing. Setting data in type may

TOOL CHANGE	STD.	
	8'	13'
ROUND NOSE	1.0	1.4
FLAT NOSE, FM.CHF.RAD OR U/C	1.8	2.6
FORM TO GAGE	4.2	5.2
TOOL BIT	.7	1.0
HEAD TO ANGLE AND RETURN	10.0	12.0
CLIMB TO AND AWAY FROM POST	.4	.5
CLIMB IN AND OUT OF JOB TO POST	.6	.7
TOTAL TOOL CHANGE		

TOOL CHANGE	STD.	
	8'	13'
ROUND NOSE	1.0	1.4
FLAT NOSE, FM. CHF. RAD OR U/C	1.8	2.6
FORM TO GAGE	4.2	5.2
TOOL BIT	.7	1.0
HEAD TO ANGLE AND RETURN	10.0	12.0
CLIMB TO AND AWAY FROM POST	.4	.5
CLIMB IN AND OUT OF JOB TO POST	.6	.7
TOTAL TOOL CHANGE		

FIG. 71. A comparison of data reduced in printing with a typed chart in 12 per inch characters.

be too expensive. That all depends upon the repetition. But printing does afford another way to reduce space. Naturally, it makes for a nicer appearance.

Printing may be utilized in two ways to reduce space. One is in type. You have a choice of sizes that enables you to condense a large amount of data into a small space. Relative proportions are shown on Fig. 71. There are compared two forms of the same chart, one in print and the other in 12-character-per-inch typewriting.

Pc.hand to hand & position or insert	.024
Insert piece in chuck	.023
Insert piece in fixture	.023
Insert pieces in gauge (Air)	.018
Insert piece in holder	.025
P/U & insert piece in chuck or fixture	.035
P/U & insert piece in holder	.037
P/U and position piece	.023

a. Data reduced by photo offset to approximately 14 characters per inch and 8 lines per inch.

P/U Gauge-Gauge Pc. & aside	.090
Gauge Width (2nd Time)	.056
Back Wheel away (Facing)	.015
Back Wheel away & Apply Brake	.046
Position Piece to Wheel	.040
Start Traverse	.014
Stop Traverse	.014
Piece out of Dog & Aside	.027

b. Standard size Pica type affords 10 characters per inch and 6 lines per inch.

Fig. 72.

The other way to conserve space by printing is through the use of the offset process. Many folks use this for everyday reproducing. If you are not familiar with it, you need to know that the process depends upon photographing the material to be printed. This step can be used to reduce the size of the data when you need to do so. A reduction is limited only by the least size of numbers and letters you can read without errors. Those shown in the accompanying illustration by no means approach that limit. Figure 72 compares a sample of reduced typing with one of full-size Pica typing, both duplicated by photo-offset printing. The one reduced in size has almost 14 characters per inch as compared with 10 in Pica typing. Notice, also, that in photography the shrinkage takes place in both directions. The result is that in the reduced sample there are nearly eight lines per inch as contrasted with the standard of six lines.

Efficient Work Sheets

As the number and ranges of your variables increase, the space required works against what I consider the ideal arrangement of having all the data on one page. An efficient data sheet is one similar to Fig. 73, originally designed by John P. Bernard. All the element standards are recorded on one side of an 8½- by 11-inch page. This sheet is duplicated like any form. One sheet is used for each standard to be set. The "form" is "filled out" by inserting the job specifications at the top. Then each of the time factors is circled and its occurrence entered in the Number column. These are extended and added to compute the operation Standard. Notice that the method just described included no mention of copying element descriptions and standards from any other record. Also notice that the variable specifications for the elements are clearly identified by drawing the circles. For example, the cope Standard of .90 minute is obviously for a 12 by 12 by 14 box, for cast iron, with a 2-inch draw. These positive identifications were made by the circles.

The emphasis on clerical details here is necessary. Such little savings will add up to equal real economy in standard setting. This is important in job-shop and non-repetitive work measurement. It is a big factor, too, when management looks at the cost of the Standards Department. It is a vital detail in the cost of maintaining your incentive plan, if that is one of your responsibilities.

The copying of information from one place to another involves chances of errors. Decimal points may be misplaced. Figures may be transposed. Then, of course, errors will creep into extensions and additions. Thus, any chart you make up for repeated use should be on *one page* if there is any practical way to achieve that result. Budget computations or cost estimates are typical examples. Even if you do not make mistakes in arithmetic, it takes time to make computations. For this reason, you should strive to reduce the number of calculations.

Direction Layout

As you take the next step to combine charts, some additional problems present themselves. Your charts become larger. As they expand, they tend to exceed the limits of paper size. If you cannot get the chart on in one direction, you may turn the sheet. Therefore, you should plan your layout.

SQUEEZER MOLDING SPECIFICATION

DATE *May 13 - 1950* BY *P. Gr.* PART NO. *47943*

PATTERN *Metal* SIZE *12 × 14*

LOOSE ___ MOUNTED *✓* PART NAME *Gear*

SPLIT ___ FOLLOW BOARD ___. WEIGHT *4½* CASTING PER MOLD *1*

METAL	FLASK SIZE	COPE DRAG	DEPTH OF DRAW IN INCHES								RAISE DEPTH	NO.	STD.
			0	½	1	1½	2	2½	3	3½	1"		
IRON	12" X 12"	COPE	.30	.50	.65	.80	.90	1.00	1.10	1.20	.30	*1*	*.90*
	12" X 14"	DRAG	—	4.06	4.18	4.29	4.40	4.46	4.57	4.68		*1*	*4.29*
BRASS	12" X 12"	COPE	.35	.60	.70	.80	.90	1.00	1.10	1.20	.30		
	12" X 14"	DRAG	—	3.05	3.15	3.25	3.35	3.40	3.50	3.60			
	10" X 19"	COPE	.45	.70	.80	.90	1.00	1.10	1.20	1.30	.40		
		DRAG	—	4.05	4.15	4.25	4.35	4.40	4.50	4.60			

MISCELLANEOUS DATA	PER	1	2	3	4	5	6	NO.	STD.
SET SOLDIERS	SOLDIER	.15	.25	.40	.50	.60	.68		
SET JOB NAILS	NAIL	.07	.14	.20	.25	.30	.35	*1*	*.25*
VENT (COPE, DRAG, OR SIDE)	VENT	.08	.15	.22	.30	.35	.40	*1*	*.15*
BLACKEN MOLD	100 SQ. IN	.06	.10	.15	.20	.23	.26		
WATER MOLD AFTER DRAW	10 LIN. IN.	.05	.12	.16	.20	.25	.29		
CUT GATE	GATE	.90	1.50	2.00	2.50	2.90	3.25		
SET, CUT AND REAM RISERS	RISER	.45	.90	1.30	1.70	2.00	2.30		
SPECIAL RAM (DRAG OR COPE)	100 CU. IN.	.30	.55	.80	1.00	1.15	1.30	*1*	*.80*
PUT PASTE ON CORES	SQ. INCH.	.05	.10	.15	.18	.20	.22		

CORE SETTING CLASSIFICATION	SKETCH OF TYPE	VOL. RANGE CU. IN.	CORES SET PER MOLD								NO.	STD.
			1	2	3	4	5	6	7	8		
STOCK CORES		0-10	.10	.20	.25	.30	.35	.40	.45	.50		
		11-20	.15	.25	.30	.35	.40	.45	.50	.55		
		21-50	.20	.30	.35	.40	.45	.50	.55	.60	*1*	*.20*
REGULAR BLOCK OR CYLINDER CORES		0-50	.20	.30	.40	.45	.50	.55	.60	.65		
		51-100	.25	.40	.45	.50	.55	.60	.65	.70		
		101-200	.35	.45	.50	.55	.60	.65	.70	.75		
IRREGULAR BLOCK OR CYLINDER CORES		0-50	.30	.35	.45	.50	.55	.60	.65	.70		
		51-100	.40	.45	.50	.55	.60	.65	.70	.75		
		101-200	.50	.55	.60	.65	.70	.75	.80	.85		

TOTAL STANDARD PER MOLD *6.59*

DIVIDED BY *1* CASTINGS = STANDARD PER CASTING USE *6.6*

FIG. 73. An example of standard data arranged to reduce clerical work to a minimum.

To make an example, suppose you have six factors of Width and eighteen of Length that you want to chart. In combination, these will make an oblong table. The narrow side will be for Width. The Length appears to be several times as great as the Width. But let's be more specific. You can calculate the dimensions in pica typewriter spacing. Using two digits, one answer will occupy a space $\frac{2}{10}$ inch wide and $\frac{1}{6}$ inch high. If you add two spaces to the width for separation, the space width becomes $\frac{4}{10}$ inch.

Under the proposal, your answer takes up a space $\frac{4}{10}$ by $\frac{1}{6}$ inch. The total width becomes 2.4 inches ($6 \times .4$), the total length 3.0

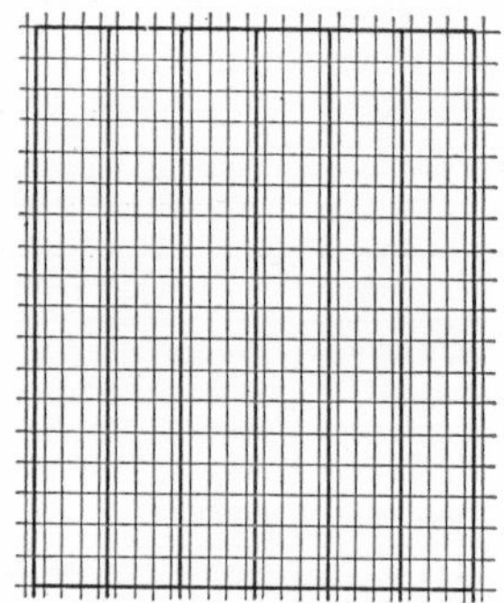

a. On Pica typewriter spacing paper, six factors across the width take up 2.4 inches. Eighteen factors placed vertically require 3 inches of page length.

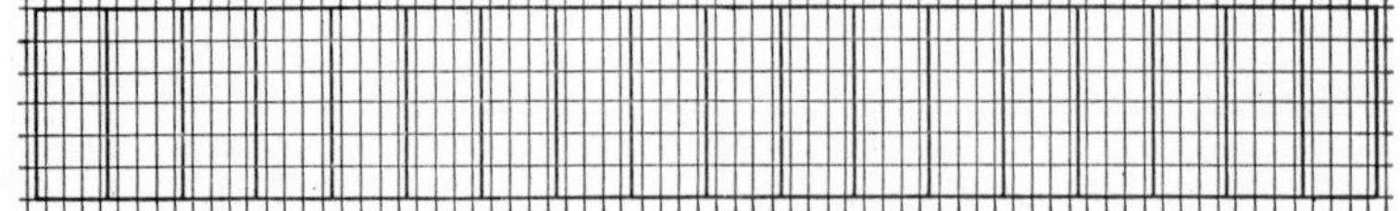

b. The same factors transposed require an elongated space of 7.2 by 1.0 inches.

FIG. 74.

inches ($18 \times \frac{1}{6}$). Normally, you would place the narrow dimension of your chart across the width of the sheet. But since we are analyzing space requirements, let's calculate width and length with directions reversed. Eighteen answers of $\frac{4}{10}$-inch width each need 7.2 inches of space width. Six rows of $\frac{1}{6}$-inch height take 1.0 inch of space height. (See Fig. 74.) So either of our two possible arrangements takes 7.2 square inches. The area will be the same either way because area is the product of all four factors. Therefore, if you are as desirous as I am to get all data on one work sheet, you will make determinations like these in planning your layout. This phase of data consolidation might be broadly summarized as

Place the short-range variables across the sheet and the long-range ones vertically.

Dividing the Variables

In our next step, we come to another question, "What should we do when there are several variables?" In answering, let me say at the outset that sometimes you may not be able to make a choice. Sometimes the variables are complex, as in certain curve families. These involve at least two variables. They are easy to handle in the initial stage of combination. They are difficult to place in subsequent stages. So we might set down a rule that

Complex families of curves are more easily combined with other factors when placed first in sequence.

If there is only one such family, it may be placed in either half of the groupings. If there are two, one may be used to start each half. This "half" idea has confused you, I know, but an explanation follows very shortly. Before leaving this detail, however, it is necessary to make another point.

Some problems involve the repetition of dimensional factors. To illustrate, with standard setting you might have more than one part of a total dependent upon Length. Each use of the Length factor as a dimension will take space. If these factors can be combined before charting, that is the obvious thing to do. But if they cannot be directly combined, then the next step is to try to utilize the one necessary space for showing the two or more factors. To attain this result may take considerable patience. If you persist, you can usually attain your objective and save considerable space. One method used to overcome duplication is explained in Chap. 19.

Now back to the halving of variables. With combinations, there are three or more variables. These may be charted all in one sequence or divided into two or more sequences. Two conventional ways of placing four variables are shown in Fig. 75. In Fig. 75*a*, the four are arranged in sequence. This shows how you might place four variables if you wanted to combine seven or eight. In Fig. 75*b*, they are divided into two groups of two each. This suggests what I meant when I said earlier to halve the variables. To conclude, let me suggest that you try to

Divide the several variables into two groups to balance the space required.

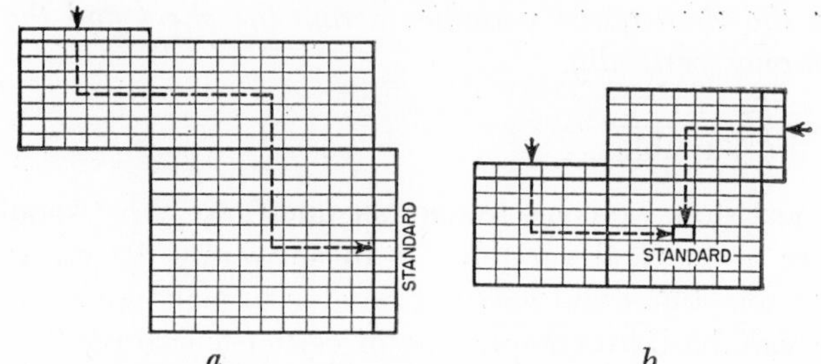

a. Any number of variables may be placed in a sequence.
b. Several variables may be divided into two groups of entering determinants.

FIG. 75.

Study the Spacing

The simple-line diagrams shown here may be confusing you because, as yet, nothing has been said about "how" to combine charts. My apologies. But I am trying to get all the discussion about space taken care of in one chapter. So if you will bear with me, we will get the mechanics immediately thereafter.

Just a few more details should be mentioned. First is the study of space taken up when we have a multi-variable chart to lay out. Two considerations have been discussed. One dealt with the area occupied. The amount and arrangements were portrayed in Fig. 74. The other stressed the halving of the number of variables.

These two considerations are brought together in Fig. 76. The illustrations show but six of many possible combinations. Several take up the same over-all box area. Each of the four factors used is indicated by the number written on the side it controls dimensionally. The extremes in arrangements are shown in (*a*) and (*f*). Diagram (*a*) occupies an area of 10.8 square inches calculated as Fig. 74 depicts. Somewhat larger areas are required for arrangements (*c*) and (*e*). In contrast, (*f*) requires only 10.7 square inches. This is computed as horizontal spaces $(7 + 10 + 1) \times .4$ multiplied by vertical spaces $(6 + 3) \times \frac{1}{6}$.

You cannot always interchange the variables as I have done in Fig. 76. You may be restricted by the mathematics. For instance, you may be required to add variables and then multiply by a factor. Also, as mentioned earlier, you may have complex variables that restrict the ease of placement. But when all variables are independent, you can elect to use the arrangement most convenient to your purposes. And in general, you will find that dividing the variables for two entries into your chart is the best layout for saving space.

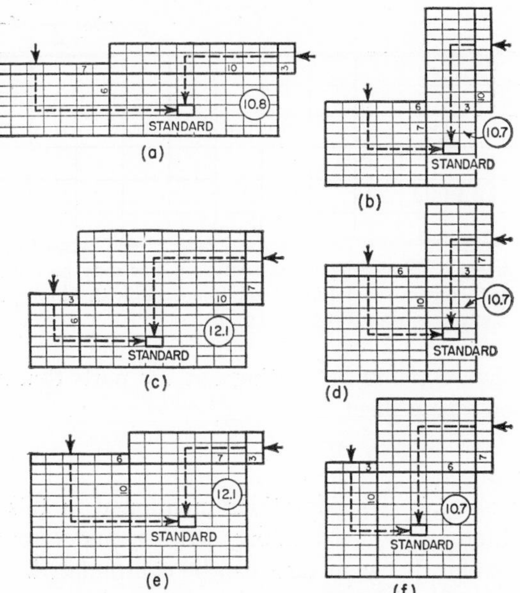

FIG. 76. Six arrangements of four variables. Many more can be made but these indicate the range in possibilities. The small numbers written on the lines indicate the number of factors in the direction shown. The figures in circles are the box areas.

Charting Paper

The line diagrams in Fig. 76 that show ways to arrange four variables are comparatively simple. Even so, you can see what is ahead if you want to build a multi-variable chart with more than four variables.

For that reason, I want to mention a final detail here. It has to do with your layout paper. My suggestion is that you equip yourself with an appropriate kind. One feature of suitability is paper already ruled. This saves time. But ruled paper often has ¼-inch squares.

Accidentally, I came across a much better ruling some years ago. It had oblong spacings, ¼ by ⅙ inch. This size is just right for chart making. You can see how adaptable it is in the small sample shown in Fig. 77. So much for the ruling.

Also, consider the size of the paper. You want a big sheet to work with when the problem is complicated. You can start in one corner and have plenty of room to change your mind, without having to start over again. This feature is especially important until you become experienced in making complex types of charts. You can save yourself much copying by having plenty of room on the sheet. Of course,

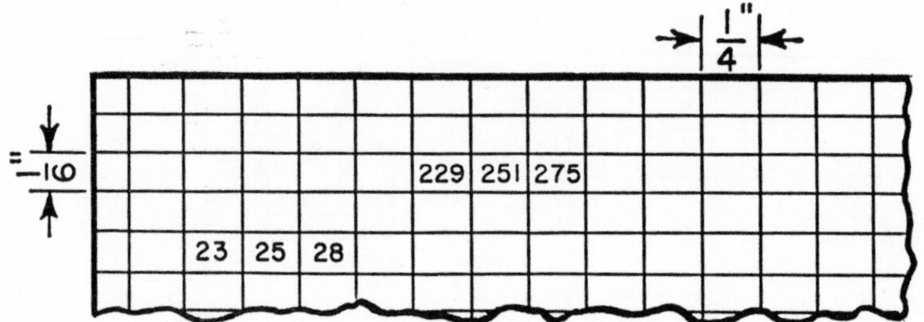

Fig. 77. Large sheets of blue-ruled cross-section paper may be obtained for chart making. The most convenient I have seen is a type with oblong spacings ¼ by ⅙ inches. This sample is almost actual size.

you can also save copying by cutting out the parts that suit you and pasting them on a new sheet.

Time Saving

The details of space considerations mentioned in this chapter are important in time saving. Handling, writing, and errors can be reduced, to the extent that your data can be consolidated. The acme is attained when all can be placed on one side of an 8½ by 11 work sheet. This ideal arrangement is often produced by those who value space. Often also, they have to do some real work to get the results they want. You are to be the judge of the proper balance between savings and cost. My suggestion is, however, that we need to give much more attention to satisfactorily explaining the results of our variable analysis. This is aided greatly when all discussion can be centered on one sheet of paper.

These several aspects of layout details should be kept in mind. They were stressed as essential groundwork behind the charting of multi-variables. With these understood, we can go on to the process itself in the next several chapters.

CHAPTER 16

Turn Inside Out

Charts of number data are made up in two general forms. One type is built up by calculating. The other is made up by changing curves to numbers. Each of these will be discussed briefly because, as a rule, we start with some form of tabulated data when we want to build multi-variable charts.

Quantity Charting

Perhaps the simplest table is one used for quantity. Usually this type is calculated. Two kinds are made. The common one is for multiples. To illustrate, here is one for a budget of Production Control expense set up for a range of Standard Minutes of Manufacturing output.

Thousands Stand. Mins....	100	120	140	160	180	200	220
Prod. Control Dollars......	3232	3340	3448	3556	3664	3773	3880

The other type is based on proration. An example from timestudy is Gauge Piece—one in 5, 10, and so on. The following chart was

Gauge, 1 in every.........	1	2	5	10	25	50	100
Micrometer...............	.12	.06	.024	.012	.005	.002	.001

computed by dividing the standard for Micrometer, .12 minute, by a series of quantities. Tables that record divisions seem more necessary to me than those for multiplications. We are more apt to make mistakes in arithmetic and decimal places when divisions are made as part of a calculating process. Therefore, you should use tables like this when dividing is a step in your computation.

Beyond the mistakes is the cost of the time used to make calculations. For these reasons, you should make up charts that eliminate calculating. The cost per answer comes down in proportion as you reduce the number of calculations. This applies particularly in timestudy work. In setting standards from data, there is the repetitive use of the same calculations. With repetition in manufacturing, you find

Miscellaneous Data	Per	1	2	3	4	5	6
Set soldiers..................	Soldier	.15	.25	.40	.50	.60	.68
Set job nails.................	Nail	.07	.14	.20	.25	.30	.35
Vent (cope, drag, or side)....	Vent	.08	.15	.22	.30	.35	.40
Blacken mold...............	100 sq in.	.06	.10	.15	.20	.23	.26
Water mold after draw.......	10 lin in.	.05	.12	.16	.20	.25	.29
Cut gate....................	Gate	.90	1.50	2.00	2.50	2.90	3.25
Set, cut, and ream risers.....	Riser	.45	.90	1.30	1.70	2.00	2.30
Special ram (drag or cope)...	100 cu in.	.30	.55	.80	1.00	1.15	1.30
Put paste on cores...........	Sq in.	.05	.10	.15	.18	.20	.22

a. A section from the Squeezer Molding data shown in Chap. 15, Fig. 73.

Wire for Plating		Loops Around			
		1	2	3	4
Twists	1	.073	.077	.080	.084
	2	.085	.089	.092	.096

b. A section from standard data for Wiring Parts for Plating.

T & L Screw by Hand	Number of Turns								
	¼	½	1	1½	2	2½	3	3½	4
Locate......	.035	.040	.050	.060	.070	.080	.090	.100	.110
Fasten......	.062	.068	.080	.092	.100	.116	.130	.140	.150

c. Data section arranged for Drill Press jig-screw handling.

Fig. 78.

ways to improve methods. You should follow the same plan in standard setting. Use more of the simple forms of tables designed to save computations similar to those shown on Fig. 78. These were set up for quantities. The necessary extensions were made once and checked. By this method, all future extensions are saved. Errors likely to occur in repeated calculations are eliminated.

Step Values

Such charts can be utilized to take care of combinations of constants and variables. For instance, notice that the Set Soldiers standards do not rise uniformly on the first line of the Chart 78*a*. For 1 we have .15, for 2 we have .25, and for 3 we have .40 minute. This results from a "Get Two" of .05 minute and a "Set One" of .10 minute. The point involved is that such necessary differences can be set up in a table very conveniently. To correctly allow them another way would require references to two or more standards and calculations—certainly addition. Many such irregularities are easily provided for in chart form.

Charted Curve Data

Tables like those illustrated are familiar to most of use. All of us have made and used them. We have often referred to similar ones

HANDLING TIME

Length	Diameter										
	1/2	5/8	3/4	7/8	1	1 1/8	1 1/4	1 3/8	1 1/2	1 5/8	1 3/4
1	.063	.072	.083	.094	.11	.12	.14	.16	.18	.20	.22
2	.064	.073	.084	.097	.11	.13	.14	.16	.18	.20	.23
4	.066	.076	.088	.10	.12	.13	.15	.17	.19	.22	.24
6	.067	.079	.092	.11	.12	.14	.16	.18	.21	.23	.26
8	.070	.082	.095	.11	.13	.15	.17	.19	.22	.24	.27
10	.073	.085	.099	.12	.13	.15	.18	.20	.23	.26	.29
12	.075	.087	.10	.12	.14	.16	.18	.21	.24	.27	.30
14	.077	.090	.11	.13	.15	.17	.19	.22	.25	.28	.32
16	.079	.093	.11	.13	.15	.17	.20	.23	.26	.30	.33
18	.081	.096	.11	.13	.16	.18	.21	.24	.27	.31	.35
20	.084	.098	.12	.14	.16	.19	.22	.25	.28	.32	.36
22	.086	.10	.12	.14	.17	.19	.23	.26	.30	.34	.38
24	.088	.10	.12	.15	.17	.20	.23	.27	.31	.35	.39
26	.090	.11	.13	.15	.18	.21	.24	.28	.32	.36	.41
28	.092	.11	.13	.16	.18	.22	.25	.29	.33	.38	.42
30	.095	.11	.14	.16	.19	.22	.26	.30	.34	.39	.44
32	.097	.12	.14	.17	.20	.23	.27	.31	.35	.40	.45
34	.099	.12	.14	.17	.20	.24	.27	.32	.36	.41	.47
36	.10	.12	.15	.18	.21	.24	.28	.33	.38	.42	.48

MACHINING TIME

R.P.M.	Strokes-Hits						
	1	2	3	4	5	6	7
228	.012	.024	.036	.047	.059	.071	.083
212	.013	.026	.038	.051	.064	.076	.089
197	.014	.027	.041	.055	.069	.082	.096
183	.015	.030	.044	.059	.074	.089	.10
170	.016	.032	.048	.064	.080	.096	.11
158	.017	.034	.051	.069	.086	.10	.12
146	.019	.037	.055	.074	.092	.11	.13
136	.020	.040	.060	.079	.099	.12	.14
126	.021	.043	.064	.086	.11	.13	.15
117	.023	.046	.069	.092	.12	.14	.16
109	.025	.050	.074	.099	.12	.15	.17
101	.027	.053	.080	.11	.13	.16	.19
94	.029	.058	.086	.12	.14	.17	.20
87	.031	.062	.093	.12	.16	.19	.22
81	.033	.069	.10	.13	.17	.20	.23
75	.036	.072	.11	.14	.18	.22	.25
70	.039	.077	.12	.16	.19	.23	.27
65	.042	.084	.13	.17	.21	.25	.29
60	.045	.090	.14	.18	.23	.27	.32

FIG. 79. Standard time data for the two parts of an operation for hot-heading bolts.

in the handbooks. Most of these have been more complex in that they have several dimensions down the left side. Some have several columns spread to the right with a variable dimension at the top. One such table frequently seen in machine shops has diameters down the left side, Surface Speeds across the top, and RPM in the body of the table. Many such tables are constructed of timestudy data.

Two such charts are shown in Fig. 79. Both of these record standard times read from corresponding curves. These were the

START WITH DIAMETER, GO DOWN THE COLUMN TO THE LENGTH, THEN TO RIGHT ALONG THAT ROW. FROM HITS, GO RIGHT TO R.P.M. THEN DOWN TO INTERSECTION

HITS	SPEED OF MACHINE IN REVOLUTIONS PER MINUTE																
1	170	112	82	64													
2		224	164	128	104	86	72	61									
3			245	193	156	129	108	92	79	68	59						
4					207	171	144	122	105	91	79	69	61				
5						214	180	153	131	114	99	86	76	68	60		
6							216	184	157	136	118	104	92	81	72	64	57
7								215	183	159	138	121	107	94	84	75	67	60

DIAMETER OF BOLT: $1\frac{3}{4}$	$1\frac{5}{8}$	$1\frac{1}{2}$	$1\frac{3}{8}$	$1\frac{1}{4}$	$1\frac{1}{8}$	1	$\frac{7}{8}$	$\frac{3}{4}$	$\frac{5}{8}$	$\frac{1}{2}$	STANDARDS IN UNITS PER BOLT TO BE DIVIDED EQUALLY BETWEEN TWO MEN																	
										4	079	087	096	11	12	13	14	15	17	18	20	22	24	26	29	32	35	38
									1	10	085	093	10	11	12	13	14	16	17	19	21	23	25	27	29	32	35	39
									6	16	092	10	11	12	13	14	15	16	18	20	21	23	25	28	30	33	36	39
								4	12	23	10	11	12	13	14	15	16	17	19	20	22	24	26	28	31	34	37	40
	LENGTH OF BOLT						2	8	18	31	11	12	13	14	15	16	17	18	20	21	23	25	27	29	32	35	38	41
							5	14	26		12	13	14	14	15	17	18	19	21	22	24	26	28	30	33	36	39	42
						4	10	19	32		13	14	15	15	16	18	19	20	22	23	25	27	29	31	34	37	40	43
					2	7	14	25			14	15	16	16	17	19	20	21	23	24	26	28	30	32	35	38	41	44
				1	6	12	20	32			15	16	17	17	18	20	21	22	24	25	27	29	31	34	36	39	42	45
				3	8	14	23	36			16	17	18	18	19	21	22	23	25	26	28	30	32	34	37	39	43	46
				4	10	16	25				16	17	18	19	20	21	22	24	25	27	29	30	33	35	37	40	43	47
			1	6	12	19	28				17	18	19	20	21	22	23	24	26	27	29	31	33	36	38	41	44	47
			3	8	14	22	32				18	19	20	21	22	23	24	25	27	28	30	32	34	36	39	42	45	48
		1	4	10	16	24	36				19	20	20	21	22	23	25	26	28	29	31	33	35	37	40	42	46	49
		2	6	12	18	27					20	20	21	22	23	24	25	27	28	30	32	34	36	38	40	43	46	50
		3	8	14	21	31					20	21	22	23	24	25	26	28	29	31	33	34	37	39	41	44	47	51
	1	5	10	16	24	34					21	22	23	24	25	26	27	29	30	32	33	35	37	40	42	45	48	51
	3	6	12	18	26						22	23	24	25	26	27	28	29	31	33	34	36	38	41	43	46	49	52
1	5	8	14	20	29						23	24	25	26	27	28	29	30	32	34	35	37	39	42	44	47	50	53
2	6	10	16	23	32						24	25	26	27	28	29	30	31	33	35	36	38	40	43	45	48	51	54
4	8	12	18	26	36						25	26	27	28	29	30	31	33	34	36	37	39	41	44	46	49	52	55
5	9	14	20	28							26	27	28	29	30	31	32	34	35	37	39	40	43	45	47	50	53	57
7	11	16	23	31							28	28	29	30	31	32	34	35	36	38	40	42	44	46	49	51	54	58
9	13	18	26	34							29	30	31	31	32	34	35	36	38	39	41	43	45	47	50	53	56	59
10	15	21	28								30	31	32	33	34	35	36	37	39	40	42	44	46	49	51	54	57	60
12	17	23	31								32	32	33	34	35	36	37	39	40	42	44	46	48	50	52	55	58	62
14	19	26	34								33	34	35	36	37	38	39	40	42	43	45	47	49	51	54	57	60	63
16	21	28									34	35	36	37	38	39	40	42	43	45	47	48	51	53	55	58	61	65
18	24	31									36	37	38	39	40	41	42	43	45	46	48	50	52	54	57	60	63	66
20	26	34									38	39	39	40	41	42	44	45	46	48	50	52	54	56	59	61	64	68
22	29										39	40	41	42	43	44	45	47	48	50	51	53	55	58	60	63	66	69
25	31										41	42	43	44	45	46	47	48	50	51	53	55	57	60	62	65	68	71
27	34										43	44	45	46	47	48	49	50	52	53	55	57	59	61	64	67	70	73
30											45	46	47	48	49	50	51	52	54	55	57	59	61	63	66	69	72	75
32											47	48	49	60	51	52	53	54	56	57	59	61	63	65	68	71	74	77
35											49	50	51	52	53	54	55	56	58	60	61	63	65	68	70	73	76	79

FIG. 80. The first multi-variable chart set up by the author in July, 1924.

charts I set up when I was on my first job as a consultant. To set a standard, as you can see, I had to read a time from each chart and then add them together. As the dotted lines show

Handling Time	= 1⅛″ Dia. × 36″ Long		.24 min
Machine Time	= 3 Hits × 81 RPM		.10
		Total	.34

After doing these three steps for awhile, I began to wonder, "Why can't I combine these charts?" So I sat, looking off into space "wondering," as I said in Chap. 2. My first multi-variable chart (Fig. 80) is not a complicated one, now that I look back on it. But the "discovery" has been applied many times since. It has many uses. Some of the different ways of utilizing the general idea will be expanded in this and the next chapters.

Turn Inside Out

The basic idea was to "turn inside out" these two-variable charts. The idea is simple enough. What it does is to get the answers on the outside of the chart instead of in the body. The reason is, of course, that we cannot add to, subtract from, multiply, or divide the answers while they are in the body of the chart. Actually, the fundamental principle involved is to

Substitute answers as one of the variables for one of the dimensional factors.

Any "efficiency expert" would say, "Why set up a chart and then turn it inside out? Why not make it right the first time?" But that is second guessing. The turning inside out only demonstrates how to get from the usual form of chart to what we want. Then, when you have seen that step of conversion and understand it, you can eliminate this unnecessary work in your future chart making.

Four Material Costs

To make an example, I set up Material Costs from part of the volume range of the four products charted in Chap. 2. These are shown as Fig. 81*a*. These are combined to form two simple tables, Fig. 81*b*. Note that here and in all chart arrangements to follow in this example, three zeros are dropped.

Step 1. To proceed, we select one of our variable factors to place outside our chart. We have two to choose from. In many instances, one is a better choice than the other. In this example, let's keep Shorts in the same top location to reduce the appearance of sleight of

SALES DOLLARS	MATERIAL COSTS			
	SHIRTS	SHORTS	SHEETS	SHOES
$40,000	$10,000	$6,000	$18,000	$16,000
60,000	15,000	9,000	27,000	24,000
80,000	20,000	12,000	36,000	32,000

a. Material Costs for part of the volume range of the four products charted in Chapter 2.

SHIRTS	SHORTS		
	40	60	80
40	16	19	22
60	21	24	27
80	26	29	32

SHEETS	SHOES		
	40	60	80
40	34	42	50
60	43	51	59
80	52	60	68

b. Two tables set up to combine Material Costs recorded in (*a*). All figures here are thousands of dollars, 000 omitted to simplify this and all subsequent charts in this example.

FIG. 81.

hand. So to start, set up the caption Shorts at the top of our new chart. Then underneath, as column headings, write in Sales Dollar volumes—40, 60, 80—shown on the original chart (Fig. 81*b*).

Step 2. Next we want to substitute material Cost for Shirt Sales. This is the step previously referred to as "turning the chart inside out." To begin this translation, we list all the different Material Costs recorded. These are written in a vertical column similar to that used for Shirt Sales, beginning with the least Material Cost at the top. One detail is changed, however. The column of Material Cost is set up on the side of the chart most convenient for combining with other variables to be included in the chart later on. The right-hand side is the location chosen in this example. The preferred location might be left side, top, or bottom in other solutions.

Looking over the Material Cost, we find the least one is $16,000. That goes in the first square at the top of the column, on the first line below the title line of Short-Sales Dollars. Then, in sequence down

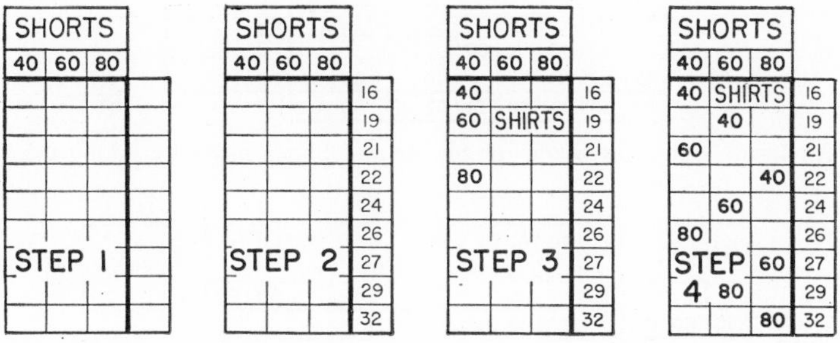

SHORTS			
40	60	80	
STEP 1			

c

SHORTS			
40	60	80	
			16
			19
			21
			22
			24
			26
STEP 2			27
			29
			32

d

SHORTS			
40	60	80	
40			16
60	SHIRTS		19
			21
80			22
			24
			26
STEP 3			27
			29
			32

e

SHORTS			
40	60	80	
40	SHIRTS		16
	40		19
60			21
		40	22
	60		24
80			26
STEP		60	27
4	80		29
		80	32

f

c. Place the title and scale of one variable across the top of your chart.
d. Set up the scale of your answers on the outside.
e. Plot the other variable dimension inside under your first variable and at proper intersections.
f. Complete your plotting to produce a chart "turned inside out."

FIG. 81. (*Continued*).

the column, write all the Material Costs 16, 19, 21, 22, 24, 26, 27, 29, and 32, omitting three zeros (Fig. 81*d*).

Step 3. In constructing the usual chart, with one variable across the top and the other down the side, the next step is to fill in the body. So now, let's fill in by plotting in their proper locations the Sales Volumes of Shirts.

Beginning with the column headed by the title for the least sales dollars of Shorts, refer to the original chart to find the Shirt Sales volume corresponding with $16,000 Material Cost. That is $40,000 Shirt sales. Record 40 for Shirts in the column under 40 Shorts and on the line opposite 16 of material cost. Then refer to each Shirt Sales volume in order, considering only 40 Shorts. Plot each one in the 40-Shorts column opposite its corresponding Material Cost. The finished result should be like that shown in Fig. 81*e*.

Step 4. Continue the process explained in Step 3 for all Shirt Sales volumes. Complete the plotting of all Shirt Sales for one selected Shirt Sales volume before taking up the next. After all are plotted, clearly label the area containing the plotted variable with its appropriate title. In this instance, it is entitled "Shirts." The end result will be a completely transposed chart like the diagram in Fig. 81*f*.

Step 5. To prepare for combining, our next step is to set up an inside-out chart for Sheets and Shoes (Fig. 81*g*). The details of plotting are the same as we used in making Steps 1, 2, 3, and 4. The only difference is in the layout. Here, we want Material Costs in a horizontal row instead of a vertical column in preparation for our next step.

40	60		80			SHOES			40	
		40		60		80			60	SHEETS
STEP 5					40		60	80	80	
34	42	43	50	51	52	59	60	68		

g. An inside out chart made for Sheets and Shoes made by taking steps 1, 2, 3, 4.

SHORTS				40	60		80			SHOES			40	
						40		60		80			60	SHEETS
									40		60	80	80	
40	60	80		34	42	43	50	51	52	59	60	68		
40	SHIRTS		16	50	58	59								
	40		19	53	61									
60			21	55										
		40	22											
	60		24											
80			26											
		60	27											
	80		29							STEP 6				
		80	32											

h. Both "inside out" charts brought together so that their partial sums may be added to get Total Material Cost.

SHORTS			40	60		80			SHOES			40	
					40		60		(80)			(60)	SHEETS
40	60	(80)						40		60	80	80	
40	SHIRTS		50	58	59	66	67	68	75	76	84		
	40		53	61	62	69	70	71	78	79	87		
60			55	63	64	71	72	73	80	81	89		
		(40)	56	64	65	72	73	74	(81)	82	90		
	60		58	66	67	74	75	76	83	85	92		
80			60	68	69	76	77				94		
		60	61	69	70	77	78	STEP 7			95		
	80		63	71	72	79	80				97		
		80	66	74	75	82	83	84	91	92	100		

i. Completed four-variable chart with construction figures omitted and a road-map dotted on to show how to read it.

FIG. 81. (*Continued*).

Step 6. Now we bring together our two inside-out charts so we can add Material Costs to get totals (Fig. 81*h*).

In the left-hand chart we plotted first, we have Material Cost of $16,000 for the sum of $40,000 Shorts and $40,000 Shirts sales volumes.

Nearest to this $16,000 is $34,000, the least Material Cost sum for $40,000 Sheets and $40,000 Shoes sales volumes.

We can add $16,000 to $34,000 to get $50,000 in the body of our chart as the total Material Cost for 40 Shorts, 40 Shirts, 40 Sheets, and 40 Shoes. In the same way, we can add every one of the Material

Costs sums in our left-hand chart to every sum in the top chart. Thus, we can completely fill the body of our four-variable chart.

Step 7. Our completed chart is Fig. 81*i*. Two of its details are called to your attention. First is the omission of the subtotals of material cost we used as construction figures to set up our two starting charts.

Second is the road map of dotted lines showing how to use the chart. This is a type of example that should be drawn on all multivariable charts. The point is that some charts can be read more than one way and wrong answers may result.

To follow the example made by the dotted lines, start at the upper left with 80 Shorts. Drop vertically to 40 Shirts, turn 90 degrees right and enter the body of the chart. Hold the line thus determined.

Enter from the upper right hand with 60 Sheets. Cross to 80 Shoes, turn 90 degrees and drop down until you intersect the horizontal line previously located.

The grand total Material Cost thus found is $81,000 for the mix of sales used in this example. Our answer checks with sum of the individual Material Costs shown in our starting chart.

Product	*Sales Volume*	*Material Cost*
Shorts..............	$80,000	$12,000
Shirts..............	40,000	10,000
Sheets..............	60,000	27,000
Shoes..............	80,000	32,000
	Total..........	$81,000

Dollar Combinations

The four-variable chart for getting Total Material Costs is but one of many you can think of that could be built to combine dollars. Budget computation is a repeating task that could be done with charts. You might say, "This chart is for budgeting material costs."

But most budgets involve a constant—the "semi-" part of what some accountants call "semi-variable expenses." How to bring in a constant has not been explained up to this point. (See Fig. 85*a*, Chap. 17.) So I elected to use Material Costs here to avoid mixing the problems of construction with those of other factors and more variables. These extensions will be described in later chapters.

Drill-time Chart

A friend once told me that his skilled professor said, "In Education, remember there are three basic rules to follow. The first and most important one is 'to repeat.' The second and equally necessary rule is 'to repeat.' The third and final rule is 'to repeat.'" If he was right, and I think he was, that is reason enough for working out another chart.

We can use a common problem in timestudy for this example. Regularly, we need to combine "Machine" time with "Handling" time

DRILL TIME CHART		DIAMETER				
		3/16	1/4	5/16	3/8	7/16
DEPTH	1/8	.05	.06	.07	.08	.09
	3/16	.06	.07	.08	.09	.11
	1/4	.07	.08	.09	.11	.13
	5/16	.08	.09	.11	.13	.15
	3/8	.09	.11	.13	.15	.18

a

DIAMETER					
3/16	1/4	5/16	3/8	7/16	

STEP I

b

a. The original chart is so arranged that the standards for drilling cannot be combined with those for handling time.

b. Place one dimensional scale at the top of a cross-section sheet.

DIAMETER					
3/16	1/4	5/16	3/8	7/16	
					.05
					.06
					.07
					.08
					.09
					.11
					.13
					.15
					.18

STEP 2

c

DIAMETER					
3/16	1/4	5/16	3/8	7/16	
1/8					.05
3/16					.06
1/4					.07
5/16					.08
3/8					.09
					.11
					.13
					.15
					.18

STEP 3

d

DIAMETER					
3/16	1/4	5/16	3/8	7/16	
1/8					.05
3/16	1/8				.06
1/4	3/16	1/8			.07
5/16	1/4	3/16	1/8		.08
3/8	5/16	1/4	3/16	1/8	.09
	3/8	5/16	1/4	3/16	.11
		3/8	5/16	1/4	.13
			3/8	5/16	.15
				3/8	.18

DEPTH

STEP 4

e

c. Write in a scale of standards to include the complete range.

d. Plot the other dimension scale values under the first dimensional scale and opposite their corresponding time standards.

e. Complete the plotting of the second dimensional scale. Now the starting chart of Drill time is "turned inside out."

FIG. 82.

to set a total operation standard time. So let's work out a simple chart that will combine these two parts of a necessary total starting with machine time. Our Original Chart for Drill Time is Fig. 82*a*.

Step 1. To avoid confusion, we will place Diameter at the top of our starting chart to keep it in the same location it originally appears. Under this title, we can copy the five diameters—3/16 through 7/16 inch—as column headings (Fig. 82*b*).

Step 2. Next, you list in order, from least to greatest, all the standard times there are in the Original Chart. The least is .05 minutes (Fig. 82*a*). The others in order are .06, .07, .08, .09, .11, .13, .15, and .18. These are placed on the right, outside column in preparation for combining later with our handling-time chart (Fig. 82*c*).

As stated about our first example, there are three other arrangements. The several ways of arranging partial charts will be discussed in our next chapter.

Step 3. Now, you are ready to plot Depth inside the body of the chart. Choosing the least Diameter 3/16 inch, what is the Depth that corresponds with .05 minutes, the least time? The Depth is 1/8 inch. Write it in the first square under 3/16-inch Diameter, on the line with .05 Minutes (Fig. 82*d*).

Continuing in the 3/16-inch Diameter column, what is the Depth that corresponds with the next higher time of .06 minutes. It is 3/16-inch Depth and is plotted in the next square under 3/16-inch Diameter on the line of .06 minutes. Going on, in the same 3/16-inch Diameter column, look on the Original Chart for all the other Depths with the times that correspond and plot each one in turn.

Step 4. Take up the next Diameter of 1/4 inch and look at the Original Chart. What is the least time shown for 1/4-inch Diameter? It is .06 minutes. And the Depth that corresponds is 1/8 inch. Plot this 1/8-inch Depth in the 1/4-inch Diameter column on the line of .06 minutes.

Carry on for all the other Depths that appear in the Original Chart for 1/4-inch Diameter. In the same way, taking one Diameter column at a time, complete this chart (Fig. 82*e*). At this stage, you have "turned inside out" the Drill Time chart and have the standard times on the outside where they may be combined with other times.

Step 5. The partial chart just completed would be on a bigger piece of paper under usual conditions. But here, because of book page limits, we have to bring it into position for the next step (Fig. 82*f*).

Step 6. Place above the body of the proposed total standard time chart, the inside out chart made up for Piece Handling time (Fig. 82*g*).

STEP 6

LENGTH					BAR SIZE
12					1 1/2
9	12				1 3/4
6 3/4	9	12			2
5 1/4	7	9	10 1/2		2 1/4
	5 3/4	7 1/4	8 1/2	10	2 1/2
.08	.09	.10	.11	.12	

g

STEP 5

DIAMETER					
3/16	1/4	5/16	3/8	7/16	
1/8					.05
3/16	1/8				.06
1/4	3/16	1/8	DEPTH		.07
5/16	1/4	3/16	1/8		.08
3/8	5/16	1/4	3/16	1/8	.09
	3/8	5/16	1/4	3/16	.11
		3/8	5/16	1/4	.13
			3/8	5/16	.15
				3/8	.18

f

STEP 7

.13				
.14				
.15				
.16				
.17				
.19				
.21				
.23				
.26				

h

f. Step 5. Set up the inverted chart for drilling.
g. Step 6. Locate the chart for Piece Handling.
h. Step 7. Add one Handling standard to all the standards for Drilling.

STEP 8

					LENGTH					BAR SIZE
					12					1 1/2
					9	12				1 3/4
					6 3/4	9	12			2
DIAMETER					5 1/4	7	9	10 1/2		2 1/4
3/16	1/4	5/16	3/8	7/16		5 3/4	7 1/4	8 1/2	10	2 1/2
1/8		DEPTH			.13	.14	.15	.16	.17	
3/16	1/8				.14	.15	.16	.17	.18	
1/4	3/16	1/8			.15	.16	.17	.18	.19	
5/16	1/4	3/16	1/8		.16	.17	.18	.19	.20	
3/8	5/16	1/4	3/16	1/8	.17	.18	.19	.20	.21	
	3/8	5/16	1/4	3/16	.19	.20	.21	.22	.23	
		3/8	5/16	1/4	.21	.22	.23	.24	.25	
			3/8	5/16	.23	.24	.25	.26	.27	
				3/8	.26	.27	.28	.29	.30	

i

i. Step 8. Complete the body of the chart. Check the answers. Then remove the construction figures and draw in a road map.

FIG. 82. (*Continued*).

This portion is an example of a direct-reading chart I will explain in Chap. 18.

Step 7. With our two lines of standard times placed at right angles to each other, you are ready to add.

All the standards for Drilling, from .05 to .18 minute, apply regardless of Handling Time. These are shown in what now happens to be the center column of the chart. You can combine any and all of these Drilling times with any and all of the Handling times. For example, you can add .08 for Handling to each of the Drilling standards. Caution! The sums must be set down in the column under the .08 minute Handling time. The first combination is .08 for Handling plus .05 for Drilling. All the combinations show in the partially complete chart, Fig. 82*h*. Next, the .09 standard for Handling is added to all the Drilling standards.

When all the combinations are made, your chart is completed except for one detail. The construction figures should be removed, from the standpoint of a finished product. Consequently, in the final chart, Fig. 82*i*, the original Drilling and Handling standards are omitted. Only the combined standards show. Your final chart is usually copied from the make-up chart. The unnecessary construction figures can be left out in this step. But they will remain on the original. This should be filed away for reference when some future revision becomes necessary.

Four-variable Chart

Now you have a chart that permits the selection of a total standard for any one of many combinations of Drilling and Piece Handling. Granted, the example is very much simpler than those we have to solve in most plants. Even so, it does show the method for putting together four different variables. That is the purpose of the explanation.

The charts we made in this chapter are simplified in other ways. For instance, only a few Sales Volumes were used in setting up the chart for obtaining total Material Cost. Too, the actual costs were used instead of approximations utilizing constant per cent increments.

Also, they are built with four variables. Naturally, you raise the question, "What about combining six or ten?"

It seemed better to make up some charts first to show how to go about combining variables. Then fill in some of the gaps. The important details omitted in this chapter will be explained in our next.

CHAPTER 17

Layout for Number Charts

We were trained as children to read from left to right. Perhaps this is why most of our handbook tables are made up to be read in that way. Notice also, we customarily lay out a table with its longer dimension running with the length of the paper. In publications, the long way of the page is usually in the vertical direction. Maybe this layout was carried over from our habit of writing letters on paper that is longer than it is wide. The example of data reproduced in chart form for ease in repeating calculations (Fig. 73, Chap. 15) was laid out this same preferred way.

Therefore, you should plan your charts to conform with our reading habit and common practice. This will place the longer variable in the vertical direction, when conditions permit. More particularly, your final chart arrangement will often be controlled by the sub-chart you set up as your starting unit. As you may have observed, Figs. 81*c* and 82*b*, developed as the starting units determined the shape of our final charts. This happened because we placed our columns of answers in desired location on the right side in the vertical direction preliminary to the next step.

The end result of roughly half of a multi-variable is the outside column of answers. This is the longer line in a vertical direction, when it can be arranged to suit normal methods of layout.

Plan of Entry

The starting units, Fig. 81*c* and 82*b*, established the direction of entry into the portions of charts built around them. Our examples required entry from the top. We placed Shorts there at the outset in Fig. 81*c*, however, because we wanted our answers to be in a vertical column. It follows that our chart entry is at right angles to our column or row of answers when there are two variables.

You may see this more clearly in Fig. 83. The schematic diagram

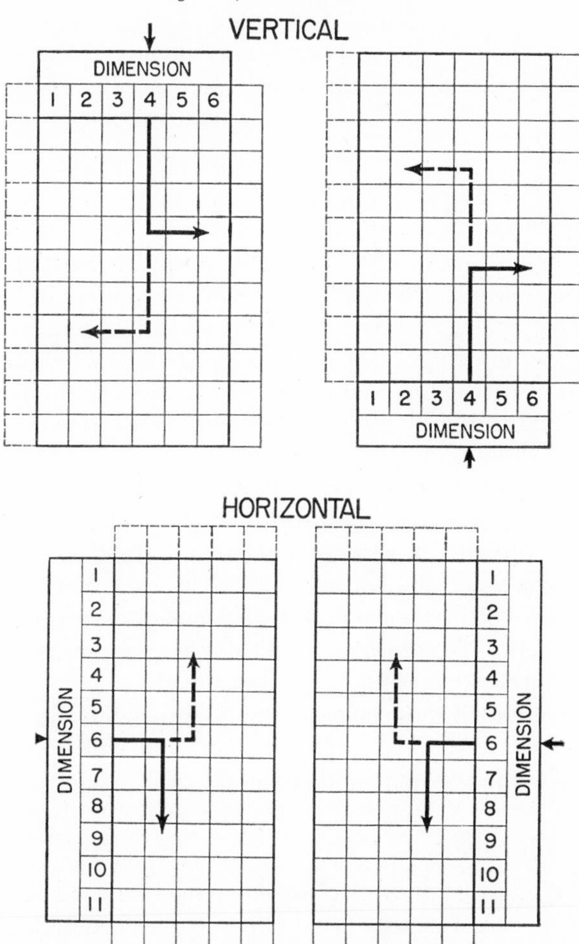

FIG. 83. Two variables may be arranged for vertical or horizontal entry. The right angle may be turned in either direction according to placement of this starting block in relation to the main body of the chart.

at the top left corresponds with those used as starting units in our previous chapter. Note that our answer scale could have been placed on the left side. Also our starting scale for Shorts or Diameter could have been placed at the bottom as shown in the diagram at the upper right. In these two diagrams, you see that the spaces provided for answers are more in number than those taken to record the Dimension scale.

In the lower diagrams, the reverse is true. More spaces are needed for Dimensions than for answers. This matter of relative space is controlled by two factors. One is the number of numbers you use in your scales. More about numbers later in this chapter. The other is the range of answers for the variable being plotted. Generally, the number of answers resulting from combining two variables is greater than the number of spaces used to record your Dimension.

Either Direction

These diagrams are inserted to portray three other details. First is that the direction of movement in the body of your chart is optional. Likewise, your scales may be placed in any convenient location and ascend in either direction. My personal preference is to arrange scales and directions so that the final chart has the least total answer in the upper left-hand corner with the maximum in the lower right-hand corner.

Second is that each step of forward movement in roughly one half of your combination requires you to turn a right angle. In this respect, your action is like that of reading any curve. Habit in curve reading causes us to start with the bottom Dimension scale, move vertically to the curve, turn 90 degrees left, and read our answer from a vertical scale on the left. That turning of 90 degrees is our way of getting from the independent variable to the dependent.

Third is that any of these layouts may be turned 90 degrees to better suit the final chart you are building. And you will have to change direction each time you add another variable.

Progressive Additions

Any of the line diagrams of chart entry may be used in a range of problem solutions. You may have either vertical or horizontal entry in either part of a multi-variable chart. The better one to use depends upon two details. First is the number of variables. Second is the way you divide the number between the two halves of your final chart.

To see some probable arrangements, take a look at Fig. 84. The outlines are hypothetical, of course. Nevertheless, they do show how you might plan a complete chart. This series is built up from Fig. 84*a* containing four variables to Fig. 84*f* including nine. As the series progresses, each added variable is joined alternately first with the left half and next with the right half. This carries out the suggestion of halving the variables.

These diagrams are misleading to some extent. They appear to over-simplify the task of multi-variable charting. More especially, they deceive with respect to space expansion as the variables multiply. The word "multiply" was used deliberately. The space required by each added variable often is a multiplication of its individual space requirement by the space factors of those variables ahead of it in the progression. This accounts, in part, for the prior extended discussion of space saving.

One more deception is concealed in my suggestion of halving your

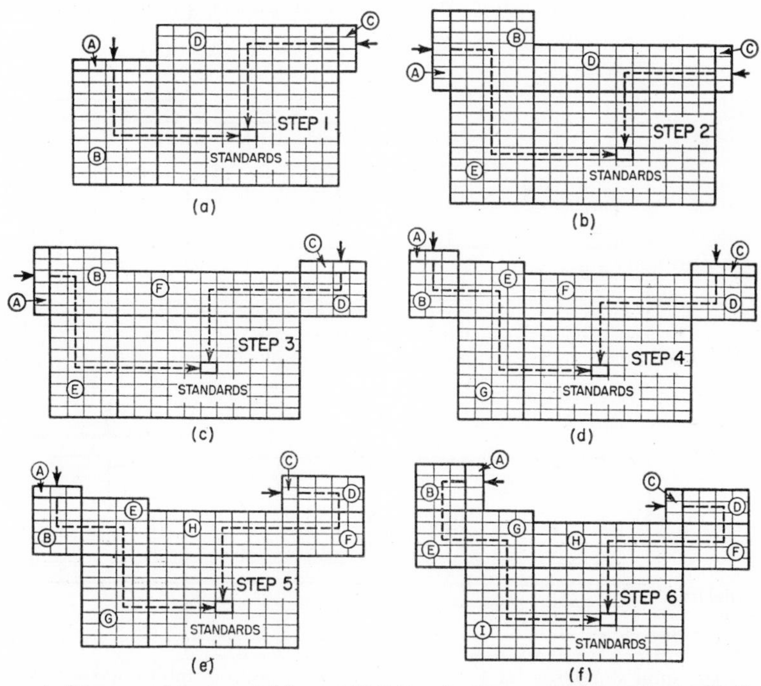

a. A diagram of four variables—*A,B,C,D*. *b.* Five variables with *E* added. *c.* Six variables. *F* has been added. *d.* Seven variables showing *G* as the new one. *e.* Eight variables including *H*. *f.* Nine variables are not the limit by any means. Our line diagrams simply conclude with the addition of *I*.

Fig. 84.

variables for double entry into your proposed final chart. Sometimes, you are limited in your choices. Let me use Figs. 81 and 82 in the previous chapter to illustrate. In charting Material Costs, we could have combined any two of our four products in either of our starting charts.

In contrast, Diameter of drill could not be separated from Depth. Our time answer depends upon these two variables in combination. The same is true of Diameter and Length of stock in Piece Handling.

Bring in Constants

You may have been misled further in that most of the comments and examples have been about adding variable answers. I guess that's because most of our combinations are made that way. And the first example in Fig. 85 is one set up to illustrate addition.

Figure 85*a* was drawn to show one way to add a constant. This is a necessary step in making many types of charts, particularly those

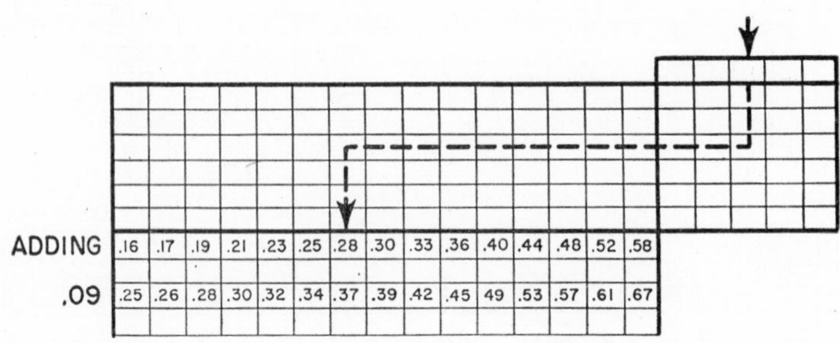

a. The combined results of a three-variable combination are increased by .09 minute.

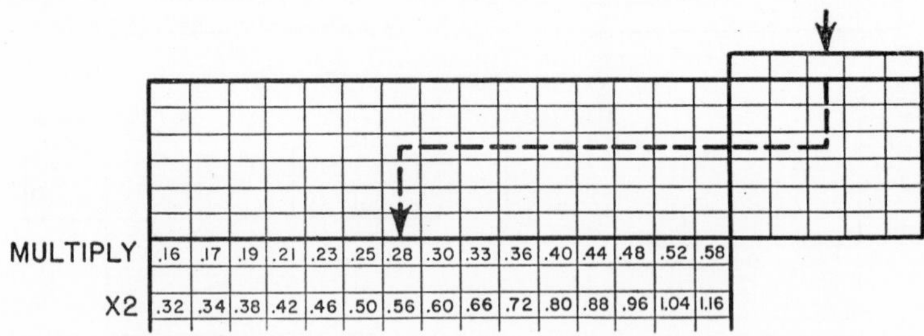

b. The total standards for three variables combined are multiplied by 2.

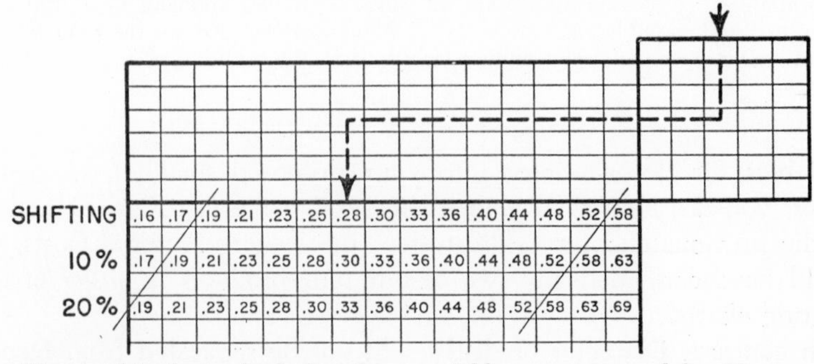

c. The combined standards for three variables are increased by 10 per cent and 20 per cent as two examples.

Fig. 85.

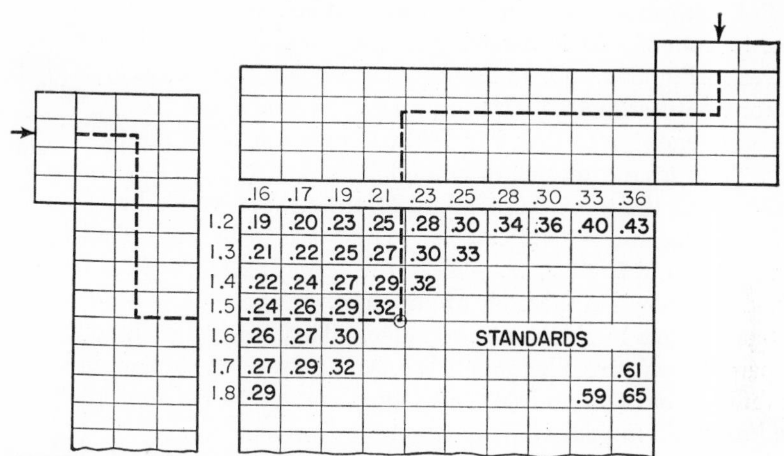

d. Three variables at the top conclude with a standard time scale. This is multiplied by factors that result from three variables combined in the left-hand portion of the chart.

FIG. 85. (*Continued*).

of standard time data. Another case was mentioned in our previous chapter—budget charting. Somewhere before you set down your final figures, you should take into account whatever constants are involved. It is easier, in my experience, to add it to one of your answer scales as shown here.

In budgets, the constant is the amount of money that causes some accountants to refer to certain expenses as a "semi-variable." One example is the minimum amount you pay in a power bill for the privilege of being connected to your public utility.

The total of these constants determines your company's breakeven point. This total constant has to be taken into account in building a chart of probable profit or loss. In this latter case, it would be subtracted instead of added.

Alter Factors

You may need to alter your chart amounts in other ways. For instance, Fig. 85*b* shows how time standards are multiplied. This is one way to provide for two sides, say of a box, when you have built a chart from length and width.

Figure 85*c* indicates a way to increase answers. The reverse plotting would serve to decrease them. Either of these sideways movements is more easily accomplished when you use the constant per cent numbers discussed in Chap. 14.

But you can see that similar results can be attained here by ordinary multiplication. To illustrate, you could multiply by 1.10 instead of 2.0 as in Fig. 85*b*. Or to reduce your answers, you could multiply by .90 or whatever factor your problem demanded.

Going one step farther, Fig. 85*d* was drawn to show multiple factoring. This is an extension of examples (*b*) and (*c*). The construction scale across the top is in Standard Minutes. The vertical scale on the left contains the several factors. These are to be multiplied by the answers .16, .17, .18, . . . , 36 in the top scale to produce the final standards shown in the body of our chart.

Such factors might be of any range. They might be divisors. Is it apparent from this illustration how you may solve similar problems? It differs from (*b*) and (*c*) indicating how a series of multipliers can be brought into your chart to affect the final answers.

In summary, you can operate on a set of answers to perform any mathematical operation. Of course, the factors have to be applied correctly from the standpoint of arithmetic. In many instances, however, the point where they are applied is optional. For example, in the nomograph chart made in Chap. 10 to calculate economical lot size, the .6 was applied at the end of the process. In this particular instance, it could have been applied at any of the stages from the first to the last.

What has been discussed here applies either to a scale of numbers or to the end results themselves. To be specific, you have seen a scale on the economical lot-size chart converted to a square root of the answer obtained by the chart. These and many other arithmetic calculations may be applied to your partial answers. They may be applied to either or both halves of charted values as demanded by the conditions.

Scale Change Points

Next is a detail of layout that can have a major effect on the size of your chart. Another way of saying this is, "You can often simplify and condense your charts by choosing the numbers you use to build it."

To make an example, I started with the Piece Handling chart shown in Fig. 79, Chap. 16. On it are shown 209 standard times. If you want to list all of these in order, you will find there are 63 different ones. These are recorded in Fig. 86*b*. Thus, to consider every different one in setting up the scale for "turning inside out" would require 63 spaces.

But many of these standard times are different by only 1 or 2 per cent. Others like .10 and .11 are 10 per cent apart. So if you think

10%	CHANGE POINT
	955
100	
	105
110	
	115
120	
	126
132	
	138
145	
	151
158	
	166
174	
	182
191	
	200
209	
	219
229	
	240
251	
	263
275	
	288
302	
	316
331	
	347
363	
	380
398	
	417
437	
	457
479	
	501
525	
	550
575	
	603
631	
	661
692	
	724
759	
	794
832	
	871
912	
	955

a

TABLE TIME	10% USED	CHANGE POINT
		.0603
.063		
.064	.063	
.066		
		.0661
.067		
.070	.069	
.072		
		.0724
.073		
.075		
.076	.076	
.077		
.079		
		.0794
.081		
.082		
.083		
.084	.083	
.085		
.086		
.087		
		.0871

TABLE TIME	10% USED	CHANGE POINT
.088		
.090		
.092	.091	
.093		
.095		
		.0955
.096		
.097		
.098	.10	
.099		
.10		
		.105
.11	.11	
		.115
.12	.12	
		.126
.13	.13	
		.138

TABLE TIME	10% USED	CHANGE POINT
.14		
	.15	
.15		
		.151
.16	.16	
		.166
.17		
	.17	
.18		
		.182
.19	.19	
		.200
.20		
.21	.21	
		.219
.22		
.23	.23	
		.240
.24		
.25	.25	
.26		
		.263

TABLE TIME	10% USED	CHANGE POINT
.27		
	.28	
.28		
		.288
.29		
.30	.30	
.31		
		.316
.32		
.33	.33	
.34		
		.347
.35		
	.36	
.36		
		.380
.38		
.39		
	.40	
.40		
.41		
		.417
.42		
.44	.44	
.45		
		.457
.47		
	.48	
.48		
		.501

b

DIAMETER												
1/2	5/8	3/4	7/8	1	1 1/8	1 1/4	1 3/8	1 1/2	1 5/8	1 3/4		
1											.063	0661
6	1										.069	0724
16	6										.076	0794
22	10	1					LENGTH				.083	0871
28	16	2	1								.091	0955
36	22	8	2								.10	105
	28	16	4	1							.11	115
	32	22	12	6	1						.12	126
	36	28	18	10	2	1					.13	138
		36	26	14	6	2					.15	151
			32	20	8	4	1				.16	166
			34	24	14	10	4				.17	182
			36	28	18	16	6	1			.19	200
				36	24	20	14	4	1		.21	219
					28	26	18	8	4	1	.23	240
					34	30	22	12	8	4	.25	263
						36	24	16	10	6	.28	288
							28	20	14	10	.30	316
							34	26	20	14	.33	347
								32	24	18	.36	380
									28	22	.40	417
									36	28	.44	457
										36	.48	

c

a. All the Piece Handling standard times Fig. 79 are listed in order with the 10 per cent selections to use the change points.

b. Table of 10 per cent numbers with change points in 10 per cent increments.

c. Lengths were plotted to the nearest corresponding 10 per cent time determined by the change points.

FIG. 86.

back to the discussion in Chaps. 13 and 14 about constant per cent increments, or relative accuracy, you can see an application here for selected numbers. More to the point, by choosing 10 per cent numbers, you can reduce to 23 the number of spaces required. These are shown in columns labeled "10% used" (Fig. 86*a*). In the next columns are noted the change points that determine groupings of the actual standard time by 10 per cent selections.

Plot the Chart Body

Both the 10 per cent numbers used as answers and those that determine the change points were taken from Fig. 86*b*. This is a list of all the numbers you need to choose a scale for any chart that is to be built on 10 per cent increments. Just remember one detail. These numbers are just enough less than 10 per cent increments to make a repeating scale.

Moving now to charting, look at Fig. 86*c*. In the right-hand columns are shown both the 10 per cent answers to use and the change points. Take another look at Fig. 62*a* and Fig. 62*c*, Chap. 13. The 10 per cent numbers designate the spaces to be used in plotting the variable Length. The 10 per cent change points tell when to change lengths by time groups. I plotted the Lengths from the table Fig. 79, Chap. 16.

This detail of chart plotting is very important. It saves time in chart reading, if you agree that chart answers should not be interpolated. By this change-point method of plotting, you record the variable (Length in this chart) points that are to be used in reading your chart. Looking at ½-inch Diameter, Fig. 86*c*, the person using the chart is expected to read .069 for any Length over 1 inch but less than 6 inches, and .076 for Lengths over 6 inches up to 16 inches. This method helps to maintain consistency in chart reading while greatly reducing the time of decision making.

Conserve Space

As another example, let's work with a more complete range of sales Dollars and Material Costs than we used in Fig. 81, Chap. 16. If you look back, you will see that we used actual Material Costs to make up a simplified chart.

All the actual costs for a wider range of variables are shown in Fig. 87*a*. These make a list of 56 different Material Costs in the range of Sales Dollars chosen. Again, these differences may be reduced by selecting constant per cent numbers to use instead. In this instance, the 13 numbers, 16 to 48, can be substituted. Their Shirt Sales dollar

SHIRTS SALES DOLLARS	THOUSANDS SHORTS SALES DOLLARS								
	40	50	60	70	80	90	100	110	120
40	16.0	17.5	19.0	20.5	22.0	23.5	25.0	26.5	28.0
50	18.5	20.0	21.5	23.0	24.5	26.0	27.5	29.0	30.5
60	21.0	22.5	24.0	25.5	27.0	28.5	30.0	31.5	33.0
70	23.5	25.0	26.5	28.0	29.5	31.0	32.5	34.0	35.5
80	26.0	27.5	29.0	30.5	32.0	33.5	35.0	36.5	38.0
90	28.5	30.0	31.5	33.0	34.5	36.0	37.5	39.0	40.5
100	31.0	32.5	34.0	35.5	37.0	38.5	40.0	41.5	43.0
110	33.5	35.0	36.5	38.0	39.5	41.0	42.5	44.0	45.5
120	36.0	37.5	39.0	40.5	42.0	43.5	45.0	46.5	48.0

a. Chart of Material Cost in thousands of dollars for combined Sales of Shorts and Shirts.

SHORTS										
40	50	60	70	80	90	100	110	120		
40									16	16.6
	40								17	18.2
50		40			SHIRTS				19	20.0
60	50	50	40						21	21.9
70	60		50	40					23	24.0
80	70	60	60	50	40				25	26.3
90	80	70	70	60	60	40	40	40	28	28.8
100	90	90	80	70	70	60	50	50	30	31.6
110	110	100	90	80	80	70	70	60	33	34.7
120	120	110	100	90	90	90	80	70	36	38.0
		120	120	110	110	110	100	80	40	41.7
				120	120	120	110	100	44	45.7
							120	120	48	

b. Inside out chart that has 13 different answers substituted for 56 in the chart above.

FIG. 87.

Grind Radius	Number of Teeth														
Up to 1/16	4	8	10	16	20	24	28	32	36	38	42	46	50	54	58
5/64–3/16	4	8	10	14	18	22	26	28	32	36	40	44	46	50	54
7/32–3/8	4	8	10	14	16	20	24	26	30	34	36	40	44	46	50
Standard..........	1	2	3	4	5	6	7	8	9	10	11	12	13	14	15

FIG. 88. Part of tool crib data for free-hand cutter grinding.

equivalents were plotted in Fig. 87*b* using the change-point method just described.

Recall again, if you will, the emphasis placed earlier on saving space. Often, you will find that arranging charts in this inside-out form will save space in some instances even when a combination is not planned. As an example, Fig. 88 shows a chart with 15 columns of numbers and standard times. To have drawn this chart in the usual manner with Number of Teeth across the top and Standards in the body, would have required 23 columns. Such a saving in space may be useful in attaining further consolidation. Therefore, consider this inside-out form of presentation as another tool in your working kit for chart making.

Per Cent in Combination

Taking up again the chart scale, I want to point out with examples another way to reduce space. Our first, Fig. 89, outlines a six-variable

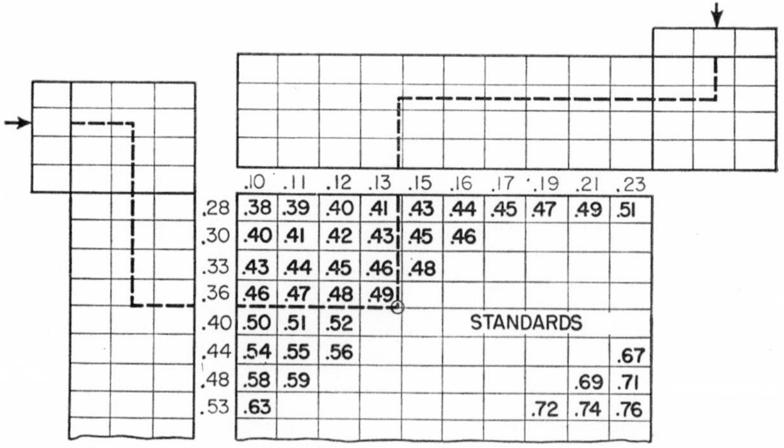

.10 .11 .12 .13 .15 .16 .17 .19 .21 .23
.28 .38 .39 .40 .41 .43 .44 .45 .47 .49 .51
.30 .40 .41 .42 .43 .45 .46
.33 .43 .44 .45 .46 .48
.36 .46 .47 .48 .49
.40 .50 .51 .52
.44 .54 .55 .56 .67
.48 .58 .59 .69 .71
.53 .63 .72 .74 .76
STANDARDS

FIG. 89. Outline of a six-variable chart showing two halves terminating with approximate 10 per cent scales and standards that differ by smaller per cents.

chart. Each half concludes with a scale of standards predetermined from 10 per cent numbers. These are shown in the row immediately above the chart body and in the column next to it on the left. These are construction figures to be omitted in the final copy. These two sets of partial standards have been added. For instance,

$$.10 + .28 = .38 \text{ minutes.}$$

Now, notice that the totals in darker figures are not in 10 per cent progression. The increment horizontally is about 4 per cent. It is less than 10 per cent vertically. This change results from addition. Per cent differences are lowered thereby. The reduction is different in the two directions because the two scales are of unlike magnitude.

With that picture, let's take another example and show how to eliminate answers so as to partially offset the variation in per cent. First, notice that the left-hand scale of numbers in Fig. 90*a* is the

6 8 … 8 10

	33	36	40	44	48	53	58	63	69	76	83	91	102
16	49	52	56	62							99	107	118
17	50	53	57										
19	52	55											
21	54												
23													
25				TOTAL MATERIAL COST									
28													
30													
33													
36													
40	73												142
44	77												146
48	81										131	139	150

Left side: 2, 4 (top); 5, 5 (bottom). Right side: 3, 3. Bottom: 6 8

a. Outside scales are 10 per cent numbers. When you add these to fill in the body of totals, most of the spreads between adjacent numbers are very much less than 10 per cent.

10 … 10

	33	38	43	49	55	62	70	78	87	97	108
16	49	54	59	65	71	78	86	94	103	113	124
21	54										
26	59										
32	65		TOTAL MATERIAL COST								
38	71										
45	78										153
53	86									150	161

Left side: 10 (top); 10 (bottom). Right side: 5. Bottom: 7

b. From the minimum total of $49,000, the minimum row and line of totals were set up in 10 per cent numbers. From these, the outside scales were computed.

FIG. 90.

same as we used in this position in Fig. 87*b*. This is the sum of material costs for Shorts and Shirts.

Across the top of Fig. 90*a* are the sums of material costs for Sheets and Shoes over the range of $40,000 to $120,000 Sales Dollars. These sums were layed out in 10 per cent numbers. Our chart is ready for completion by adding the vertical to the horizontal scale of sums to fill in the body of total material costs. A few are filled in.

Outside the scales are the per cent differences between the adjacent sums in the body. Notice how they differ. If both scales were of equal numbers, the per cent differences between the smaller sums would be about 5 per cent. Since the material cost totals for Sheets and Shoes are about double those for Shorts and Shirts, the per cent differences in grand totals vertically are about half those horizontally.

You can't attain the uniform per cent difference I have suggested when you add numbers as we have here. So I made up Fig. 90*b* to suggest a way to accomplish three results—to reduce differences in per cents, to save space, and to eliminate calculations. First, I added the minimum sum of $16,000 for Shorts and Shirts to $33,000 for Sheets and Shoes. This is the total material cost of $49,000. Then I set my slide rule at 110 and read off each successive number from 49 up to 86 in the vertical columns of totals and 49 up to 124 in the horizontal.

My next step was to subtract each total from its 10 per cent higher neighbor. These were recorded outside Fig. 90*b*. Using these increments to fill in the body of totals reduces the per cent differences. Of course, these per cents are 10 in the vertical and horizontal lines of minimums. And at the maximums in the lower right-hand corner, the per cent is 7 horizontally and 5 vertically.

Variable Dimensions

The changing per cent just discussed presents another kind of problem to prepare for. It occurs when you have any two or more variables you can combine before charting.

You may take your pick of examples. One might be standard times for several different elements of work that were dependent upon Length. Another might be budget dollars for several different staff functions that were dependent upon volume of production.

Probably, curves for either set of answers would have different constants and different slopes. That means if you took your variable dimensions from 10 per cent increments on your answer scales, the dimensions read off for one curve would differ from those for the others. Thus, you would be unable to plot one set of dimensions for the sums of your curve readings. As a matter of fact, you couldn't add to get sums. Here are samples from budget curves with 10 per cent increments in dollars and corresponding volumes in standard minutes.

Volume Stand. Mins.....	176,000	216,000	250,000	294,000	340,000	394,000
Production Control......	$47,900	$52,500	$57,000	$63,100	$69,200	$75,900

Volume Stand. Mins.....	154,000	192,000	230,000	270,000	322,000	374,000
Standards..............	$69,200	$75,900	$83,200	$91,200	$100,000	$110,000

Volume Stand. Mins.....	110,000	191,000		286,000		382,000
Accounting.............	$91,200	$100,000		$110,000		$120,000

As you can see, there isn't any logical way for us to add these. Thus, we have to take a different approach somewhat akin to that used with total material cost in Fig. 90*b*. Remembering that per cent increments decline when you add, one solution is to lay out the per cent increment suitable for your problem on the curve having the largest amounts. Read the dimensions that correspond. Then use these dimensions in reading the answers from the other curves that are to be combined with it.

The details of layout explained in this chapter come into your charting as you begin to combine more variables. They are pointed out here so you will understand what is taking place as we work out and show some more complex charts in the following chapters.

CHAPTER 18

Make Charts Direct Reading

Conversion factors are used every day to change dimensions from one form to another. The one I seem to encounter most often is the rate per gallon of gasoline that converts my dollars into fuel to get me places. Similarly, we convert inches to feet, volumes to pounds, and tons to dollars.

When these conversions are repeated calculations, charts can be made to save the work involved and the errors that may result. We find such charts in handbooks that show, for example, squares, cubes, square roots, cube roots, and reciprocals. All are functions of the numbers listed in the left-hand column. Another common chart is one showing payroll amounts for ranges of hours for each of many wage rates.

Conversion takes another form where charting can be used. This is in the many instances where we want to use equivalents. An example is to find material costs when we know sales dollars. Or maybe we want to get budgets in dollars from volumes of sales or production measured in standard time—hours or minutes.

Still another degree of conversion is illustrated by our common thermometer. With it, we read off degrees of temperature from inches of mercury or colored alcohol.

Putting these two conditions together, conversion factors and repeated calculations, I want to stress another detail of charting. I call it, "making charts direct reading." The most common case I have seen is in standard setting. It occurs where the blueprint (dimensions) and standard data (time) are brought together for the purpose of setting work standards for operations. In this step, calculations may be necessary.

Starting Factors

Perhaps the simplest illustration occurs where in drill-press work we have to consider drill-point depth. This is usually taken as

.3 × Diameter. Perhaps, also, some lead or overrun depth must be included. These distances greater than the drawing dimensions may be added in either of two ways. Usually, they are added to the drawing depth of the hole. Then the time assigned is for the total depth. This method requires one or more extra steps. There are several if the standard setter refers to auxiliary tables for drill-point lengths and overrun distances. Always, he must take account of the extra depths. If he forgets, an error is created.

The extras we are interested in are time values beyond those directly related to drawing dimensions. The arithmetic is like the markup in department-store pricing. Why not apply the same principle in standard data? Since drill point is .3*D*, it can be added in time in any data tabulated by diameter. Said another way, the drawing dimensions can be plotted against a time scale offset enough to add the required time.

The same applies to overrun. When this extra applies singly for blind holes and differently for through holes, two columns are suggested. One set of times is read directly to include drill point and approach. The other includes the additional time for break-through overrun. Two such columns might merge into one where the per cent difference becomes too small. The principle involved is to avoid the repetition of calculations by converting your data to drawing dimensions.

This improvement in method is one you can look for whenever dimensions are the starting information. You should try to eliminate steps taken to transform starting dimensions to some other figures. Charts may be worked out to save these computations. But you should go one step further. You should try to arrange your data to conform with dimensions available to you. With such conformations, you can eliminate references, computations, and interpretations.

Construct charts that utilize dimensions readily available to those who will use them.

Dimensions of Weight

Suppose the time to "handle" the part to be worked on is related to its weight. However, the blueprint shows only its dimensions. One solution is to calculate weight from dimensions. Another is to convert weight to dimensions.

Either way can mean repeated calculations. So first, charts can be made to record the answers and save time. Second, we can make charts to read in terms of available information. This is the conversion step implied in the term "direct reading."

To work out an example, I used the original chart of Weights built into Fig. 82*g*. These are shown in Step 1, Fig. 91*a*, with dark figures

WEIGHT				
6	8	10	12	14
.08	.09	.10	.11	.12

ORIGINAL CHART

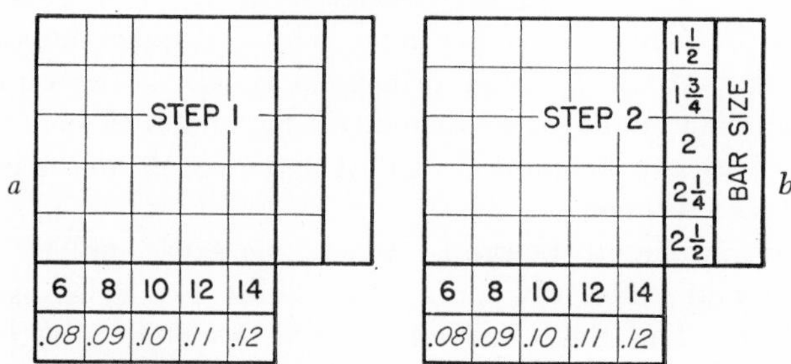

a. In place of pounds, we want direct-reading dimensions. So lay out a chart with pounds as construction figures.
b. Place one dimensional scale at right angles to start the two-variable chart.

FIG. 91.

6 to 14 representing pounds and light figures .08 to .12 their corresponding time standards in minutes. Then diameters of round bar stock were written in as one variable outside the chart (Step 2, Fig. 91*b*). Step 3, The next move was to look up in a handbook the lengths of bars of given Diameters that correspond with Weights. A 1½-inch round bar of steel that weighs 6 pounds is 12 inches long. So I wrote 12 over 6 on the 1½-inch diameter line. A 1¾-inch bar that weighs 6 pounds is 9 inches long. Successively, I found the other lengths shown in the column over 6 pounds in Fig. 91*c*. Step 4, in the same way, I plotted the other lengths of bars to correspond with weights 8, 10, 12, and 14 pounds.

Now we have a chart that enables us to select the correct standard time without having to compute weight. This illustrates an important conversion. It shows the two steps

1. How to set down information you want to apply in terms of measures that are available, and
2. How to record computations so as to eliminate the rework of doing them over and over again, as well as the errors that may occur

Area-volume Chart

Let's carry this approach a step further. You can use it to solve problems that have two or more interrelated factors. One example is suggested by a foundry operation. In such work, a molder fills a "box" with sand. The time to do so is related to the volume of the flask he uses (Fig. 92*a*).

After other elements of work are done, he scrapes off the excess sand so it is level with the rim of his flask. This is called "Strike Off." The time required is affected by the area he scrapes (Fig. 92*b*).

Thus, our problem is to compute two related dimensions—area and volume. I say "compute" because jobbing foundries have many different flask sizes. But we can set up a chart that will give us areas and volumes while retaining our starting dimensions of length, width, and depth. Such a chart will enable us to go "direct" from available (blueprint) dimensions to the answers (standard times) we seek. Let's work out an example.

Step 1. Lay out scales that take in the ranges of sizes. In this case, we are concerned with length, width, and thickness. Figure 92*c* shows only a few widths listed in the upper left side of the diagram. Crosswise are recorded 10 per cent numbers for area. Vertically at the lower right are volumes in 10 per cent steps.

Step 2. Next we divide areas by widths to get lengths (Fig. 92*d*). Area 100 divided by width 10 equals length 10. Our answer is plotted over area 100 on the line of 10 for width. We continue dividing width 10 into each area in turn and plotting until the maximum probable length is recorded.

Then we take width equals 11. Here we could get lengths of 9 and 10 but I do not record these. My reason is to avoid interchanging

c

		STEP 3				BAR SIZE
12					$1\frac{1}{2}$	
9					$1\frac{3}{4}$	
$6\frac{3}{4}$					2	
$5\frac{1}{4}$					$2\frac{1}{4}$	
					$2\frac{1}{2}$	
6	8	10	12	14		
.08	.09	.10	.11	.12		

d

		LENGTH				BAR SIZE
12					$1\frac{1}{2}$	
9	12				$1\frac{3}{4}$	
$6\frac{3}{4}$	9	12			2	
$5\frac{1}{4}$	7	9	$10\frac{1}{2}$		$2\frac{1}{4}$	
	$5\frac{3}{4}$	$7\frac{1}{4}$	$8\frac{1}{2}$	10	$2\frac{1}{2}$	
.08	.09	.10	.11	.12		

STEP 4

c. Plot in the other dimensional scale after computing it.

d. Complete the second set of dimensional factors by computing or by looking up in tables.

FIG. 91. (*Continued*).

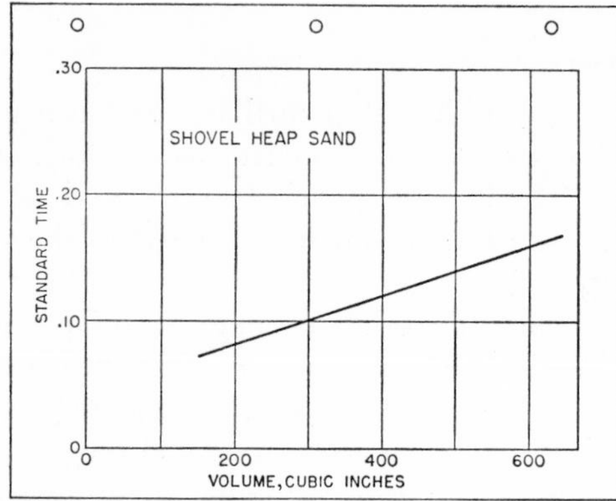

a. Curve of element standard time for filling flask with sand.

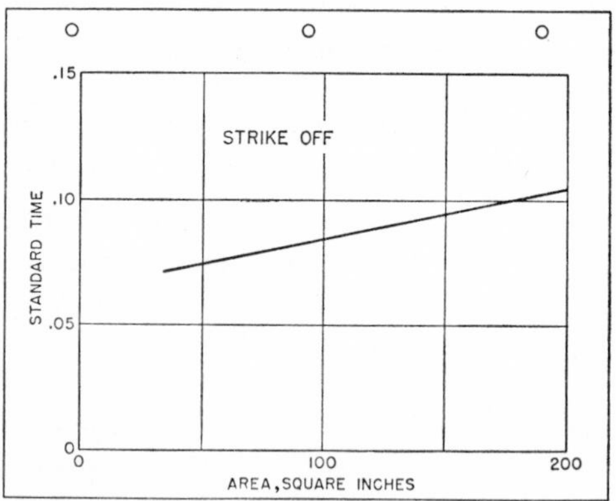

b. Element time to scrape excess sand off of the top of the filled flask.

WIDTH	LENGTH							
10								
11								
12								
13								
AREA	100	110	120	132	145	158	174	VOLUME
DEPTH								398
								437
								479
								525
								575
								631
								692

c. Chart laid out to include the ranges of width, area and volume.

WIDTH	LENGTH							
10	10	11	12	13	15	16	17	
11			11	12	13	15	16	
12					12	13	15	
13							13	
AREA	100	110	120	132	145	158	174	VOLUME
DEPTH	4							398
		4						437
	5		4					479
		5		4				525
	6		5		4			575
		6		5		4		631
			6		5		4	692

d. Lengths are plotted by dividing areas by widths, depths by dividing volumes by areas.

FIG. 92.

WIDTH									
10	10	11	12	13	15	16	17		
11			11	12	13	15	16		
12	LENGTH				12	13	15		
13							13		
	100	*110*	*120*	*132*	*145*	*158*	*174*		STANDARD
STAND.	.083	.085	.087	.090	.092	.095	.098		
	4							*398*	.12
		4		DEPTH				*437*	.13
	5		4					*479*	.14
		5		4				*525*	.15
	6		5		4			*575*	.16
		6		5		4		*631*	.17
			6		5		4	*692*	.18

e. Times for Shovel Heap Sand are read from curve (a) and recorded by corresponding volumes, those for Strike Off from curve (b) recorded by equivalent areas.

WIDTH									
10	10	11	12	13	15	16	17		
11			11	12	13	15	16		
12	LENGTH				12	13	15		
13							13		
	STRIKE OFF								STANDARD
STAND.	.083	.085	.087	.090	.092	.095	.098		
	4							SHOVEL HEAP	.12
		4		DEPTH					.13
	5		4						.14
		5		4					.15
	6		5		4				.16
		6		5		4			.17
			6		5		4		.18

f. Final chart has element names substituted for dimensions used in construction.

Fig. 92. (*Continued*).

width with length. In some charts you could get wrong answers were you able to interchange dimensions. Therefore, I recommend that you make charts that can be read only one way whenever you can do so.

Depth is our next factor. To get these dimensions, we divide volumes by areas. To illustrate, Volume 398 divided by Area 100 gives us a Depth of 4. This is plotted under 100 on the line of 398.

Two other details should be mentioned here. One is to record nominal dimensions—4 instead of 3.98. The other is to use dimensions that are customary or available. For instance, flask sizes are given in inches and fractions—not decimals.

Step 3. Our actual conversion is made at this point. We are ready now to insert the time equivalents of areas and volume. Refer to the curve Fig. 92*a*. Here we read the time standards for Shovel Heap Sand that correspond with our several volumes. These are written alongside our scale of volume in the lower right-hand portion of Fig. 92*e*.

We use the same procedure for areas. We read the times for Strike Off on our standard data curve Fig. 92*b*. These are recorded under their corresponding areas across the near middle of our chart Fig. 92*e*.

Step 4. Figure 92*f* is our completed chart. But let me explain a bit of sleight of hand. It appears that areas and volumes have been erased with the titles "Strike Off" and "Shovel Heap Sand" written in their places. This is only to save space in this illustration.

In practice, I recommend that you write construction figures like areas and volumes in colored pencil. All other figures should be in black. The original should be preserved for reference, perhaps use, when extensions may be required at some future date.

Thus, Fig. 92*f* should be looked upon as a copy made for reproduction and daily use. Actually, you might prefer to start with three rows and columns. One each for title, dimensions, and time standards. Then those used for colored construction figures would be omitted in the copying stage.

Easy Dividing

To find and plot the lengths in chart Fig. 92*e*, we divided area by width. In this process, we can make use of the preferred numbers

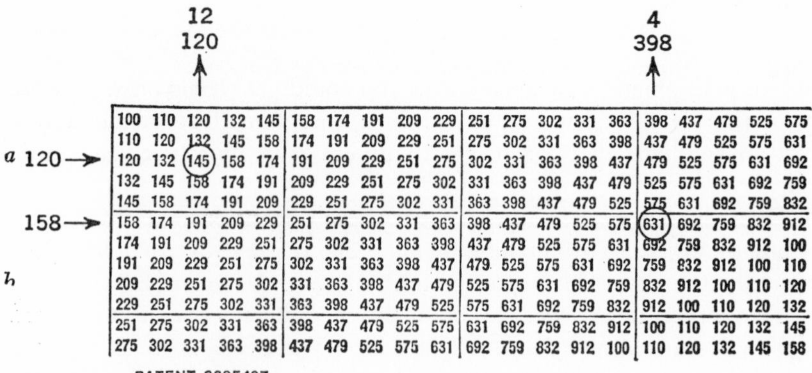

12 / 120 ↑ (above third column); 4 / 398 ↑ (above sixteenth column)

	100	110	120	132	145	158	174	191	209	229	251	275	302	331	363	398	437	479	525	575
	110	120	132	145	158	174	191	209	229	251	275	302	331	363	398	437	479	525	575	631
a 120 →	120	132	(145)	158	174	191	209	229	251	275	302	331	363	398	437	479	525	575	631	692
	132	145	158	174	191	209	229	251	275	302	331	363	398	437	479	525	575	631	692	759
	145	158	174	191	209	229	251	275	302	331	363	398	437	479	525	575	631	692	759	832
158 →	158	174	191	209	229	251	275	302	331	363	398	437	479	525	575	(631)	692	759	832	912
	174	191	209	229	251	275	302	331	363	398	437	479	525	575	631	692	759	832	912	100
	191	209	229	251	275	302	331	363	398	437	479	525	575	631	692	759	832	912	100	110
h	209	229	251	275	302	331	363	398	437	479	525	575	631	692	759	832	912	100	110	120
	229	251	275	302	331	363	398	437	479	525	575	631	692	759	832	912	100	110	120	132
	251	275	302	331	363	398	437	479	525	575	631	692	759	832	912	100	110	120	132	145
	275	302	331	363	398	437	479	525	575	631	692	759	832	912	100	110	120	132	145	158

PATENT 2295497

FIG. 93. Part of a 10 per cent unit card used here to divide. *a.* Take 120 in the left-hand column as width equal 12. Move to right to 145 as area and find 12 (120) at the top of that column as length.

b. Take 158 in the left-hand column as area. Move right to 631 as volume and find 4(398) as depth in the top row.

described in Chaps. 13 and 14. Figure 93 is part of a "unit" card of 10 per cent numbers described in Chap. 14 and reproduced here for convenience. Let me try to show how I would use it to save work.

Take width 12 inches. Look at the left-hand vertical column of figures to find 120. Disregard decimals. Now move to the right along the row of numbers thus established until you come to 145 as the area. Glance up to the top-row figure of this column to find 120 or 12 the length. Now try another. Next to the right of 145 is 158 area. At the top of the column over 158 is 132 or 13 length.

Using this same chart, we can find depth by dividing area into volume. Take 158 as an example of area. Start with 158 in the left-hand column and move right along the row it determines. When you come to volume 631, glance up to the top of that column. There you see 398 or 4 as the depth.

This chart aids in division because the product of any number in the left-hand column multiplied by any number in the top row is found in the body of the chart at the intersection of the two rows determined by the two numbers chosen. Thus, this preferred number chart is a time-saving gadget you can use for many calculations or conversions.

Box Dimensions

The direct-reading approach has another common application. This one is related to volume or weight. It occurs often where piece-handling time is involved. We can get weights, for example, when we take timestudies of the operations. But, we can't weigh a piece we haven't made. That is where we find ourselves when presetting standard times for work measurement or cost estimates.

So the question is, "Can we convert weights to available dimensions"? Often, you can. One substitute is what I call "box dimensions." These are length × width × thickness taken from specifications.

To utilize box dimensions, you should test two different kinds of relations. First is to make sure that time is related to weight over the range you plan to chart. It may be. But, too often, we oversimplify. Sometimes we overlook the fact that a sheet or a bar weighing 50 pounds may take longer to handle than a chunky piece of the same weight.

Second is to study shape. The "box" that a piece may fit into may have little or much empty space. Also, a piece may fit into a box while most of the space is air because the piece is hollow. These varied conditions tell us to look for classes of pieces. The need for classes is determined by the range in degree of error you would make if you were to use an average. The number of classes you need may be found by applying the 5 or 10 per cent analysis described in Chap. 4. The classes you need to look for are the several degrees of weight per cubic inch of volume that occur in the range of your answers.

The examples shown here are but a few of many. They may suggest ways to use equivalents in order to make your charts "direct reading." When you can apply this principle, you can save both time and errors of computing.

CHAPTER 19

Building Complex Variable Charts

Making charts to combine variables may appear as a "technique" to you. It is a tool—a very useful one. But it is more than a tool. Let me try to explain.

One engineer who became skilled in chart making said, "Phil, learning to chart gave me a pattern of thinking." Charting will give you a pattern of thinking, too, if you analyze what takes place as you work with multi-variables.

My simplest way to explain is in terms of juggling. You or I can juggle one orange at a time. But to keep five or six in the air at the same time takes very unusual skill. So it is with the mental consideration of the many variables in a complex problem. Most of us cannot keep in our minds all the factors of combinations of variables.

However, we can work with an unlimited number by taking them one at a time. That is what we do when we chart them. And, apparently, this way of working out complex problems one factor at a time is what my engineer-friend meant by his term "pattern of thinking." Perhaps this value of charting will be seen more easily in example form.

Multi-factors

Many factors enter into our American customer choice system of free enterprise. One set every business manager inevitably must face is the combination of variables that determines his Profit and Loss Statement. Three we all recognize are Price, Volume, and Cost. Each of these is a variable. We have

1. Actual versus quoted price
2. Real versus apparent volume
3. Actual versus standard cost

The end result of any combination of these might be shown on a chart. But space in a book does not permit. Even so, we can work out part of such a problem.

The example I plan to use is a variation of Fig. 8, Chap. 2. The figures used are shown in Fig. 94 and are taken from Fig. 4, Chap. 2.

Before going into the method of charting, however, I want to stress one fundamental that may not be readily apparent. It is that charting is a way of putting numbers together—any numbers. Therefore, the use here of dollars does not in any way suggest that you cannot follow the same method for combining standard times or other sets of numbers. Actually, this and other examples in the book were worked out

THOUSANDS SALES INCOME	VARIABLE COSTS AND MARGINS							
	SHIRTS		SHORTS		SHOES		SHEETS	
	COST	DIFF.	COST	DIFF.	COST	DIFF.	COST	DIFF.
$40	$32	$8	$28	$12	$44	$-4	$36	$4
60	48	12	42	18	66	-6	54	6
80	64	16	56	24	88	-8	72	8
100	80	20	70	30	110	-10	90	10
120	96	24	84	36	132	-12	108	12
	PLUS $30,000 CONSTANT COST							

FIG. 94. Chart showing thousands of dollars of sales at the left with corresponding variable costs and differences (plus or minus) together with the $30,000 constant cost used to build up the product mix combinations.

to show the opposite—that charting has many applications beyond those of combining standard times for setting work measurement standards.

Sales-dollar Error

Also, let me point out that this example of a common every day problem is chosen for a couple of reasons not related to charting. First is to show that sales dollars are not the consistent measure of volume some managers seem to think. They are not because (1) material content varies greatly—costly or cheap, purchased or fabricated—and (2) profit or loss differs from one product to another.

My second reason is to show what changes in product mix can do to profit or loss. My hope is that this example may help some managers to see how they can chart their products in order to predict the probable results of marketing decisions they may make to change the mix.

Four-product Mix

To chart such a problem, we begin with the range of one variable. Figure 95*a* shows a range of $40,000 to $120,000 of Shirts sales.

Step 1. Our first step is to set down underneath these sales dollars their corresponding profit margins. These are taken from Fig. 94 and are the differences between sales dollars and variable costs.

Step 2. What we do next is a matter of choice. One choice is to introduce another one of our variables. This has been the method followed in most of our prior examples. To vary, let's bring in our "constant cost" at this point. To do so is logical. Our constant cost must be overcome by profit increments in sales income before the break-even point can be reached.

So we should treat our constant cost of $30,000 as a loss from the standpoint of net profit. Combining our minus $30,000 constant cost with the range of plus differences for Shirt sales, we get a series of losses. These are shown in tabulation Fig. 95*b* as varying from —$22,000 for $40,000 Shirt sales to —$6,000 for $120,000 Shirt sales. These losses are recorded in Fig. 95*c* under their corresponding volumes of sales.

Step 3. Now we can bring in our second variable, Short sales. This has a spread of plus $12,000 for $40,000 sales to plus $36,000 for $120,000 sales, Fig. 94. By combining this range of plus differences

SHIRTS				
40	60	80	100	120
8	12	16	20	24

a

SALES SHIRTS	40	60	80	100	120
SHIRT VAR. COST	32	48	64	80	96
DIFFERENCE	8	12	16	20	24
LESS CONSTANT	−30	−30	−30	−30	−30
NET	−22	−18	−14	−10	−6

b

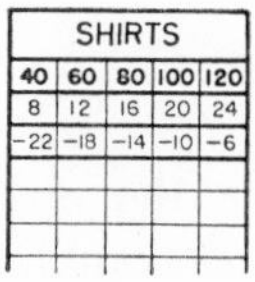

SHIRTS				
40	60	80	100	120
8	12	16	20	24
−22	−18	−14	−10	−6

c

a. Step 1 is to lay out the range of Shirt sales with corresponding profit differences.

b. Step 2 is to combine Shirt sales differences with the constant cost of $30,000.

c. Net results of Step 2 combinations are recorded in our starting chart (*a*).

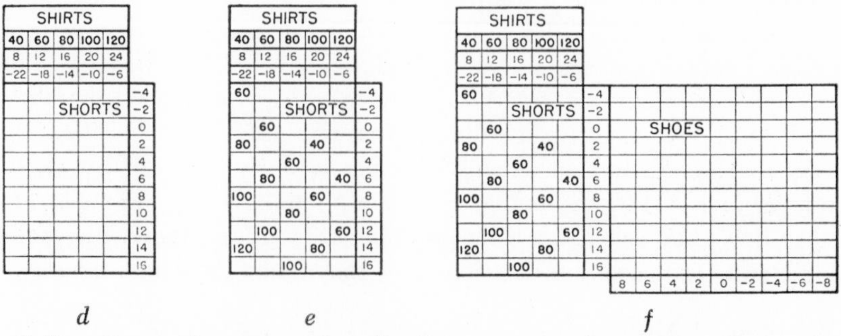

d *e* *f*

d. Step 3 provides area and scale of net answers for plotting Short sales volumes.

e. Step 4 consists of plotting Shirt sales in their proper locations.

f. Step 5 is to lay out area and scale for our third variable Shoe sales.

Fig. 95.

with the range of minus differences set up in Step 2, we determine our scale of values for plotting Short sales. I have omitted the extremes to reduce space. So in Fig. 95*d*, you see a scale in the right-hand vertical column that ranges from —$4,000 to +$16,000 net. I chose steps of $2,000 dollars for ease of plotting. This layout, you will recall, is just like all the previous examples of two variable combinations.

Step 4. Our next step is to plot Short sales. Choosing $40,000 Shirt sales, our starting figure is $22,000 loss. This loss will drop to $4,000 when we sell $60,000 of Shorts having a profit margin of $18,000 shown in Fig. 94.

Short Sales	$60,000	$80,000	$100,000	$120,000
Short Profit Margin	18,000	24,000	30,000	36,000
Loss $40,000 Shirts	−22,000	−22,000	−22,000	−22,000
Net	− 4,000	+ 2,000	+ 8,000	+14,000

So we plot the figure 60 for Shorts sales under 40 of Shirts sales on the line of —4 (—$4,000) of net loss on Fig. 95*e*.

Again, $40,000 of Shirts with its loss of $22,000 when combined with $80,000 sales of Shorts (+$24,000, Fig. 94) will result in a net of +$2,000. This is shown by plotting 80 for Shorts sales under 40 of Shirts sales on the line of 2 for net profit.

Following the same procedure, we obtain the locations for plotting the rest of the Short sales volumes. Here is one more table of combinations. It is for Shirt sales of $60,000.

Short Sales	$60,000	$80,000	$100,000
Short Profit Margin	$18,000	$24,000	$ 30,000
Loss $60,000 Shirts	−18,000	−18,000	−18,000
Net	0	+ 6,000	+12,000

At this point, we have completed the combination of two variables as in many earlier charts.

Step 5. Here is a departure. Rather than add two more variables set up in a similar chart, as heretofore, we start to add two onto our chart Fig. 95*d*. This procedure is intended to show how to tackle the charting of part of more than four variables.

Our initial step is to lay out an area for plotting our third variable. Then at right angles, we set up a line of answers. Taking Shoe sales as our third variable, we get a range in net profits of plus $8,000 to minus $8,000, Fig. 95*f*. Again omitting some extremes, this spread is obtained by combining the range of Shoe losses (Fig. 94) with the net values in Fig. 95*e*.

Shoe Sales	$80,000	$40,000
Shoe loss...........	− 8,000	−4,000
Scale range..........	+16,000	−4,000
New scale...........	+ 8,000	−8,000

We can start any place to locate our plottings for Shoe sales. Let's begin near the middle because some extremes answers are omitted. We can do this by setting down the range of Shoe sales.

Shoe Sales	$ 40,000	$ 60,000	$ 80,000	$ 100,000	$ 120,000
Shoe losses......	$−4,000	$−6,000	$−8,000	$−10,000	$−12,000
Scale answer....	+8,000	+8,000	+8,000	+ 8,000	+ 8,000
Net..........	+4,000	+2,000	0	− 2,000	− 4,000

Step 6. These net figures give us locations Fig. 95*g*. On the horizontal line of 8 (+$8,000) of our vertical scale of previous answers, we plot 40 for $40,000 Shoes sales over 4 for $4,000 net in our new horizontal scale of answers.

Still on the line of 8, we plot 60 over 2, 80 over 0, 100 over —2, and 120 over —4 of our horizontal scale.

Step 7. Now we can progress either up or down to fill in plottings of Shoe sales (Fig. 95*h*). Moving upward to the line of 6 (+$6,000) in our vertical scale, we can spot the locations of extremes of Shoe sales.

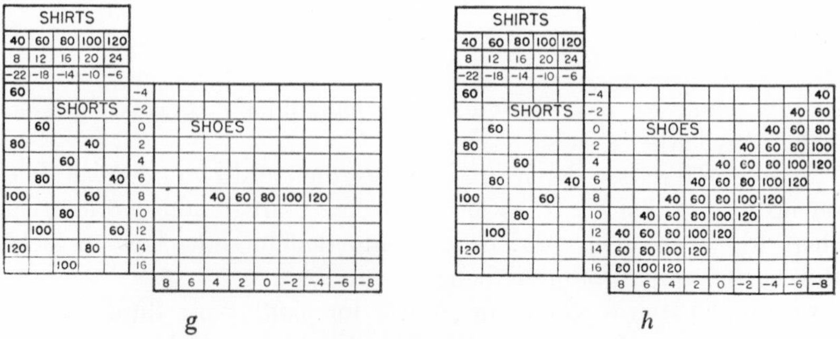

g *h*

g. Step 6 is to locate and plot one range of volumes of Shoe sales.
h. Step 7 is to complete the plotting of Shoe sales volumes.

Fig. 95. (*Continued*).

Shoe Sales	$ 40,000	$ 120,000
Shoe loss............	$-4,000	$-12,000
Scale answer.........	+6,000	+ 6,000
New scale.........	+2,000	− 6,000

Plotting, we write 40 for $40,000 Shoe sales on the line of 6 on our vertical scale over 2 for +$2,000 net shown on our new horizontal scale. Similarly, we plot 120 for $120,000 sales over −6 for −$6,000 loss. Continuing, keep one eye on the differences for Shoe sales shown in Fig. 94. We combine these with our vertical scale and plot all the other locations for Shoe sales in Fig. 95*h*.

Step 8. To add our fourth variable, Sheet sales, we turn a right angle and lay out an area for plotting Fig. 95*i*. Next, we set up a vertical scale of answers to cover a new range of net profits or losses.

Sheet Sales	$40,000	$100,000
Sheet Profit Margin.........	+4,000	+10,000
Horizontal Scale............	−8,000	+ 8,000
New scale..............	−4,000	+18,000

Step 9. Again, let's pick a figure near the middle of the horizontal answer scale we got for the combination of Shirts, Shorts, and Shoes.

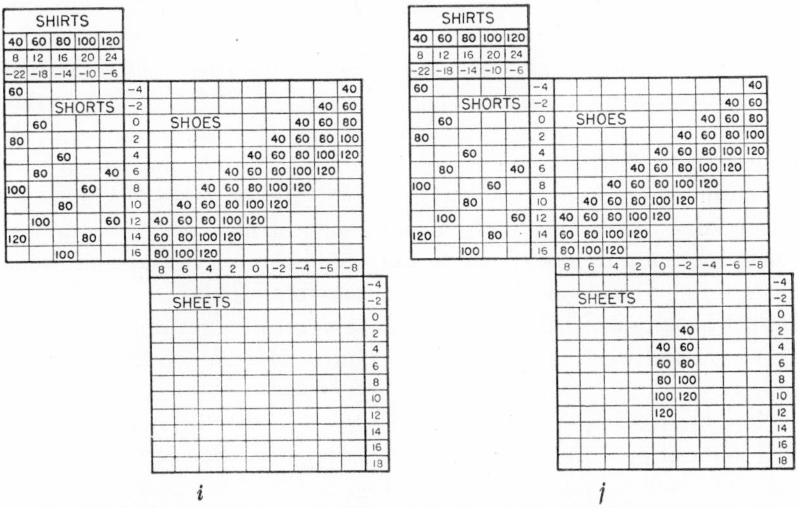

i *j*

i. Step 8 is to provide an area and a new scale of net answers for plotting Sheet sales volumes.

j. Step 9 is to locate and plot two sets of Sheet sales volumes.

FIG. 95. (*Continued*).

Suppose we choose 0. With this net result, we can locate the squares for plotting one column of Sheet sales volumes.

Sheet Sales	$40,000	$60,000	$80,000	$100,000	$120,000
Sheet difference........	$ 4,000	$ 6,000	$ 8,000	$ 10,000	$ 12,000
Scale answer..........	0	0	0	0	0
Net...............	4,000	6,000	8,000	10,000	12,000

Our net figures tell us where to plot Sheet sales, Fig. 95*j*. For example, we write in "40" for $40,000 Sheet sales in the vertical column headed by 0 in the horizontal scale, on the line of 4 for $4,000 net in our new vertical answer scale. Sheet sales of 60 for $60,000 are plotted in the same 0 column on the horizontal line of 6 for $6,000 net. Similarly 80 is plotted on 8, 100 on 10, and 120 on 12.

Continuing as with Shoe sales, you complete the plotting of Sheet sales. Let's set up one more column of Sheet sales locations just to make sure the method described in Step 6 is understood. Suppose we pick the next vertical column headed by —2 for —$2,000 in our horizontal scale.

Sheet Sales	$40,000	$60,000	$80,000	$100,000	$120,000
Sheet difference.......	$ 4,000	$ 6,000	$ 8,000	$ 10,000	$ 12,000
Scale answer (−2)....	−2,000	−2,000	−2,000	−2,000	−2,000
Net...............	2,000	4,000	6,000	8,000	10,000

We write in 40 for $40,000 Sheet sales in the vertical column headed —2 for —$2,000, on the horizontal line of 2 for $2,000 in our vertical scale of final net profit or loss. In the same column headed —2, we write 60 Sheet sales on the line of 4, 80 on 6, 100 on 8, and 120 on 10.

Continuing in the same way, we plot all the other locations for Sheet sales within the limits of our range of final net profit or loss. These plottings are not shown in Fig. 95*j* to avoid pictorial confusion.

Step 10. Our final chart of four variables is shown as Fig. 95*k*. Here I have omitted the three scales of figures we set up successively as we added each new variable. Only the scale of final answers shows.

Note the road map. It shows how to correctly read our final chart. It is laid out purposely to show the same combination of product sales and net profit as that mapped on Fig. 8, Chap. 2. You start at the top left with $60,000 Shirts. Dropping vertically in this column to $100,000 Shorts, you turn right. Continue on that line to $40,000 Shoes. Turn 90 degrees and drop vertically in that column to $80,000 *k.* Step 10 is our final chart that combines four variables with a road map showing how to read it.

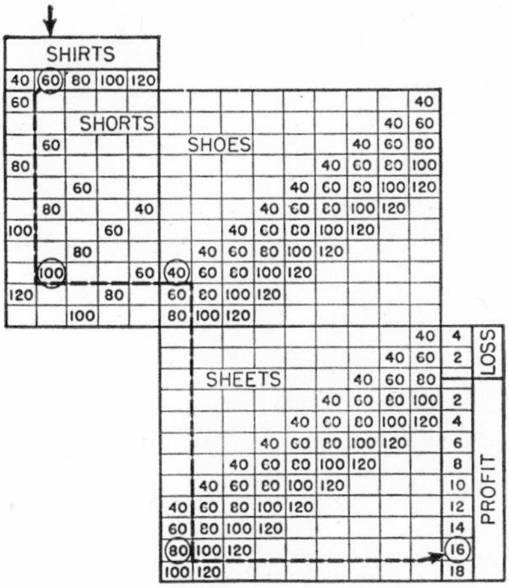

FIG. 95. (*Continued*).

Sheets. Again turning right, you move along that line to read $16,000, the combined profit for this product mix of $280,000 sales.

Many Variables

You can see, I'm sure, from the steps taken in charting the four variables of product mix that we could combine any number. The only limitations I find are space and patience.

For example, you can readily see how we could set up four more like these we have just combined. If we started with the first of these four laid out in a vertical column, the final answers would lie in a horizontal line. Were this line of answers to start just above —4 of our final answers, Fig. 95*k*, then we could combine our two sets of answers. The net sums for eight products would lie in a chart bounded by our Fig. 95*k* answers and our new set of answers for an additional four-product sales.

You can see how, for example, we could have combined more or less than four products by the method used in building Fig. 95*k*. The same applies to the additional products we might set up as another chart to combine with our first one. In other words, you can think of Fig. 95*k* as roughly half a chart. The other half can be built up in like manner to meet it at right angles as in the many earlier charts of four variables. Such a chart of seven variables is shown on Fig. 96.[1]

[1] Carroll, Phil, "Timestudy for Cost Control," 3d ed., p. 204, McGraw-Hill Book Company, Inc., New York, 1954.

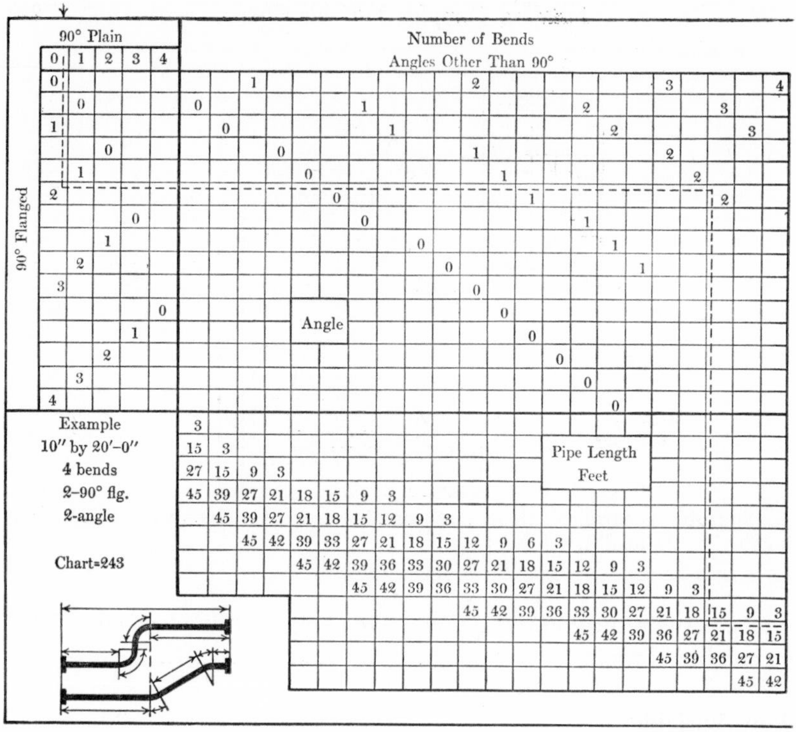

90° Plain

Number of Bends
Angles Other Than 90°

90° Flanged

Angle

Example
10" by 20'-0"
4 bends
2-90° flg.
2-angle

Chart=243

Pipe Length
Feet

FIG. 96. Chart of seven variables showing

Zero Factors

Notice one detail in Fig. 96 that is new. It is the use of a zero in plotting variables. This is to show that a variable factor is to be omitted when reading the chart. You can see one example of where to place 0 if you will look at Fig. 95*g*. Suppose you wanted to omit Shoe sales from your product-mix chart reading. Then you would place 0 in the square to the right of 8 in the vertical column over 8 in the horizontal scale of new answers.

Now if you move on to Fig. 95*h*, you can imagine a whole line of 0's going diagonally upward across the chart two squares away from the line of 40 Shoe sales.

You may have such problems to solve in charting standard time data. It occurs where you add standard time for part of an operation under certain conditions but omit it for others.

In such charts, you must insert a row of 0's for every factor that may be omitted. The row of 0's marks the location where you turn a right angle to avoid changing the answer previously obtained. Observe 0's in the first three variables in the upper left-hand portion of the chart, Fig. 96. These allow for the selection of any one, two or three different types of bends according to the job specifications.

Solution

Start at Left with Number of 90° Plain Bends, down to Number 90° Flanged, right to Number of Angle, down to Length, right to the Intersection. Start at right with Number of Bends and the Different Angles, left to Diameter, then down the column to Intersect above line.

Inches Nominal Pipe Diameter																						Bends: Radii of Bend	Bends: Number
3	8	14	20																				1
				3	8	14	20															Same	2
						3	10	20														Diff.	
									3	6	10	18	20									Same	3
										3	6	10	18	19	20							2 diff.	
												3	6	10	18	20						All diff.	
															3	6	18	20				Same	4
																3	10	18	20			2 diff.	
																	6	10	18	20		3 diff.	
																	3	6	10	18	20	All diff.	
76	79	83	86	108	113	118	123	131	140	146	153	159	166	172	179	188	204	212	221	231	242		
79	82	86	89	111	116	121	126	134	144	150	157	163	170	176	182	191	207	215	224	234	245		
83	86	90	93	115	120	125	130	138	148	154	161	167	174	180	186	195	211	219	228	238	249		
87	90	94	97	119	124	129	134	142	152	158	165	171	178	184	190	199	215	223	232	242	253		
91	94	98	101	123	128	133	138	146	156	162	169	175	182	188	194	203	219	227	236	246	257		
95	98	102	105	127	132	137	142	150	160	166	173	179	186	192	198	207	223	231	240	250	261		
100	103	107	110	132	137	142	147	155	165	171	178	184	191	197	203	212	228	236	245	255	266		
105	108	112	115	137	142	147	152	160	170	176	183	189	196	202	208	217	233	241	250	260	271		
110	113	117	120	142	147	152	157	165	175	181	188	194	201	207	213	222	238	246	255	265	276		
115	118	122	125	147	152	157	162	170	180	186	193	199	206	212	218	227	243	251	260	270	281		
120	123	127	130	152	157	162	167	175	185	191	198	204	211	217	223	232	248	256	265	275	286		
125	128	132	135	157	162	167	172	180	190	196	203	209	216	222	228	237	253	261	270	280	291		

zeros (0) to indicate omits from consideration.

Duplicated Variables

Opposite the 0 factor, you might say, is that of the variable you may have to take into account more than once. In such cases, you have the choice between repeating the variables in your chart or finding means for making repeated references to the variables shown only once.

An example is in foundry molding and the chart, Fig. 97, shows one solution. Many false starts were made before I found out how to get the answer. So it may be worth while to explain here how the problem was solved.

Note that three factors repeat. These are Type of Pattern, Hundreds Cubic Inches, and Depth of Draw. Taken together, these determine the cope or the drag standards. So my problem was to add two separate standards together because the molder made both halves of the mold.

The addition was made by means of a diagonal reference line. To show how it was determined, an enlarged section, somewhat different from the original, is set up as Fig. 98.

Step 1. Part of the plotting of volume of sand in hundreds of cubic inches is shown here. This is like most charts we have drawn. The

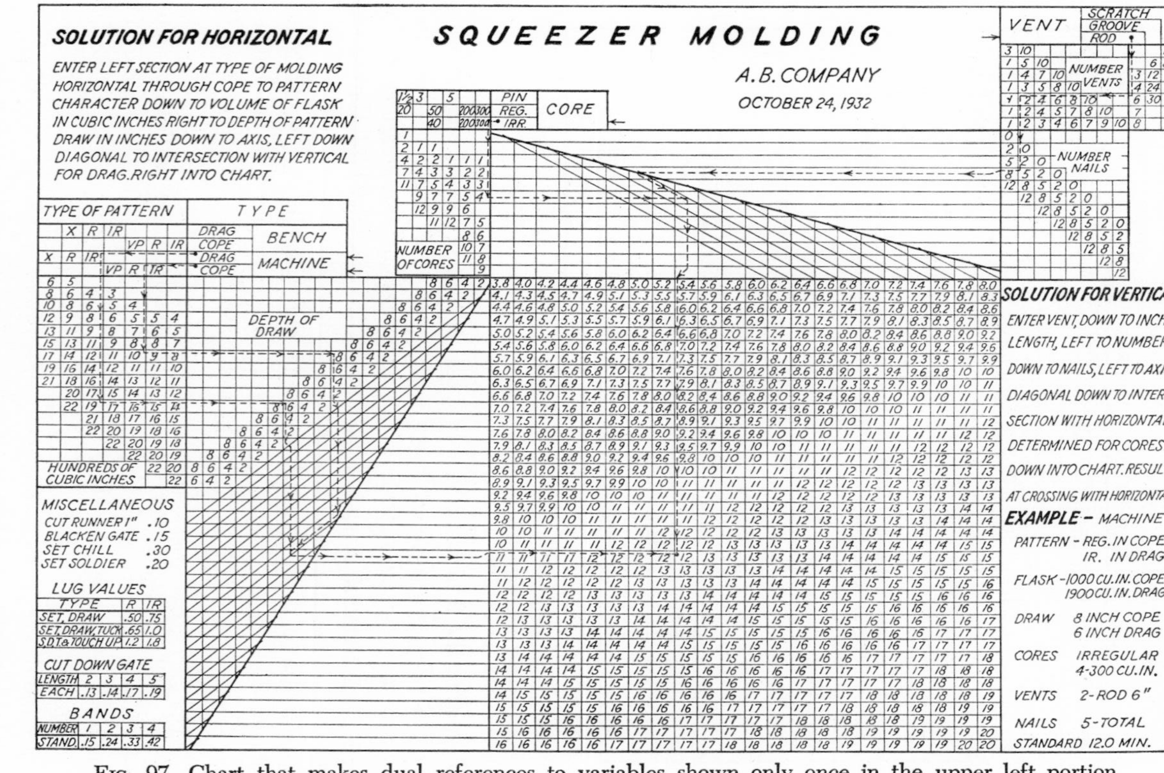

FIG. 97. Chart that makes dual references to variables shown only once in the upper left portion.

TYPE OF PATTERN								TYPE	
	X	R	IR					DRAG	BENCH
				VP	R	IR		COPE	
X	R	IR						DRAG	MACHINE
			VP	R	IR			COPE	
13	11	9	8	7	6	5		2.6	
15	13	11	9	8	8	7		2.9	
17	14	12	11	10	9	8		3.2	
19	16	14	12	11	11	10		3.5	
21	18	16	14	13	12	11		3.8	
	20	17	15	14	13	12		4.1	
	22	19	17	16	15	14		4.4	

STEP I

a. A section of standard times is laid out and volumes in hundreds of cubic inches are located according to type of mold.

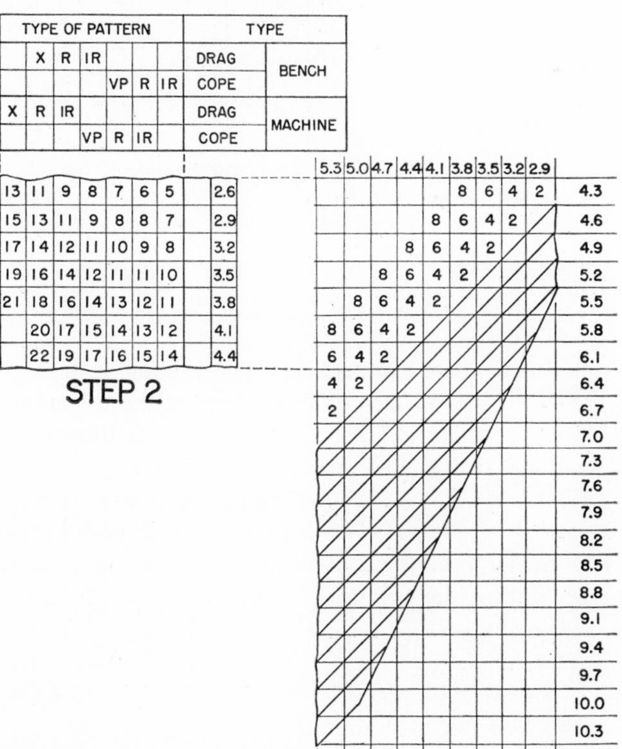

b. A scale is located at right angles across the top so that Depth of Draw time can be added. Then a double scale is set up vertically for locating the diagonal line that combines.

FIG. 98.

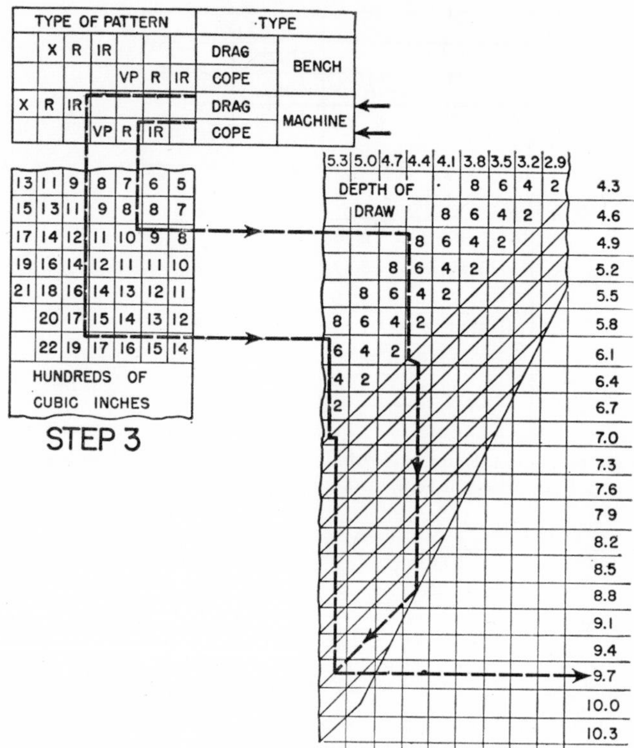

c. Road maps show how two references are made from one set of charts and their results added.

Fig. 98. (*Continued*).

standard times of 2.6 to 4.4 are reached by entering with the selection of Bench or Machine type of molding. Next is the selection of Drag or Cope. Moving left to character of pattern, you drop vertically to volume of sand and turn right to read standard time.

Step 2. First, a scale was set up at right angles to provide locations for plotting Depth of Draw. This is seen across the top instead of the bottom as in earlier examples. The locations for one row of depths are found by noting the relations of the following figures to their placement in the chart.

Depth of Draw	8″	6″	4″	2″
Draw pattern	1.2	.9	.6	.3
Time first block	2.6	2.6	2.6	2.6
Time on top scale	3.8	3.5	3.2	2.9

Now for the tricky step. Note that if you start with 2.9, drop to the main diagonal line, and turn right, your answer on the vertical scale is 5.8 mins. Starting with 4.7, you get 9.4 as your answer. Thus, we have provided for roughly double the standard time for either cope or drag.

Step 3. Now, let's take the next step. Start with 4.4 at the top, drop to 8.8, and then follow down the line that takes off to the left at that point. You will see that as you move one square, you add .3 minutes, that is 8.8 becomes 9.1 minutes. That is because the top and vertical scales have the same increments. Said the other way, the family of lines taking off to the left bisects the squares because the two scale increments are the same.

In reading the chart, you pick up twice the lower standard in the right-hand portion. Then as you move left down the line of the family thus determined, you add .3 minutes for each square moved. Continuing, you accumulate enough to equal the difference between the smaller and the larger standard.

Going down the line from 4.4 in Fig. 98*c* to the column headed 5.3, and then reading the answer thus determined, you get 9.7 minutes in the vertical column. This is 4.4 plus 5.3 and is also 8.8 plus .3 × 3 squares moved. Probably there are other ways to overcome duplication of variables in charting. Here at least is one you can use when you encounter the problem.

Label Each Variable

When you build up complex charts, you should properly identify each of the variables by name. Usually you can place labels in the blank triangles left by the plotting of the numbers. Maybe there can be no mistakes made in reading certain charts because the numbers representing the variables are not interchangeable. Yet, this is not always the case. If numbers can be interchanged, it is obvious that the resulting answers may be in error. For this reason, it is usually necessary to use the chart in the same manner it was constructed. Therefore, proper identification of each of the variables is very necessary.

The method for using the chart should be further defined by inserting a road map that shows both direction and sequence to follow in solving a problem.

Further detailed explanations may be placed in the blank spaces provided around the outside of the charts. Such available areas may be used for the recording of auxiliary charts and standard data. Examples of how these spaces can be used are shown on Fig. 97.

That brings us to the end of these complex combinations. I hope the examples shown will enable you to figure out how to expand upon the methods of combining variables in chart form. The number you may combine is limitless. But of course, there are restrictions imposed by size and practicality. Problems of revision and of understanding must be considered also. These restrictions, along with the costs to make the chart, have to be balanced against the savings attainable through less expensive computations charts make for you. Remember that better methods are what we are seeking to save time and errors in repetition calculations.

CHAPTER 20

Charts for Setups

Most of the charts constructed in the prior chapters have been combinations of ranges of variables. These seem to be the more difficult to understand. Hence, they were given more explanation.

Even so, there are complex combinations of constants, as contrasted with variables, that charting can help you to make. The most common example I see has to do with setting standards for machine setups. Similar problems occur in many assemblies. About the only difference between the two is in the procedure. With setups, you take out (tear down) as well as put in (set up). With assemblies, you put in only. Perhaps then a discussion of how to chart setup times, the more difficult combining, will be helpful to you.

Why Skip Setups

Many timestudy men appear to shy away from setting standards for the necessary work of setup. Skipping this part of work measurement is easy to do when "setup men" do it. As a result, in too many cases, incentive payments are made to these men on the basis of the earnings of those they service. Looking ahead toward what we call "automation," you can readily see there will be no "operators" as we now think of them. Hence, this abortive way of paying incentive will diminish.[1]

In most of my experiences with "tailor-made" products, mechanics make their own setups. Here it becomes necessary to measure their setup work. This may, and often does, amount to a bigger part of the day than what we call "direct labor."

Common Methods

Those more progressive timestudy men who attempt to measure setup work generally use one of three methods. Perhaps, the cheapest

[1] Carroll, Phil, "Better Wage Incentives," p. 90, McGraw-Hill Book Company, Inc., New York, 1957.

of these from the standpoint of standard setting is to use an average time for the job being set up. This may work out satisfactorily if there are several setups made during the day. The several may average the bitter with the sweet.

A second choice is to use the "laundry ticket" method. This allows for changes made in major groups of element times. This method considers tear down as well as setup. Sometimes the mechanic marks a check list to report what he does.

A third procedure gets even closer to the right answers. This, in reality, is setting standards from elements for the work that was done. My chief objection to it is that it costs too much. Each standard set has only one application. Then the standard setting must be done again and again because rarely are two change-overs alike.

Mileage-fare Charts

The simplest way to explain the approach I plan to describe is to recall for you the way you read the mileage chart on your automobile map. You follow across the line from one city, say Columbus, to the intersection with the column headed by another city, say Cleveland. There you find the distance between them—141 miles.

Or suppose you want to find the plane fare from Chicago to El Paso. You move across the line from El Paso to the column headed Chicago. There you find $84.30, before taxes, for one-way first-class fare, subject to change without notice.

This "from–to" relation underlies the pattern of most setups. They are made to change the machine *from* the setup required for the previous job *to* that needed to turn out the next job to be done. This may involve any combination of four kinds of work. These are

1. Taking out some tools and equipment
2. Putting in some tools and equipment
3. Rearranging some tools and equipment
4. Doing certain tasks that go with setups

It is in the differences that existed between requirements 1, 2, and 3 that I got bogged down recently. I tried to use charting methods like those described in our earlier chapters to determine standards for setup on big shears for cutting sheet metal. I relied on taking differences between totals. That will work under many conditions. But when you have three different times, say 1.0 minutes to tear down one tool, 5.0 to set up that tool, and 3.0 minutes to rearrange it, change-overs involving several tools can cause major differences in total times.

The possible combinations made this problem one of the most complex I have tried to work out. Its solution depended upon the development of another form of charting.

Look for Similarities

Let me point up the underlying approach we used by referring again to assemblies. One key is found in Peter Drucker's description of the correct meaning of mass production. He says, "It rests on *uniform parts* which can then be mass-assembled into a large variety of different products."[1]

Think of assembling parts to make "a large variety of different products." When you do, you have the standard data approach that looks for the similarities instead of the differences. As for the parts, they were described for us by Frederick W. Taylor when he said,

> "Add together into various groups such combinations of elementary motions as are frequently used in the same sequence in the trade, and record and index these groups so that they can be readily found."[2]

Using the "pattern of thinking" one reader said he got from the first edition of this book, we utilized a chart to assemble the parts described by Taylor as "various groups."

Wholesale Method

I call it the "wholesale method" when we use similarities to set standards by the mass-production approach outlined by Drucker. We used charting to take advantage of three simple principles of repetition. These are

1. Groups of elements that repeat in the same sequence
2. Recordings of groups so they are readily found, and
3. Analyses of the tools and equipment required in a complete setup

The first two of these are parts of Taylor's prescription for setting up standard data. The third is nothing but recognition of the fact that the tools and equipment required in a setup the mechanic is about to make are the same tools and equipment that will be present at some other time when his work is to tear down. This is like your mileage or fare chart. Either enables you to get from any city listed to every

[1] Drucker, Peter F., "The Practice of Management," p. 100, Harper & Brothers, New York, 1954.

[2] Copley, F. B., "Frederick W. Taylor," vol. I, p. 227, Harper & Brothers, New York, 1923.

other city on the chart. The mileage from Columbus to Cleveland is the same as from Cleveland to Columbus.

But there is one big difference. A chart of setup or change-over times must be read only one way. The change-over from Job *A* to Job *B* may take half or twice as long as to change from Job *B* to Job *A*.

Classify Work

Two major variables controlled the solution. One was the type of shearing to be done. The other was the sheet size.

Thus, the first step was to make floor layouts. We knew, as you would assume, that one layout may serve for several types of shearing.

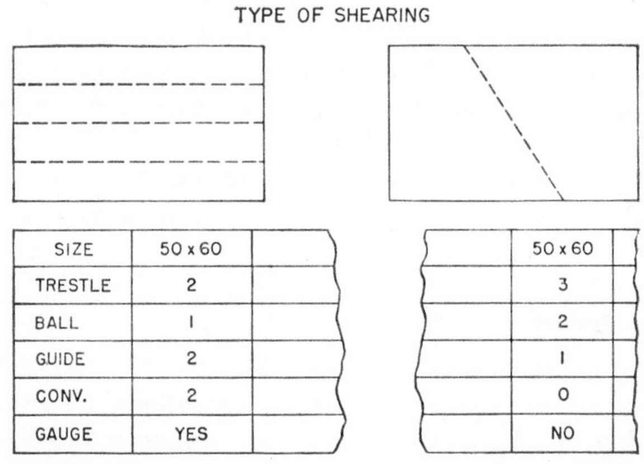

SIZE	50 x 60			50 x 60	
TRESTLE	2			3	
BALL	1			2	
GUIDE	2			1	
CONV.	2			0	
GAUGE	YES			NO	

Fig. 99. Simplified form of a chart used to record number and type of equipment needed by type of setup.

The next step was to relate the 80 types of shearing to our layouts. In this way we found out how many different types of setups we had to consider. These types enabled us to condense the 80 different ones to 7 groups. So we noted carefully all the tools and equipment needed for each type of completed set up. In Fig. 99 you see a simplified form of this record.

Sheet Size

The other major variable, sheet size, was then studied. Its effects were taken into account in two steps. First was to determine what of the many possible sizes would cause increases in equipment as we moved from small toward larger sheets. Thus we reduced a multitude to five sheet sizes.

For these, we could make transparencies. Placing these over the layouts, we could determine how many accessories were necessary and where to place them. In this way, the variations caused by sheet size were determined separately from those related to type of work.

Figure 100 shows how the simple layout for one type of change-over portrayed in Fig. 99 was expanded to record differences caused by sheet size. Then for convenience, we used multiples of this small

TO GROUP 2					
50 x 60	70 x 90	70 x 120	70 x 160	70 x 192	SIZE
3	4	4	5	6	TRESTLE
2	3	4	5	5	BALL
1	1	1	1	1	GUIDE
0	0	0	0	0	CONV.
NO	NO	NO	NO	NO	GAUGE

	SIZE	TRESTLE	BALL	GUIDE	CONV.	GAUGE					
FROM GROUP 1	50 x 60	2	1	0	2	YES					
	70 x 90	3	1	0	2	YES					
	70 x 120	3	2	0	2	YES		EACH ONE OF THESE SQUARES WAS LAID OUT LIKE FIG. 101			
	70 x 160	4	2	0	2	YES					
	70 x 192	5	3	0	2	YES					

FIG. 100. Chart shown in Fig. 99 was expanded to accomodate five sheet sizes and provide spaces to record the number of accessories by types.

sheet rather than go to a big one that could contain our 49 (7 from $\times$7 to) change-overs.

Chart Design

Moving on to the construction chart, the next step was to provide the means to get *from* one setup *to* another setup. So like cities on the mileage chart, we put all the setups across the top and down the side. We called those down the side the "existing" setups—the *from* portion. Those across the top were the "required" setups—the *to* part.

The space at the intersection of horizontal row and vertical column

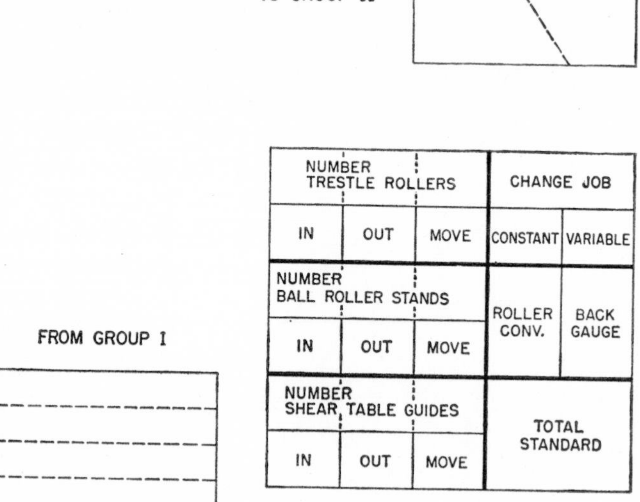

FIG. 101. Key to the layout of one intersection of the "from-to" chart used to compute change over standards.

was complex. It looked something like Fig. 101. Three spaces had to be provided for several types of equipment so that correct standards could be inserted for

Number of pieces of equipment
1. Added to the setup
2. Taken from the setup
3. Rearranged within the setup

Spaces were provided also for other parts of the change-over, such as Set Back Gauge, Place Material Table, Place Stack Racks.

Two squares were allotted for the recording of the Change Job times for the types of setups. These varied depending upon what the mechanic was expected to do in each type. One common element of work was Read Blueprint. Another was Check by Template.

The one big square in the lower right-hand corner was for the total of all the times in the several squares.

Saving Rework

Now let me try to explain how this chart helped to save endless hours of work. It eliminated what Harold Smiddy calls "reinventing the wheel." It saved the making and remaking of thousands of decisions about what work elements go into any particular setup. Making many decisions is what the timestudy man must do who follows the third method mentioned earlier in this chapter.

Take the simplest example. Suppose the constant standard of 4.4 minutes applies to every setup. Having made that determination, you

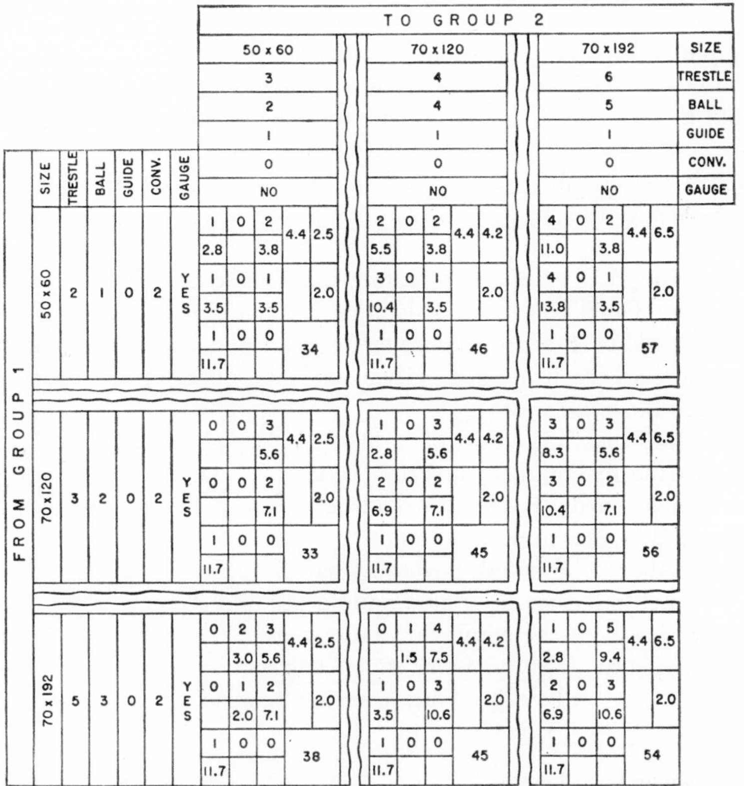

FIG. 102. Section of construction chart showing quantities of accessories and appropriate work standards in minutes with the total for the changeover in the lower right hand corner.

write 4.4 in the proper box in every location. Note its repetition in Fig. 102.

As a next degree of simplicity note that 2.5 minutes of variable Change Job repeats vertically in the section for 50 × 60 to Group II. Similarly, 4.2 and 6.5 minutes repeat vertically. If you have several different constant standards, the recording in proper locations takes only a little more concentration.

Now let's consider the chief complexity—tool changes. Since there are two Trestle Rollers in the Group 1 50 × 60 setup and three in the Group 2 50 × 60 setup, you know (1) one tool is to be added and (2) none are to be removed. So 1 is placed in the In space and 0 in the Out. The other determination is (3) how many are to be moved. From the transparencies, we find that 2 are to be moved.

The decision made about one type of equipment for one type of change-over then applies to all of that kind. The variant in this example is number. This may increase as you change, meaning (1) to add, when the new setup is for a bigger sheet size. The reverse would be true, (2) to remove, were the new setup for a smaller sheet size.

When the quantities of every kind are recorded, as shown in Fig. 102, you post the proper standard under each. Again, repetition is utilized.

Reviewing for emphasis, charting saves time in solving complex problems. Once you make a decision about the effect of one factor, you write down the proper answer for that detail in every space on your chart where it applies. Then you take up the next factor and treat it in the same way.

Thus, you take advantage of similarities. You save time, work, and errors to the extent there are similarities. As Auburn Shuff puts it, "the wrinkles in my forehead would be six less if I could have turned to Chap. 20 a year and a half ago to get answers to some of my problems. It should be noted, however, that the principle described here can be used to reduce the time required to build direct reading charts for simple as well as complex operations other than setup. We used this principle to chart our fabrication, construction, erection and foundry operations and reduced the charting time from around six man weeks to forty man hours."

Change-over Standards

The final chart is a copy of the Setup Types, Sheet Sizes, and total times only. The totals are illustrated in Fig. 102 by 34, 46, and 57 in the lower right-hand corners of the top row. The completed chart takes a space smaller than 8½ by 11 inches.

From it, correct standards can be predetermined when the sequence of jobs is known as in any well-run production scheduling. Or standards can be set on the floor as the jobs change. They can be set at the end of the day when job sequence is recorded on the log-type of time sheet.

What Type Machine

Setups have another underlying question. This relates to quantity. What is the lot size that determines when to change from one type of machine to another?

One plant used a rule of thumb based on 50 pieces in a lot. That quantity seemed reasonable until we began to do some figuring on break-even points. Then we found that the change-over point might be nearly any quantity. So we worked out a chart to answer the question because it came up frequently.

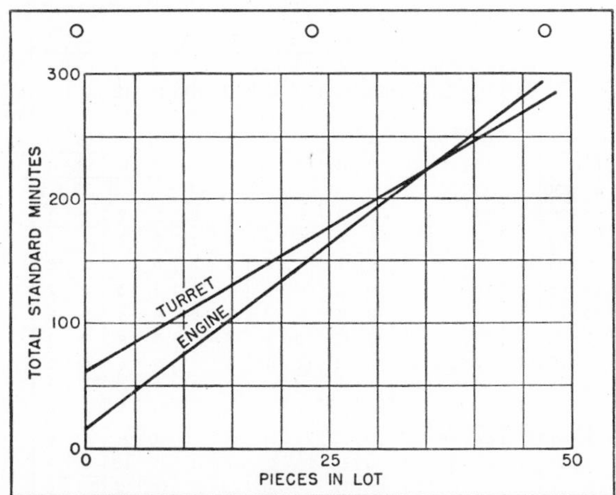

FIG. 103. The economical point to change method is where the total minutes to process a lot are the same for either choice.

The break-even point is illustrated by Fig. 103. It is at the quantity where the total time for the lot is the same for either method. Total time equals Setup plus Quantity × Standard time per piece. Using Turret Lathe and Engine Lathe as examples of method, the break-even point is found by setting two expressions equal to each other.

$$\text{Setup } E + Q \times \text{Standard } E = \text{Setup } T + Q \times \text{Standard } T$$

$$Q = \frac{\text{Setup } T - \text{Setup } E}{(S_E - S_T)}$$

Chart Break-even Point

To chart a solution to this problem, I set up two lines of differences. These are shown in lightface on Fig. 104. Vertically they range from

10.0 to 91.2 and horizontally from 1.00 to 9.12. They are every other number taken from my 10 per cent chart shown in Fig. 66, Chap. 14, and Fig. 93, Chap. 18. I refer you to the latter illustration in particular. There I show how to use these preferred numbers to divide. That was the first step in construction.

Let's take one example. The difference 2.51 in Standards divided into 52.5 difference in Setups equals 21 pieces. Looking at Fig. 93, you locate 251 in the left-hand column. Then move to the right until

OPERATION STANDARDS													TURRET LATHE
4.0	4.2	4.5	4.7	5.1	5.5	6.0							3.0
4.6	4.8	5.1	5.3	5.7	6.1	6.6	7.2			ENGINE			3.6
5.4	5.6	5.9	6.1	6.5	6.9	7.4	8.0	8.8		LATHE			4.4
6.3	6.5	6.8	7.0	7.4	7.8	8.3	8.9	9.7	11				5.3
7.3	7.5	7.8	8.0	8.4	8.8	9.3	10	10	11	12			6.3
8.6	8.8	9.1	9.3	9.7	10	11	11	12	13	14			7.6
10	10	10	11	11	12	12	13	13	14	15	16		9.1
11	11	11	12	12	13	13	14	14	15	16	18	19	10

SET-UP TURRET LATHE																			
44	53	63	76	91	100		1.00	1.20	1.45	1.74	2.09	2.51	3.02	3.63	4.37	5.25	6.31	7.59	9.12
34	43	53	66	81	90	10.0	10	8	7	6	5	4	3	3	2	2	2	1	1
32	41	51	64	79	88	12.0	12	10	8	7	6	5	4	3	3	2	2	2	1
29	38	48	61	76	85	14.5	15	12	10	8	7	6	5	4	3	3	2	2	2
27	36	46	59	74	83	17.4	17	15	12	10	8	7	6	5	4	3	3	2	2
23	32	42	55	70	79	20.9	21	17	15	12	10	8	7	6	5	4	3	3	2
19	28	38	51	66	75	25.1	25	21	17	15	12	10	8	7	6	5	4	3	3
14	23	33	46	61	70	30.2	30	25	21	17	15	12	10	8	7	6	5	4	3
8	17	27	40	55	64	36.3	36	30	25	21	17	15	12	10	8	7	6	5	4
	9	19	32	47	56	43.7	44	36	30	25	21	17	15	12	10	8	7	6	5
		10	23	38	47	52.5	53	44	36	30	25	21	17	15	12	10	8	7	6
ENGINE LATHE			13	28	37	63.1	63	53	44	36	30	25	21	17	15	12	10	8	7
				15	24	75.9	76	63	53	44	36	30	25	21	17	15	12	10	8
					9	91.2	91	76	63	53	44	36	30	25	21	17	15	12	10

FIG. 104. Chart showing quantities that are proper change points from one method to the other.

you come to 525. Directly above 525 in the top line is 209 or 21 pieces. This is the way I filled in the body of the chart.

At a glance, you can see that the quantities set a pattern. This happens because I used the preferred numbers. So after you look up enough to determine that pattern, you can write in the others.

Next I laid out horizontally at the left some likely Turret Lathe setup times in rounded preferred numbers. These minus the differences 10.0 through 91.2 placed vertically to compute pieces gave the Engine Lathe setup times.

When I began to place the operation standards in the top section, I reversed procedure. Here I wanted to place the Turret Lathe standards outside the chart to correspond in relative location with their setup standards. So mentally I reversed the positions of these in the divisor of our equation to read as

$$-S_T + S_E$$

Then I could add the horizontal row of differences 1.00 through 9.12 to the column 3.0 through 10.0 representing Turret Lathe operation standards. Thus the upper section of the chart of Engine Lathe standards was filled in by adding instead of subtracting.

Take one case to see how the chart is used. Start with *TL* Setup of 63 minutes and drop down to *EL* Setup of 19 minutes. The quantity we are looking for is in the row of answers on the line of 19 minutes. Now, start with *TL* standard 4.4 and move left to *EL* standard 5.6 minutes. Move down in the column established by 5.6 until you intersect the row determined from 19. There you find the break-even quantity of 36 pieces.

Proof: *TL* 63 min + (36 × 4.4 min) practically equals *EL* 19 min + (36 × 5.6 min)

Broad Applications

Charts like those built up in this chapter seem important to me. They suggest ways to solve problems that come up repeatedly in job-shop operations. In all such work, setup can be a big per cent of labor cost.

But I hope they will indicate approaches you can use for other and different applications. I like to believe they are but examples of "patterns of thinking" you can utilize to solve complex problems of many types.

CHAPTER 21

Utilize Charted Data

The success of most companies depends upon making reasonable profits. Even non-profit organizations must succeed in breaking even by some definitions. Their successes are determined by manager decisions of several kinds and degrees.

The manager decisions we usually think of at the mention of "profit" are translated into one, two, or all of the three factors we call "price, volume, and cost." Another factor not thought of often enough is product mix.

How some of these factors affect profits have been shown in several charts. Such charts made for existing companies could help in the making of better decisions about what products to push.

What about Cost

On the other side is the question of costs. These, too, have been charted in some forms. Material cost is one. This suggests how to make up charts for budgets or expense forecasts of almost any type you may need.

More importantly, the two examples of material cost combinations, Figs. 56 and 81, indicate how to set up better budgets. These charts show how to take account of changes in product mix. Said the other way, we should set our expense budgets so as to allow different rates of expense according to the different types of products in the sales forecasts. Here is one place to improve our controls of overhead costs.

But there is another, more fruitful way open. That is to measure the work done by the overhead people and utilize incentives to reduce its cost. This is a course that more companies will be taking for several reasons.

First is that overhead costs are skyrocketing. They bulge in every direction because the usual budgets are not based on reliable facts. Most of them are patterns taken from past experience—past errors, if you prefer. They neither specify what work is to be done for the dollars allotted nor how often.

Second is the threat of pricing ourselves out of business. Evidences appear here and there that seem to show we can barely afford to buy the things we make in America.

Third, and I think this important, most of our costs are wrong because we spread overhead expense with a shovel. So we need to take apart this big unknown to find out where our profits or losses really are.

Measure Indirect

We can do a lot about all three of these problems by measuring the work of overhead people. They are a big part of that cost. I checked recently and found that in two typical companies, over 70 per cent of their overhead was people cost.

However, the survey of Wage Incentives and Work Measurement by Robert S. Rice reports only about 40 per cent of the overhead hours measured (70 per cent coverage times 57 per cent by measurement).[1] Then further on at Item 29 is the question, "Why not extend your incentive plan to non-covered works?" Meaning both direct and indirect. Under this are two answers I want to discuss. "Impractical to Measure," say 53 per cent and "Uneconomical to measure" say 49 per cent.

Extend Incentives

My suggestion is that these two answers, "Impractical" and "Uneconomical," are based on experiences with commonly used methods. We are using the standard-setting methods taught for use with repetitive operations. This is fallacious. With large-quantity production, the cost per standard is relatively unimportant. Almost any reasonable cost may be insignificant in comparison with the gains achieved. I might add also, that the time taken to set the standard is usually very much longer than it need be. In one plant, the average number set per man per day was 5.7 "rates."[2] Urgency is lacking. This is because the operation will be continuing next week, next month, and perhaps next year.

These are the experiences men think with when they say "Impractical" and "Uneconomical." According to the survey, more than half are using timestudies to set "rates" instead of building standard data.

From my point of view, we need to reduce the costs of timestudy results so we can get wider application. The problem is analogous to

[1] *Factory*, McGraw-Hill Publishing Company, Inc., New York, April, 1959.

[2] Carroll, Phil, "Better Wage Incentives," p. 38, McGraw-Hill Book Company, Inc., New York, 1957.

that of every business with respect to its product. The lower the cost, the wider the distribution.

To gain our objective, we should analyze and improve our timestudy methods. We should effect economies. We should utilize all the principles of repetitive application that we can borrow from manufacturing methods. We should devise "tooling" that brings about the lowest total cost.

In this effort, the methods described in preceding chapters have some place. They suggest different types of "tooling" that can be used to increase production. You can utilize at least some of the ideas in this book to make your timestudy work more constructive.

Quantity Factors

Of course, incentives must pay for themselves. The returns should include intangibles like employee satisfaction, advancement, and objective measurement of individual skill and ability. In a large degree, results depend upon the methods used.

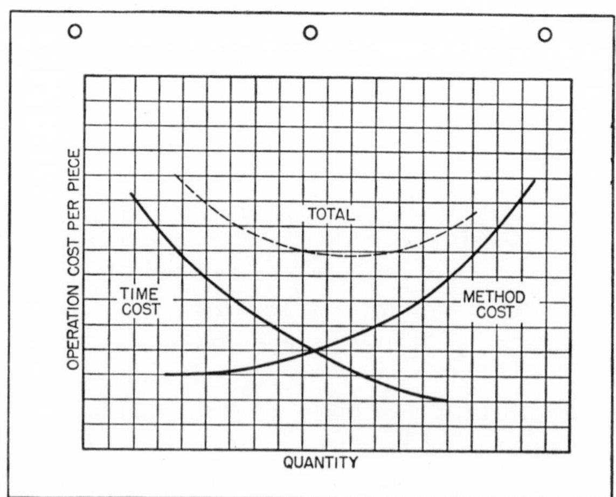

Fig. 105. Within limits, we can afford to spend more money for methods improvement as quantities rise.

All methods cost money to install and to operate. Each should make a profit. If each is not self-supporting, it consumes part of the gains made by the others. Each has its own break-even point with respect to quantity. One portrayal of this effect is shown in Fig. 105. The diagram indicates that we can economically spend more and more for method improvements as quantities increase, up to a point. The total cost of method plus time declines until a saturation point is reached. Then the total begins to rise. This is often true generally.

But our two curves are based on one type of method improvement. Should we change to another, two more cost curves would be introduced. Either might be higher or lower than its corresponding curve in this diagram. And this applies to our analysis of charting data. The important difference is that quantity here is number of standards set, not pieces on the order. Also, as with tooling methods, we must consider the probable number of standards to be set before a revision in data makes our chart obsolete.

Choosing Methods

Our criterion is the total cost per standard. This is made up of the prorated cost of our chart plus the cost to set one standard with it. These considerations are limited solely to the per standard cost. They should not include costs of the many other functions that may be carried on by the timestudy man. Our best analysis may show that we can afford an intricate chart for setting standards on one-piece orders. At the opposite extreme, it may cause us to conclude that a very simple chart is least expensive for another condition. These are tangible cost considerations. But in addition, we must reckon with errors created and explanations to be made.

To get at relative costs per standard, I had a study made of the times required to apply the same standard data arranged in six forms. Two tests were made. One was of time to set standards, the other was of errors made. Several men were asked to set five work standards each for five sets of conditions from standard time data prepared in six forms. Each form was based on the same four variables. Actual times tabulated from these tests are the averages of five trials. The average times taken and the per cent each is of the lowest time are listed together with the forms of standard time data.

Type of Data Form	*Minutes to Set One Standard*	*Per Cent of .42, Shortest Time*
1. Equations	4.75	1130
2. Family of curves	1.06	253
3. Nomograph	.92	219
4. Two curves	.66	157
5. Two tables	.47	112
6. Four-variable chart	.42	100

These summarized results definitely point out the relative economies of the several forms of this four-variable data, considering only the time to set standards.

Form Influences Consistency

Besides the cost of time, you must concern yourself with the probability of error. Obviously, some of these methods include more chances for mistakes than others. To bring out this phase, the per cents of variations from the standards set from the four-variable chart are compared.

Data Form	*Per Cent of Variation*
1. Family of curves	130
2. Nomograph	107
3. Two curves	43
4. Equations	41
5. Two tables	16
6. Four-variable chart	0

These tests are by no means conclusive. They represent only the results from one set of data conditions. Probably, also, the results are distorted by lack of expertness with all the forms of data used in the tests. Nevertheless, the comparisons show that some of the better "tooling" described in our earlier chapters can drastically reduce the cost per standard.

What to Do

It must be remembered, however, that this case example involved only four variables. Also, all four variables entered into every standard. Of course, when more variables are added, the charting becomes more complicated. When some variables affect certain types of answers but not others, the charting is complex. Yet we should not take an "all or none" attitude in approaching a solution. Nor should we limit the types of solutions to a few, either because we know only those or because we settle into routines. Our approach should be the same as with all types of methods improvement. "Is there a better way?" we must continually ask. "Will it pay for itself in a reasonable time?"

Let me repeat, "We do not perform all lathe work on an automatic." In fact, many of the job shops I have worked in do not own such machines. The quantities run are too small to permit the practical use of such equipment. In its simplest terms, the setup cost per piece would be prohibitive. So it is with our methods study of charting.

Chart Perfection

The test results show that it is faster to trace through four charted variables than through two pairs in separate tables. Most of the difference is consumed in writing and adding two answers. In addition, there were 16 per cent more errors created by the writing and adding. This clearly points out that the ideal solution is a chart showing total answers.

Notice also that both time and error are reduced when numbers are used instead of scale divisions. Remember, however, that those who took the tests were not equally expert in using all six forms of data. Make certain that you recognize the necessity for prior training before you conclude to accept or to reject any specific forms of data.

You want the best. But the ideal solution is not always attainable. It may cost too much. It may be too large and unwieldly. Therefore, you should balance advantages against disadvantages. You should weigh the setup cost per answer against the savings in cost per answer. You should seek the economical solution to your problem.

More Tools

Each form has its field of application. Each is like a tool in a kit. In different situations, each may be substituted for the other. The

Type	Advantages	Disadvantages
Curve	Simple to prepare Conservative of space	Tendency to interpolate Slow to read Probability for error Subject to faulty extension
Chart	Easily understood Simple to prepare No interpolation	Slight chance for error Most space uncombined Certain inherent error
Equation	Requires least space Simple to combine with others	High cost per standard Mysterious to many users Difficult to determine Probability for error
Nomograph	Small amount interpolation Least space to combine	Probable error in reading Mysterious Difficult to construct
Family of curves	Small space required Simple method of combining Easy to revise	Errors in tracing Opportunity for interpolation
Multi-variable chart	Practically no error Most efficient No interpolation	Most costly to make Difficult to revise Most space required

Fig. 106. Comparative summary of six methods for consolidating basic data.

well-trained analyst should know how to construct and use all six. Without such skill, I don't see how we can make the proper choice of method to be used. For that reason, the important factors that affect each type are summarized on Fig. 106.[1]

Many of the comments given there are indicative only. Many concern intangibles that are difficult to evaluate. Even so, my hope is that you can be saved some mistakes by analyzing your problems with these advantages and disadvantages before you.

The important considerations are those of cost and understanding. These two are somewhat interdependent. Any form that requires endless explaining is costly. And here I assume that lack of understanding is real and not political. It is sometimes difficult to distinguish between these two conditions. In general, we must assume that the "mystery" is a result of our failures in attempted explanations. We must try again. We must use more understandable terms and forms.

Forms for Explaining

But do not conclude that the "mystery" of a form should eliminate it from use. In contrast, it may require that you use two forms. One is the most efficient form for the purpose you plan to serve. The other is a form you may have to use in order to explain the results of your work.

The problem is similar to that involving Instruction Cards. Instructions are very necessary when training new people or retraining present employees. The emphasis is on training. Instruction Cards, films, visual aids, operation drawings, and all sorts of supplementary devices are desirable in training. But they become less and less important as knowledge and understanding are acquired.

The same is true of your standard data. Why should you use a cumbersome form every day simply because you may sometime need that form for explanatory purposes? Take a simple example. I have a strong feeling against the use of a slide rule in the shop. It is something "mysterious." We should use pencil and paper to do whatever calculating is necessary. Our computing should be carried on as slowly as the pace of our questioner requires. If he fails to keep pace, we must go back over the arithmetic and explanations. Understanding is what we are striving to attain. But the fact that longhand figuring is a good way to explain to shop men does not make it obligatory for us to throw away our slide rules. We may make a thousand

[1] Carroll, Phil, "Timestudy for Cost Control," 3rd ed., p. 200, McGraw-Hill Book Company, Inc., New York, 1954.

calculations in the office for every one we compute in longhand in the shop.

Let's remember also that explanations must be repeated. There will always be the new manager, new accountant, new foreman, new time-study man, new employee, and new steward. All may have questions that should be fully answered. We must gain their understanding in order to attain their confidence in our charted answers.

Choose Economical Tools

My personal preference is to use multi-variable charts expressed in numbers. But one method in charting cannot be the best. Relative costs are too important to be disregarded. So you should choose the form that most nearly fits your specific conditions at the time. This means, perhaps, that you may change forms as you move from one stage to another with the same data.

To offer some indicator of choice of solution according to the problem you want to solve, I include a rough sort of guide. You may find assistance in the "guesstimated" chart, Fig. 107. In this, the attempt

APPLICATION OF TYPICAL FORMS OF WORKING DATA

Number of Standards	Type of Operation			
	Simple	Normal	Complex	Very Complex
Thousands........	Element	Equation	Table	Table
Hundreds.........	Equation	Table	Multi-variable	Multi-variable
Tens.............	Table	Multi-variable	Multi-variable	Family
Occasional........	Curve	Multi-variable	Nomograph	Formula*
Rare.............	Curve	Family	Nomograph	Formula*

**Note.* The term "formula" is used to distinguish an equation that has been determined from the plotting of a large number of total standards.

FIG. 107. A rough guide suggesting the type of solution suitable to the conditions.

has been made to suggest the type of solution to use according to the complexity of variable elements in the standard and the number to be set.

The methods brought out are by no means all-inclusive. They are limited principally to those designed for standard data application. You might say they are the "jigs and fixtures" for gaining more complete work measurement and incentive coverage.

Much of America's greatest productivity came from using better "jigs and fixtures in our shops." Why not use better tools to raise timestudy productivity? We should. We must improve the productivity of all those people we call "overhead" or "indirect." We must reduce the costs of the work they do by eliminating the unnecessary operations and wasted efforts that go on day after day simply because we have not studied and analyzed what is done.

As a result, and to me the most important reason, we should find out what products cause these overhead expenses. Then we can more correctly determine what our several overhead "rates" should be. Then we can get correct product costs. Only then can we correctly determine where profits are made or lost.[1]

Make Better Decisions

I hope you have seen also that all the examples in this book are but methods of combining numbers. Such methods can be used to solve many complex problems some people now think only Operations Researchers can work out. And there is an important difference.

Charts can be used to *simultaneously portray* the results of several different courses of action. To achieve this result was the reason why I devised what I call my "rubber profitgraph." I wanted to show how changes in rates of income and in costs would affect both profits and break-even points.

Progressive managers need more of such charted data. They are invariably forced to choose from among alternatives. What course of action will give us the best end results? "Optimization" is the $10 word some people use to designate this process.

Progressive managers spend money to make money. They try to make the highest return on any investment. At the same time, they must choose where to allot the funds that are available for making profits. Thus, managers are always faced with what I call the "choice of disadvantages"—it costs money whatever the choice.

Many multiple-choice problems can be charted. Their several different answers can be shown with their interrelations. Thus, the effect of each variable on the end result can be seen. This is an important advantage in decision making that charts of data can provide. So I urge you to learn better how to chart variable data in order to help your company managers make more right decisions.

[1] Carroll, Phil, "How To Control Production Costs," p. 163, McGraw-Hill Book Company, Inc., New York, 1953.

Index